# THE CLINIC

# THE CLINIC

A Novel

*Anthony Pietropinto, M.D.*
*and*
*Elaine Piller Congress, M.S.W.*

**Times**
BOOKS

All of the characters in this book are
fictitious, and any resemblance to actual
persons, living or dead, is purely coincidental.

Published by TIMES BOOKS, a division of
Quadrangle/The New York Times Book Co., Inc.
Three Park Avenue, New York, N.Y. 10016

Published simultaneously in Canada by
Fitzhenry & Whiteside, Ltd., Toronto

**Library of Congress Cataloging in Publication Data**

Pietropinto, Anthony.
The clinic.

I. Congress, Elaine Piller, joint author.
II. Title.
PS3566.I426C58    1980    813'.54    80-5137
ISBN 0-8129-0887-2

# THE
# CLINIC

# 1

"THEY TOOK MY BABY AWAY. TWO MEN. I THINK ONE OF THEM was Billy." She clenched her eyelids shut, and two more large teardrops cascaded over her plump cheeks as she shook her head from side to side, either to dispel or unscramble the painful images, I couldn't be sure which.

"Billy? Your first husband? Do you mean they took Cheryl?" I probed.

"No, it wasn't Cheryl," she groaned. "This was only an infant. They took it from my arms."

Lisa had spoken of this before, always when she was losing contact with reality—seeing men appear in her house, watching her children's faces "change," feeling the powerful influences of unseen forces "messing with" her mind. The story could not have possibly happened as she recalled it, but its recurrence whenever her defenses broke indicated that the assault and her loss of a baby represented more than a random nightmare or poorly organized delusion. Lisa had abandoned her oldest daughter, then five years old, to the custody of her first husband when she fled a California mental institution and returned east about seven years ago. Was the lost infant only a symbol of Cheryl, or had she lost an earlier child through miscarriage, abortion, or adoption, then repressed the memory? Once again, I was pursuing this distressing shadow, one that emerged only when Lisa was least able to cooperate in the therapeutic ghost hunt.

"Billy was holding me down. If it was Billy. Maybe my father-in-law was the other. He raped me once . . ."

An agonized shriek rattled the opaque glass window, as though to punctuate Lisa's numb statement. Two audible gasps followed, then again the wail arose, resounding through the waiting room and the horseshoe of offices that surrounded the bright orange and blue plastic chairs where our patients awaited our summonses in grim rows.

I winced as the disconsolate "Ayyyyyy" roused Lisa from her waking nightmare and routed her personal demons with its own unrelenting demands. That scream was a hellish blend of anguish and despair, a cry from that "place void of all light which bellows like the sea in tempest, when it is combated by warring winds," as my old countryman Dante Alighieri once put it—and it would have rattled both patient and psychiatrist, as it did the windows, except for Lisa's apparent difficulty in distinguishing external stimuli from her own internal chaos and my own familiarity with the source of that unearthly sound. I even anticipated the harsh buzz of the intercom.

"Vince, can you come outside right away?" Dolores's apprehensive voice pleaded.

"I'm with a patient," I grumbled testily, knowing the receptionist was quite aware that Lisa was in session.

"I know, but there's a very sick lady. She needs help right away."

Murmuring a vague apology to Lisa, I entered the waiting room and saw, as anticipated, Wanda Gonzalez, her two-hundred-pound bulk convulsed in wall-shaking sobs as she sprawled over the better part of two seats clutching an official letter. This happened at least every six months, and I knew why without asking. The letter was from the Social Security office, informing Wanda that her case had been closed and no more checks would be forthcoming because she had failed to appear for a face-to-face recertification interview, as mandated by law. Wanda had ignored, as always, the appointment letter—for some good cause, such as accompanying her daughter to a colitis clinic or sleeping off a two-day migraine—and was now in a state of crisis, having been cruelly abandoned by her one source of support, the United States government. I quickly strode over to Wanda, scanned the letter, and nodded with authority; patting her hand, I said firmly, "Okay," several times, a word which is Spanish for "okay." Wanda sniffled appreciatively and reduced the intensity of her laments to a rhythmic series of low-pitched moans.

Dolores returned my steady gaze with trepidation as I approached the reception desk opposite Wanda with a was-it-really-necessary-to-disturb-the-medical-director-of-this-whole-damned-mental-health-clinic-with-such-nonsense glare. "Dolores," I hissed informatively, "that is *not* a 'very sick lady.' It is merely a loud, hysterical lady. Now, see that old woman quietly conversing with the trash container? *That* is a very sick lady!" Turning to Connie, who was now manning the phone and who had enough experience with the unit to know a very sick lady from a very loud one but had been on her coffee break when Wailing Wanda began her routine, I wrested the phone receiver from its cradle and pressed a button on the intercom while asking, "Is Pat in session?"

"She's with a patient," Connie drawled lackadaisically, noting that I had already interrupted the clinic coordinator without waiting for an answer to my question.

"Pat, get a Spanish-speaking assistant to baby-sit Wanda until we can free up a doctor to give her a magic letter," I commanded. "She's waking up the winos out here." Without waiting for an acknowledgment, I hung up and instructed Dolores, "As soon as one of the doctors is free, have him give her a letter to take to the Social Security office saying she should continue to receive disability because she's a very sick lady. I'll pull her chart for you."

Planning to leave Lisa alone with her tormented thoughts for only a few more minutes, I paced down the corridor to the records area, where nearly a dozen metal file cabinets held the charts of our 1,917 active cases and a second bank of file cabinets, only half as many, held the inactive records of those who had more or less permanently dispensed with our services through geographic relocation, apathy, death, or (if such a thing exists in the field of mental health) cure. I never got to pluck Wanda's bulging chronicle from the half-drawer of Gonzalezes because secretary Carmela Perazzo, whose ignorance of Spanish rendered her unable to communicate with nearly half our clientele and doomed her to exile among the files, turned from the window and announced, more in aggravation than horror, "A woman just got shot outside. They're bringing her in."

I was midway downstairs to the first landing before I had the presence of mind to ask myself whether I was indeed heading in the right direction. Getting shot in our neighborhood was not a unique occurrence. Nearly one weekend a month would be highlighted by such a happening in one of the dingy nests the newspapers called social clubs. Add to these social events the random murders that flared periodically after sundown outside corner taverns or under the elevated highway, and reported homicide accounted for enough deaths in our immediate area to rate its own national charity research fund. Getting shot at 11 A.M. on a busy street directly outside *my* community mental health clinic did, however, bring the problem uncomfortably close to home.

By the time I reached the second landing, my muddled brain was acknowledging that it was not concern for my staff that was motivating my foolhardy dash to danger, even though the Department of Mental Health had been recently "freezing" personnel lines in an attempt to cut budgets through attrition and would probably not let me replace a psychologist or clerk-typist gunned down on their lunch hour. They would have to replace the medical director, I presumed, but I was certainly in no hurry to sacrifice myself for the staff simply because I was the most replaceable, hence expendable, body in the budget.

And I certainly was not going to be of much help to the bullet-ridden victim, unprepared as I was, without even a Band-Aid. Then, in those final seconds before my pounding feet hit the ground floor, I finally recalled the purpose of my mission—to make sure that the misguided samaritans who were bringing the lady in got her to an emergency room as quickly as possible and did not blunder into conveying her upstairs, where six crack psychiatrists could do little more than write a concise letter certifying her eligibility for Social Security income on the basis of physical disability and emotional sequelae.

I timed my arrival perfectly. A thin copper-skinned woman,

about thirty-five years old, was walking in under her own power, her elbows supported by our security guard on one side and a maintenance man on the other, trailed by three solicitous neighbors. Her right hand was bleeding profusely and she was crying and moaning, though compared with Wanda upstairs, she was a model of genteel stoicism. She was led to the guard's swivel-chair, where a clean towel was pressed into her wounded hand, which I gazed at with numb detachment, as if observing a pathology slide in a medical school lecture. Her hand was puffed up to nearly twice its normal size and seemed to be oozing blood from many points where the skin was cracked open, rather than from one wound. There were charred flecks that looked like burned paper over her palm, which I presumed to be burned skin. At first I feared she was missing the terminal joint of her thumb, but as the towel soaked up some of the blood, I was relieved to see that all parts of her flexed fingers were intact.

Nobody seemed to expect me to do anything, which was just as well, since I was totally unprepared for what I encountered. I had expected them to carry in someone shot in the chest or abdomen, or at least in the leg. I had somehow gotten through medical school, an internship, three years of psychiatric residency, and even two years in Vietnam with the Army without ever seeing a gunshot wound. It took a job in a community mental health clinic to provide me with my first experience. Since the Lone Ranger and Roy Rogers routinely shot their adversaries in the hand, I suppose I once believed such wounds to be about as noxious as mosquito bites—you remember how it was, the villain glaring malevolently while rubbing the back of his hand as the hero delivered a brief sermon on the virtues of good and the folly of evil. Well, five years of medical training had somehow imbued the concept that bullets cause holes, and I expected to see at least a neat little aperture through the lady's palm as I kept mentally chastising myself for not knowing what the hell I was looking at, much less what to do about it. Fortunately, I was saved by an ear-splitting police siren, and I dashed outside to see a squad car speeding the wrong way up our street, spinning into a broad U-turn outside our door. "In here! Woman's been shot!" I beckoned authoritatively.

The two cops moved in crisply and solicitously, helping the

sobbing woman to her feet and easing her outside. They never even blinked when the guard drawled, to my dismay, "A cherry bomb exploded in her hand." Dummy! I shrieked inwardly at myself, standing by the elevator and hoping the security guard had not heard my inept corroboration of Carmela's diagnosis-by-hearsay. It's things like this that give us psychiatrists a bad name. One look should have told you that there were no entrance and exit wounds, that the stuff that looked like charred paper *was* charred paper, that the hand looked like something had exploded in it because . . . hell, isn't this elevator working? Shoemaker, stick to your last, and head-shrinker, stick a desk between you and your patient so that you are never tempted to touch the bodies you've forgotten how to treat. Stick to those nice, harmless psychotherapy sessions—nuts, I'd forgotten about poor Lisa, staring at my empty chair upstairs while I played frontier doctor. I took the stairs two at a time and returned to the office where Lisa was smoking placidly.

"Sorry," I muttered. "Another emergency."

"I forgot where I was," Lisa smiled apologetically.

"You started to say something about being raped by . . ." I saw from Lisa's alarmed stare that the dream, fantasy, screen memory, delusion, or whatever it was had burrowed back into its unconscious recesses and there was little point in raking the muck, especially with Lisa's hour and the rest of my schedule shot, you should pardon the expression. "Let me give you your shot . . . uh, injection . . . Lisa, and I'll see you again Friday, if you can make it." I gave her two cc's of Prolixin decanoate, an antipsychotic agent that has a two-week effect, apologized again for the interruption, and even walked her halfway to the reception desk in a futile effort to make amends. This gave Patterson, the clinic coordinator, the opportunity to move in behind me and station herself at my office door, which she deferentially held open for me, though her own arms were encumbered with a small stack of new charts. Slipping into the office after me, she cheerfully reported, "Maria's talking with Wanda in the back, Chief, and Dr. Martinez will give her a letter before he takes off for lunch." Since Pat handled this sort of crisis several times a week, there was no need for this perfunctory report and I knew she really had come in to get an update on the

woman downstairs, Pat having the uncanny ability to learn everything that's going on in the clinic and within a radius of ten blocks
while juggling thirty-odd patients in mid-therapy without missing
an appointment. I was in no mood to talk about the morning's
incident, but when Pat broke down and asked, "How's the lady
they brought in? Was she one of ours?" I was not about to indicate
that I had handled things with anything but professional expertise
and aplomb.

"No, but I suspect she'll wind up here soon, possibly this very
afternoon, with a referral from the emergency room for treatment
of her nervousness," I scowled. "She wasn't shot, by the way . . ."

"I know, it was a firecracker," she interrupted, usurping the
narrative. "Her bastard of an old man threw it at her, and she
caught it, and it went off."

"And where did you get that piece of fantasy from?" I challenged.

"Connie heard it a few minutes ago from the woman's neighbor,
who saw the whole thing. She and her *marido* are always fighting,
and today he called to her from the window and threw the
firecracker down. The poor woman unthinkingly caught it . . ."

"Aw, come on!" I implored. "I saw her hand. It had been resting
squarely in her right palm when it exploded, and no woman could
have made a catch like that with Johnny Bench's mitt, let alone on a
reflex impulse. Your sweet, defenseless little woman intended to
throw that thing herself, only the fuse was defective or she was too
wishy-washy to lob it in time."

Pat seemed more pleased at the woman's aggression than
dismayed at losing another example of man's inhumanity to
woman. "Well, good for her! Too bad she didn't hit the bum with
the firecracker."

"It is quite probable," I informed her, "that rather than hurling
her violence at some laudable target, such as an adult male, your
heroine was 'fragging' *us*. Three months ago, this building had five
broken windows and now it has nine. It's bad enough when our
own psychos take out their frustration on us, but when outsiders
start picking on us for downgrading their ghetto, I start worrying
about our image."

"Now, Chief," Pat cajoled, "you don't know for sure that she was aiming at us. What probably happened was, there are so many things and people on this street that deserve to be blown up that she couldn't make up her mind once she lit the firecracker."

"Cherry bomb!" I corrected. Pat looked puzzled. "Do you mean," I said, "that an informed, street-wise social worker like yourself doesn't know what a cherry bomb is?"

"I wasn't into juvenile delinquency as a kid," she confessed. "I waited till I was ready for the adult variety."

"Well, that's why women shouldn't mess around with fireworks. No preparation for it. Still, I'm surprised they didn't give you a course in elementary explosives in that liberal social workers' school you went to."

Pat shrugged as she exited. "Sorry, I majored in arson."

See, Patricia Patterson got here first, one of the few members of the staff here ahead of me and one of the three professionals I never got to choose personally. It took me nearly four months after I became director to get even a resume from her, and when I finally did, I was sorry I had ever asked . . . and asked . . . and asked.

"This is it?"

"Sure, Chief," she said amiably. "Everything relevant is there."

"*Everything?* All I've got here is your name, address, phone number, Berkeley for your master's degree and your certification. Where's the rest of it?"

"Like what?" she asked blandly.

Exasperated, I pulled open the file drawer of my desk and withdrew a neatly typed three-page resume submitted by Chris Pappas, one of our female psychologists. "Like this!"

Pat gingerly picked it up, avidly assimilating the data in that voracious memory bank of hers, yet shaking her head in dismay all the while. "Date of birth. Now, Vince, you *know* the law does not permit employers to discriminate on the basis of age, so why should someone have to tell when they were born?"

"The law also does not permit the employment of minors! Suppose I got a resume from a twelve-year-old?"

"Hah, I can imagine how far this resume would have gotten if

Chris were fifty instead of twenty-five!" she scoffed. "Look at this—weight: one hundred twenty—which Chris probably last weighed in the eighth grade. Would you have liked someone to decide he wasn't going to hire Dr. Bellino because you were forty pounds overweight?"

"Forty pounds!" I exclaimed. "Listen, I may not eat that bacteria-ridden curdled glop you subsist on, but I am not *that* . . ."

"*I* don't care what you weigh," she assured me magnanimously.

"So why should you want *me* to list my height?"

"Who said you had to list your height? I can *see* you're five-nine."

"Five-eight," she corrected. "I'm just as tall as you are."

"And *I'm* five-nine," I persisted.

She looked at me skeptically. "Is that with or without your clothes on?"

"What the hell have clothes got to do with height?"

"Well, maybe you had on shoes with higher heels on the day you measured," she said helpfully.

"I wouldn't be buried in shoes with high heels!"

"Well, you don't have to feel that way about it. A lot of short men wear . . ."

"I am not a short man. I am of average, i.e., normal, height. *You* are a tall woman."

"Which makes me abnormal, I suppose. You see what happens when you ask personal questions about all these sensitive areas, like weight and height and place of birth."

"Place of birth?" I questioned. "What the hell's so controversial about that?"

"Are you kidding? You wouldn't dare ask my race, but suppose I listed my place of birth as Ghana. Or San Juan, Puerto Rico?"

"In this community, you would have gotten the job automatically," I reassured her.

"And this one's the worst—marital status! Does being married make Chris Pappas a better psychologist? Does it make her more reliable?"

"Possibly less so. We certainly lose more married women to maternity leaves," I conceded.

"I'm sure Chris is too liberated to let her husband keep her barefoot and pregnant, the way you Latin men want your wives to be," Pat sneered.

"Now, that's unfair," I retorted calmly. "Haven't you heard of Gucci? Our wives wear some of the finest shoes in the world. And Chris, despite the extreme hazards of marriage, seems to be free from imminent childbearing and athlete's foot, and quite happy with her identity as a married woman."

"Why should identity have anything to do with marriage?" Pat protested. "All women should be addressed as Ms."

"On envelopes, maybe. But admit it, Pat, nobody *calls* you Ms. Patterson. Half your patients call you Miss, half Mrs., and the rest, caught up in the spirit of universal sisterhood, call you Pat. However, far be it from me to meddle in a case of Ms.-taken identity," I assured her. "Still, wouldn't you like to provide us with a nearest of kin in case you lose one of your battles with the forces of evil and the American Psychiatric Association? Parent, child, husband, boyfriend, girlfriend, rebel leader?"

"You're really dying to know about my personal life, aren't you?" she taunted, hands on her hips.

"Your personal life couldn't possibly concern me less!" I answered, feeling my face flush. "I don't give a damn about your lifestyle, past or present affiliations, race, weight, height, measurements, pedigree, or extracurricular acts in violation of criminal, moral, or natural law, as long as you show up on time and do your job! As medical director, all I have to know about you is whether you meet the qualifications of your job description."

Far from looking dismayed by my uncharacteristic outburst, Pat looked serene and vaguely triumphant. "It's all there on the resume, Vince," she smiled, indicating the half-filled, triple-spaced sheet she had offered me.

By now, you are probably asking the same question I have asked myself dozens of times: How did a rational, conservative, medically disciplined psychiatrist like myself get saddled with an insubordinate, bleeding-heart ultraliberal like Patterson as coordinator of my community mental health clinic? Well, you probably haven't asked it in so many words, since I'm sure you don't know what a clinic coordinator is. You probably don't even know what a community mental health clinic is—much less care.

So let's start at the beginning, with why you should care. If you're an American, the odds are four out of five that you have some kind of a psychiatric symptom: anxiety, depression, insomnia, irritability or, more likely, the kind of a headache, backache, or bellyache for which your kindly old family doctor has been scribbling prescriptions for years without its getting any better. And if you're like most Americans, you shrug off the symptom and keep plugging away at your routine, figuring there is nothing you can do about it anyway. One in five of you does not keep plugging away with the same efficiency—that symptom is actually interfering with the way you function. The one statistic that has always freaked me out is that at least one in ten Americans will be admitted to a mental hospital at some point in his life. It freaks me out because it's something nobody ever talks about and you forget it happens. People love to talk about their operations and their ulcers, but who is going to admit to a nervous breakdown or that their dear old mother is rotting away somewhere in an upstate asylum?

Now if you're among the eighty percent who are suffering from psychiatric symptoms, the one thing you are least likely to do about it is to see a psychiatrist. First of all, you may be suffering but you're not crazy, and everyone knows that a psychiatrist treats people who are crazy, right? Secondly, if you happen to have a psychiatrist in your neighborhood, chances of which are slim if you don't live in New York or Los Angeles, he will charge you anywhere from thirty to seventy-five dollars for a short-weighted hour (something on the order of forty minutes), and laying out that kind of money at least once a week for months or years at a time either indicates you are crazy enough to need it or crazy to be laying out that kind of money, if you aren't desperate.

Alternatives? You could try your family doctor, who by now has been replaced by a specialist in internal medicine or an equally trained specialist in family practice—they charge fifteen or twenty dollars for ten minutes, which some simple multiplication will show is worse than what psychiatrists charge. Since they want to waste neither their precious time nor that of the people in their bulging waiting rooms talking out your emotional problems, and are not about to insult you or lose you as a patient by referring you to a psychiatrist, they treat you in the quickest, most economical way possible—which is why Valium is by far the most widely prescribed drug in the country. You could try your clergyman, if you're a churchgoer—a rather iffy business, since he may be no more qualified to do psychiatry than he is to practice gynecology—especially since he can't fall back on Valium unless he gives you some of his own.

What you need, of course, is a *community mental health clinic*, a neighborhood center staffed by competent professionals who will diagnose and treat you immediately at a price you can afford—or possibly at no cost at all; a clinic that can stop your weird uncle from hallucinating, keep your spouse from drinking, help your son kick drugs, find out why Johnny can't read, rid your sister of those migraines that have plagued her for years, get mother out of her depression, and help you find some meaning and satisfaction in your life. You need a place where you can get a staff member to accompany you to family court to keep your old man from battering you or to visit your home to evaluate the daughter who hasn't gotten out of bed except to urinate for the past two weeks.

But chances are that if you start cruising around your neighborhood in search of your friendly community mental health center, you'll find that it's never been constructed. If four out of five Americans had pain in their toes, you can bet your boots there would be a low-cost community foot clinic on every other block before throngs of irate citizens marched (despite their painful toes) on their city halls demanding something be done. But when it comes to mental health, people suffer in silence, because they know they're not crazy yet and they don't want anyone to suspect they are and, besides, they figure their anxiety and depression is the normal state of mind—which, in view of the prevalence of such symptoms, is true to some extent.

The community served by St. Dymphna's didn't have a community health center in the true sense of the word; I mean, not one of those big, modern comprehensive centers that includes an in-patient psychiatric unit with a color television in every room to watch the paranoids, seclusion rooms with upholstered walls, and electroshock units also wired for quadrophonic high-fidelity amplification, the kinds of psychiatric Disneyworlds that were being thrown up like pup-tents at a Boy Scout jamboree around the country during the federal construction boom in the sixties. By the time our sleepy community woke up to the notion that there was money around for new mental health centers, the wave of optimism was over, and it was like arriving at the buffet table to find your selection limited to lemon wedges and parsley sprigs.

We started with a modest staff in a small clinic located in a crumbling, semiabandoned building and have been cruising downhill from there. The St. Dymphna Community Mental Health Clinic, which I direct on its precarious route, is but an arm of a proud, rejuvenated, fully equipped medical center—well, more its armpit. We're not even within a half mile of the rest of the hospital, which is not an unusual situation among medical centers; after all, everyone in the neighborhood says, "A mental health clinic is a great idea, but not on *my* block," and the parent hospitals themselves tend to hold the same philosophy. If you ever find a medical center with both a leprosarium and a mental health clinic, the leper colony will be the one closest to the main building.

We were housed in a grim brick building with nine (at last count) broken windows and walls that still show in spots the scars of fires started periodically by the derelicts who inhabited it between owners. I'm not sure what function the building previously had—it is rumored to have sheltered a telephone company, a public library, a police station, and a venereal disease clinic, possibly all simultaneously, before it was ultimately abandoned. The community kept vandalizing and defacing it, probably under the impression that it was a welfare center, so the landlord was only too glad to accept us as tenants for the community to use as a target for its hostility, and save wear and tear on the property.

To be honest about it, I wasn't always that enthusiastic about community mental health myself. I always figured that after my residency I would take a job at some university-affiliated hospital for a few hours a day while I built up a pleasant private practice of cooperative and insightful patients and, after a year or so, would devote my life fully to doing the sort of thing you read about in the analytic journals or, better yet, watched on the movie screens— you know, helping a gorgeous lady executive like Ginger Rogers in *Lady in the Dark* face up to her latent penis envy and rise radiantly from your genuine cowhide couch ready to chuck her unfulfilling career and find happiness in the arms of a strong, benevolent man. I should have realized back then that a kid who grew up loving pizza and stoop ball on the streets of Manhattan could never have settled into that sort of dreary though lucrative lifestyle, even though I had been able to hold my own against more traditional types on their ivy-covered academic turf. I was a natural for community psychiatry, but that's always the last chapter in the thousand-page textbook, and they never get to cover it in the lectures.

We never covered military psychiatry in the course of my training either, but that didn't dissuade the U.S. Army from pressing me into service for two years. Subsequent potential employers were not as eager to conscript me and, as a 32-year-old jobless vet, I found my prospects apparently limited to methadone clinics or Medicaid mills that doled out prescriptions for barbiturates and tranquilizers on demand. Then, St. Dymphna's and I found each other. They needed a director for their newly funded mental health clinic and, though it would be my first real job, my administrative experience in the Army and my academic background impressed the administration enough for them to hire me, especially since what St. Dymphna's had to offer was hardly likely to entice an experienced clinic director to switch realms.

Before the clinic opened, St. Dymphna's was providing some limited mental health services at the main hospital through a pair of psychologists and two psychiatric social workers, who were loosely attached to the Social Service Department. A couple of psychiatrists with established private practices were also on the payroll and came in for a few hours a week to prescribe medication and do evaluations. The docs had no role in the new clinic, which was budgeted for half a dozen full-time psychiatrists and had no need for by-the-hour consulting types. The other professionals had been assured of continued employment at the new clinic, leaving the incoming director no real choice in the matter. However, the senior psychologist, a lady Ph.D., exercised *her* choice in the matter by resigning before I was hired, miffed at the hospital's insistence on filling the top slot with an M.D. after she had been so capably running its skeletal mental health operation.

Her resignation left me with three professionals, two aides, three secretaries, and a bunch of promises for my newly acquired staff. It was only after my arrival that I learned that while we indeed had a firm commitment from the federal government and the New York City Department of Mental Health, with a legitimate contract, there would be a slight delay in the translation of the inky budget figures into negotiable dollars while various papers bobbed around the bureaucratic channels between Albany and Washington. Now, as wasteful and absurd as it sounds, it is not that uncommon to have a new facility constructed and a staff hired and then have to wait several months to begin clinical services, during which time the hirelings attend meetings, make plans, read professional literature, and otherwise waste time. Our problem was the opposite; since St. Dymphna's had been providing mental health services, we already had an active case load. Moreover, that case load would grow rapidly, as hospitals and agencies throughout the city had been informed that St. Dymphna's now had a brand new mental health clinic, ready to receive referrals of clients from our surrounding area.

The "slight delay" in getting funds with which to hire a respectable staff ultimately amounted to three months, during which time we had to meet the onslaught of depressed, deranged, and destitute patients with our small squad of holdovers and rejects.

With the departure of the senior psychologist, Patricia Patterson, M.S.W., though still south of thirty, became the senior clinician. Tall, slender, and tanned, she looked nothing like the dumpling-shaped, oxford-shod, wry-faced crones whose images the words *social worker* evoke, but beneath those long, straight brown tresses rattled the saberlike invectives of Germaine Greer and Kate Millett, whose landmark feminist tomes were just then beginning to reach the paperback trade. I'm sure Pat would have preferred the leadership of a female Ph.D. to a male M.D., and served under me just about as willingly as I had served in the Army.

The remaining psychologist was Carl Brock, a prodigious former linebacker whose knee injury in a game against Ohio State during his junior year led him to stay on for an M.A. in psychology instead of going on to the greener fields of Astroturf in the NFL.

Our other psychiatric social worker was Sandy Silverstein, a no-frills native New Yorker who wore blue jeans to work long before Gloria Vanderbilt made it respectable. Sandy had the invaluable asset of fluency in Spanish, which she attributed to her high school courses. I personally doubted that the old textbooks, with their pretty farm houses and aristocratic *haciendas*, contributed much to her understanding of faulty plumbing, defective heating, and nondomesticated resident fauna when one of our local clients listed everything wrong with her apartment in a forty-five-second tirade. I held more stock in the scuttlebutt that Sandy had shacked up with so many of our local Latinos that by now her verbal productions during orgasm came out in Spanish.

The hospital was benevolent enough to assign us two of its clinic aides, whose prime qualifications seemed to be the desire for a transfer—I'm not sure whose desire, their own or the hospital's. Well, expansion teams don't get staffed with all-stars and neither do newly formed clinics, exiled blocks away from the motherland. Maria Sanchez was reputed to have a quick temper and a sharp tongue, while Amos "Molasses" Mosley had a slow metabolism and a dull wit.

Molasses was out "in the field" most of the time, making home visits to patients without phones when they missed appointments, running (well, actually, shuffling) messenger service to the main hospital, and bringing lunch to clinicians who didn't mind eating it at 4 P.M. If you sent him out for a container of hot coffee and a cold Coke, the drinks always came back at the same temperature.

Since neither Carl, Pat, nor I spoke Spanish, Maria was generally shuttled from office to office to interpret for Hispanic patients:

"Ask her how she feels, Maria."

*"Como esta usted, Señora?"*

*"Me siento mala."*

"Doctor, she don't feel so good; this lady's got asthma a long time, and she's got headaches, too, and she's very nervous. Her husband, he's been seeing another woman, he don't give her no money, her oldest son is in trouble with the police, and she thinks her daughter's on drugs."

Since Maria knew everyone in the neighborhood intimately, this saved us considerable time in history-taking; but even with her expertise in rapid translation, Maria was hard pressed to spread herself around when three or four Puerto Ricans were simultaneously undergoing some form of diagnostic evaluation or treatment. It was not unusual in those days for us to pull one of our two receptionists from the front desk to serve as emergency interpreters, exposing them to more stirring and pathetic real-life drama in one day than they could have absorbed in an entire week of watching *novellas*, the UHF-TV Spanish soap operas. The more experienced of the pair was Connie Rodriguez, a thirty-five-year-old transfer from the medical clinic who, in spite of her reddish-brown hair and alabaster skin, persisted in classifying the bulk of our patients as either Spanish or white. (We whites called ourselves Anglos, whether Italian, Greek, or Argentinian.) Connie's brunette sidekick, twenty-year-old Dolores Santiago, had a more typical dark Latin complexion and a most delightfully atypical body; when it came to holding down the reception desk, Dolores could not match Connie's front-line experience, but neither Connie nor anyone else could match Dolores's own spectacular front line.

The final member of our shorthanded team was Rosie McGonigle, whose unimpressive official title was secretary, but who, because the clinical demands on me as the only psychiatrist left little time to handle even the most mundane of administrative chores, became a self-appointed administrator of sorts. Rosie was the world's oldest forty two year old, a tall, broad-hipped spinster with graying hair like straw yanked painfully back from her perpetually creased forehead. She squinted at an ill-run world through rimless lenses as thick as Maria Sanchez's accent and seemed to be constantly shaking her head in shocked disapproval of one more irregularity discovered in someone's performance, demeanor, dress, or general existence. Shuttled from department to department at St. Dymphna's for a quarter of a century, ever since leaving high school with her perfect attendance award clutched to her maiden form, and now foisted upon our defenseless infant program, Rosie openly complained or secretly seethed about the deterioration of the neighborhood, the increase in bureaucratic paperwork, the replacement of aristocratic doctors and starched nurses by denim-clad, careless vagabonds masquerading as professionals, and a general erosion of medical and moral standards comparable to that of tooth enamel immersed in a fluoride-free sea of taffy. Rosie lived for only two things: the clinic and her mother, one occupying her days, and the other her nights and weekends. Her mother, Ethel McGonigle, actually occupied quite a bit of clinic time as well, with phone calls and drop-in visits. In shameful delight, we watched the otherwise ultraefficient Rosie squirm in anguished embarrassment like a victim of Montezuma's revenge on a nonstop bus trip from Mexico City to Tijuana every time mother interrupted her meticulous routine of fee-collecting, statistics compilation, and office espionage.

Rosie, as abrasive and fault-finding as she was, unconsciously served the invaluable function of holding the rest of us together in those difficult early days, for no matter how much we got on one another's nerves, our common animosity toward Rosie locked us in an indissoluble alliance. It made us as oblivious to our inherent differences as Rosie was; Connie Rodriguez summed up Rosie pretty well when she said, "A lot of people say Rosie McGonigle is prejudiced, but it's not true. She treats everybody rotten, no matter what color they are."

Not that we had much opportunity to fight Rosie or each other—we were kept busier than a spider addicted to Methadrine back then. Carl, Sandy, and Pat alternated intake duty while attempting to provide ongoing psychotherapy and social services to patients already on the rolls, while I had to evaluate each new case as soon as possible after intake, as well as prescribe medication, some form of which more than half of our charges received. After three months of this, I had almost forgotten that somewhere in the distant past St. Dymphna's had been promised a staff commensurate with its clinical responsibilities. When administration called with the glad tidings that the funds to hire a dozen professionals had finally been made available, I truthfully was apprehensive about tampering with our hectic but functioning operation by adding horses in midstream.

Well, overconfidence once cost the Mets fifth place and the clinic was getting a little spooky with just the nine of us rattling around its spacious though decrepit interior, so I baited the outside world with a few ads and wrote letters to the hospitals with psychiatric residency programs and within six weeks we had enough staff to be at each others' throats over adequate office space.

Our newly formed roster had the international composition of the Ringling Brothers' circus and I felt like a ringmaster trying to keep three rings running without getting trampled by a herd of elephants or sabotaged by a bunch of clowns in the process. The newcomers included psychiatrists Sharon Schaeffer, Dimitri Niarhos, Diego Martinez, Ilse Krumpel, Iderlina Feliciano, and Harry Chong; psychologists Nunzio Scaglione, Ramon Montalvo, Chris Pappas, and Dennis Boyle; social worker Dave Goldman; and nurse Jackie Callahan. More than half were foreign born and even the rest made Pat, the only WASP on staff, feel like a member of the diverse minority groups she so liberally championed.

Faced with the formidable task of converting this ragtag batch of rookies into some semblance of a team, I cast about for some help and hooked Pat, realizing that mental health clinics make stranger bedfellows than even politics.

"How would you like to be clinic coordinator?" I offered one morning.

"How much does it pay?" she asked.

"Nothing. It's an internal title. No hospital-wide recognition, no raise, just extra work," I explained.

"Sounds great. I'll take it," she agreed.

"Not so fast!" I cautioned. "I'm not giving you the job unless I understand why you're taking it. If you don't have a sane reason, you default by reason of insanity."

"Then who will you give the job to?" she asked.

I thought a moment. "I don't have anyone else."

"That's why I'm taking it," she explained. "I had the count already. What do I do?"

"Help me organize things a little more tightly," I explained. "Our intake system is haphazard. We've been assigning one social worker or psychologist to intake every morning or afternoon and whoever comes in, they win as their personal case, after a psychiatrist does his own evaluation right on top of theirs. The only thing in favor of picking up patients that way is that unless the Supreme Court declares the law of averages unconstitutional, cases should ultimately even out."

"The law of averages does nothing to prevent losing streaks," Pat observed. "Some clinicians can run three straight intake days without a case while others get blitzed with six in one afternoon. Then, it doesn't make sense for a therapist who can't speak Spanish to be running around the clinic like a horse-trader, trying to unload a Puerto Rican patient he shouldn't have been involved with in the first place."

"So," I continued, "why don't we get the psychologists and social workers off intake altogether. Leave the whole procedure to the psychiatrists, who have to see each new patient for diagnosis and evaluation anyway. Then, the clinic coordinator—that's you—can review the intake chart and make a leisurely, sensible assignment based on the patient's needs and the therapist's existing case load. It will also spare an impatient patient from having to recite his life history twice in two hours."

"What else do I coordinate?" Pat asked.

"Anything that looks uncoordinated," I advised.

"That should take in just about everything but Dolores Santiago's walk," she noted.

"Yes, please do not mess with that!" I begged. "When all else is in ruins and shambles, and despair reigns throughout our realm, we can always send Dolores down the corridor and watch her walk."

"That's not going to do much for me," she complained.

"I could get Ramon Montalvo, that new Argentinian psychologist who looks like Zorro, to twirl his moustache for you," I offered.

"Amazing what some allegedly modern men think will turn a woman on!" she exclaimed caustically.

"Oh, I don't subscribe that much to moustaches and muscles, as you may have noticed," I hastened to assure her. "For a real turn-on, I'll still put my faith in a good old-fashioned power switch."

Incredible to relate, within a month of expanding our staff, the clinic pace was as frantic as it had been prior to the arrival of our reinforcements. A steady stream of referrals inundated us: state hospitals turning out thirty-year tenants in an ill-advised house-cleaning spree; county hospitals turning away would-be admissions for being sane enough to request admission; guidance counselors using us in lieu of the hickory stick for their unruly charges; medical clinics tired of hearing complaints ill matched to normal laboratory tests and well-functioning bodies; and word of mouth from satisfied customers to dissatisfied neighbors. We were now averaging more than a hundred new cases and logging over five hundred visits each month.

Pat, who led our league in the patients-carried department, was now busier than ever: working with me and Rosie to cope with the increasing paper work; indoctrinating new clinicians in proper charting procedures; holding down the fort while I forayed out to various agency and community meetings; and refereeing patient-receptionist, receptionist-clinician, clinician-patient, and sundry other hassles filled any spare minutes between patients of her own that she did not spend reviewing and assigning new cases. I still had one more massive burden to foist on her, however.

I will never forget the day Pat learned she was about to become a mother. I will never forget because I was the one who broke the news to her—the tidings that she was about to acquire the direct responsibility of a brood of seven fledgling paraprofessional assistants of assorted sex and color, in various stages of underdevelopment.

"Good morning, Pat," I intoned with mellifluous authority, trying to emulate Charlie Townsend about to send his Angels merrily off on a life-threatening mission. "I've received a bit of somewhat disturbing news. It seems some help is on the way."

"An unwanted kind of help for an operation that is as short-handed as a five-armed octopus?" Pat mused. "My leader speaks in riddles. You mean, perhaps, some sort of unwelcome administrative or community surveillance in the name of improving our services?"

"No, nothing like that," I reassured her. "This involves actual additions to our staff. Mental health assistants!"

"But what *kind* of assistance?" she asked impatiently.

"Assistants. With a *t*—as in trauma. I mean, as in trustworthy, tried, and true."

"Vince," she observed, "you look as though you have just won your choice of a weekend in Sheboygan, Wisconsin, or fifty pounds of sheep dip. Whence cometh these assistants that you are awaiting with such keen revulsion?"

"From our very community they cometh, sons and daughters of our teeming environs," I revealed.

"Home-grown products of our native soil?" Pat waxed metaphorical.

"That's dirt, not soil," I corrected. "But, yes, they'll be hand-picked from our asphalt garden by that motley gang we call a community advisory board, who have had their fingers in our pie since St. Dymphna's started this half-baked operation."

"Look, so far all I've managed to piece together is that someone from the neighborhood is sending someone else from the neighborhood to give us some help that you'd rather not have. Could you possibly be just a little more specific?"

"Page one," I began. "The federal government, under the auspices of the Department of Labor, has made money available to certain low-income communities to train unemployed people for hospital jobs. Certain hospitals, including ours, have agreed to sponsor some of these trainees and guarantee them jobs upon successful completion of their nine-month training period. Some will be trained as operating-room technicians, some as medical-records clerks, and some, God help us, as mental health assistants."

"How many are we getting?"

"Seven," I moaned. "As in the deadly sins or the plagues of Egypt."

"Well, *I* think it's great!" Pat declared. "It's about time we started giving more jobs to the people around here whose Medicaid cards we make our livings from."

"Yes, but in less time than it took me to complete the first grade they are supposed to undergo a metamorphosis from unskilled drifters to knowledgeable psychotherapists," I griped.

"Since it took you only nine months to progress from a one-celled organism to a ten-toed little human," Pat pointed out, "is it too much to expect some small measure of educational progress over that same period of time?"

"It depends on what you are expecting it from," I replied. "I can think of any number of creatures with ten toes who never learn to count on them. You have to consider the nature of the species we are trying to train."

"I don't expect you to be a flaming liberal like me," Pat smoldered, "but you don't have to assume that anyone who happens to be born into a different socioeconomic or ethnic group from your own is uneducable."

"While I can't predict with absolute certainty the caliber of trainees we'll get when the big wheelers and dealers of our community back the protégé, cousin, or paramour of their choice, I know exactly who our first two trainees will be," I revealed. "This clinic's very own dynamic duo, Maria Sanchez and Amos Mosley!"

"Great!" Pat exulted. "I should hope our benevolent administrators would begin their charity on the home front. Those two have been with the hospital since the Social Service Department started mental health services—long before *you* arrived—and they deserve a chance to be something more than interpreters or errand runners."

"My optimistic colleague," I sighed, "you must have been the kind of a kid who would find a stocking full of horse manure on Christmas morning and joyously look for a pony. Just what do you expect to fashion out of old Mosley? In nine months, Molasses probably wouldn't finish filling out his registration cards, much less suffer direct exposure to the training process. Neither of them has been inside a classroom in over twenty-five years, and the last time they dropped in was just before they dropped out. And do you think our community is going to dredge up anyone more promising, considering that Molasses and Maria, despite their considerable limitations, managed to avoid the legions of the unemployed from which our other recruits will be drafted? What, realistically, will we have to work with?"

"People who actually live in this community and are well acquainted with its problems and resources!" Pat answered.

"Well, *those* criteria would be met by the entire membership of the Spanish Skulls," I noted. "They're not only familiar with the community's problems, they cause a great number of them. Likewise, they are thoroughly familiar with such indispensable indigenous resources as pushers, fences, loan sharks, and arsonists."

Pat seemed to be truly relishing my discomfiting misgivings. "Like it or not, Vince," she crowed, "the days when the rich professionals held a monopoly on all the health services are at an end—and good riddance, too! I'm sure that the new mental health assistants will work out just fine."

"I'm sure they will," I gently affirmed, then added ominously, "under your able supervision."

Pat's eyes widened as she suddenly perceived that into our ideological arena a few real lions had been turned loose. "*My* supervision? Just what exactly is that supposed to mean?"

"The nine-month training period," I explained, "will be only partly spent in some distant classroom learning the basic principles of psychology, sociology, elementary English, and whatever other fields are remotely connected with or presumed to supply some sort of foundation for the shifting, crumbling structure of the community mental health system. Much of the trainees' time— and, once their instructors get an idea of how little time it will take to saturate their capacity for absorbing formal education, I daresay *most* of their time—will be spent right here with us, learning the nature of the real world of mental health, a world into which the writers of textbooks never venture. Pat, are you listening to me? I seem to have lost you somewhere."

"Try looking for me back at 'under your able supervision,'" she said helpfully.

"Ah, but who else would I possibly choose, having already elevated you to the exalted rank of clinic coordinator . . ."

"Stop the elevator!" Pat commanded. "Where would I find the time, between treating my own patients and trying to hold this place together while you attend those leisurely community coffee klatsches you call meetings. You're not sticking me with shepherding a flock of kids. Who'd want to?"

"Hmmm, Sandy Silverstein might," I speculated. "Especially when she realizes that such a flock could make her pastures a little greener. Your rabble-rousing union demands a salary differential for social workers with supervisory responsibility—somewhere between one and two grand a year, as I recall. And Sandy is always bitching about the high cost of pot. She'd probably jump at . . ."

"Listen, Bellino," Pat snapped, rising to her feet. "Do you think I'm going to let you promote that girl over me when I've got two years' seniority in the Social Service Department here? I'm sure the union would have something to say about *that*! That kid wouldn't know how to begin to manage a trainee, and furthermore . . ."

I leaned back contentedly in my chair. "Okay, Pat," I grinned, "you've convinced me. You can supervise the trainees, if that's what you want."

She stopped her tirade and glared at me, then shrugged. "I guess I did want it, after all. But don't ask me why!"

"Oh, I don't have to," I said. "It's simply because you could never stand to watch somebody do an important job that you know you could do better."

"An insight you picked up in one of your courses on Freudian psychology?"

"No, it goes back a little earlier," I answered. "Plato, I believe. He said that no wise man would ever choose to govern, except out of fear of being ruled by someone less capable than himself. In any event, Pat, I'm sure that once you get to know your new charges, you'll soon come to love them."

She shook her head ruefully. "The feeling, I assure you, will be strictly platonic."

And so, with five new assistants-to-be joining Maria and Molasses, the clinic staff was finally complete. Some of the newcomers were eager to be molded into the brilliant, empathetic type of therapist Joanne Woodward winds up playing on "The Monday Night Movie," while others, who never watched Joanne Woodward movies, were merely grateful for a regular pay check and would have initially been just as content to be file clerks or laundry workers had the feds deposited equal grants in those vocational areas.

The quintet consisted of Carmen Ortiz, twenty, single, and just out of a two-year college program leading nowhere; Pablo Suarez, eighteen, a local kid with no foreseeable future once he'd left high school and the street gangs until an aunt with a strong community connection came through with this assignment; Jeanne Ellis, twenty-three, black, divorced, mother of two, ready for anything we or life could throw at her; Andrew Canfield, articulate, unattached, and twenty-one, with a thoroughly useless B.A. in psychology and a thoroughly useful uncle on the hospital's board of trustees; and Evelyn Larsen, a thirty-five-year-old divorcee with three kids, who had bounced around as a real estate agent, teacher's assistant, welfare mother, and civic-minded volunteer, a woman who had experienced a broad spectrum of highs and lows, economically and emotionally.

"I do not expect you to become junior psychoanalysts," I told them at our first meeting.

"And why not?" Evelyn retorted, rising to the challenge.

"Because I already have plenty of those," I explained, "and there are more important things you'll have to learn to do—such as making sure your patients and their families have adequate funds for groceries and clothing, adequate living accommodations, and are emotionally together enough to be able to take advantage of the benefits they're eligible for, including the opportunity to get therapy here. Psychotherapy is fine, but food has to come first. Or as my sainted grandfather, Vittorio Bellino, would always greet his guests, 'First, eat—then let's talk!' Welcome aboard."

With twenty-two clinicians on staff, including six psychiatrists, I suppose I could have asked Pat to reassign the cases I had picked up during our staff-poor months so, like all the self-respecting clinic directors I had ever known, I could devote all my time to administrative matters. But, hell, I went through four years of medical school, a year of internship, and three years of residency because I wanted to be a *psychiatrist*, and you couldn't pay me enough to give that up to push papers around full-time. Patients seem to me to be as essential to doctoring as booze to bartending or fish to fishmongering.

How does somebody give up patients? Laurie, for example, had started treatment with me five years ago—God, that's practically half of my adult life! Oh, I haven't seen her continuously; she was one of the first cases assigned to me as a resident, and she looked me up when I got out of the army—still, I've been an important part of her life for years, as I have for many patients, and I'm not going to deny that they're important to me, too. How do you close up shop on that kind of existence and say, "I'm not seeing patients anymore?"

I've seen Laurie through three hospitalizations, several suicide attempts, two divorces, a few job changes, and innumerable relationships, most somewhat traumatic. This week's crisis was a rather benign though significant one.

"I don't know how you're going to feel about this, but I've got to tell you," she began, excitement in her eyes. "I'm going to get a tattoo."

I very carefully raised an eyebrow.

"Yeah," she assured me. "I've always wanted one. As a kid, I used to buy those washable ones in the five-and-ten. My mother hated them, so I'd put them way up my arm where my sleeves would cover. I'd apply them in the bathroom and throw the used sheet in the toilet. One time it didn't go into the water and clung to

the wall of the bowl, so when I flushed, the design wound up
imprinted on the toilet. It was a really gruesome skull with a snake
crawling out of its eye. My mother went wild!

"Jerry, that guy I've been seeing, has a tattoo. It's a panther, up
on his bicep; it seems to be clawing his arm, and there are little
drops of blood tattooed, too. It's a real turn-on."

"Laurie," I groaned, "you're *not* getting a panther, I hope."

She grinned elfishly. "No. First I thought I wanted a butterfly,
but now I'm sure I want a rose. A pink tea-rose, just beginning to
open, with a green stem. My girlfriend knows a guy in Westchester
who does it great. I'm going to put it right here." She pointed with
her index finger to her jean-clad right thigh, at the hip socket. "It
won't show even if I'm wearing a bikini. I mean, to see it, someone
will have to be already *very* intimate with me. It will be a nice
surprise for him—I'm not using it as a come-on. I was going to do it
last summer, but Roger was so much against it."

Roger was a twenty-six-year-old commercial artist, eight years
younger than Laurie. He had been seriously involved with only
one other woman, was strongly under his parents' domination, and
was ambivalent about Laurie's age, her past, and her numerous
male friends; still, the relationship had survived a stormy two-year
course.

"Roger says if I want to change my body, I should have cosmetic
surgery on the stretch marks on my abdomen. Or have the scars on
my arm taken off, where I used to slash myself. He doesn't
understand that I don't want to hide my past—I accept it as part of
myself. I have stretch marks because I had babies—I'm a thirty-
four-year-old woman, not an eighteen-year-old girl. I'm still
beautiful, but it's a different kind of beauty.

"Roger says, 'Suppose you meet a serious man who wants to
marry you. How do you know he'll accept a tattoo?' Shit, anyone
who wants me has got to accept a hell of a lot more than a tattoo!
I've got two Mexican kids by my first husband somewhere. I was in
a state hospital. I've tried to take my own life. A tattoo is the least!

"When I was only fifteen years old, I carved the word KILL at the
top of my arm with a compass point. You can still see it if the light
is right. Funny, Jerry went through a lot and he cut himself, too—

but he carved a heart. I mean, here he's so tough and wears leather and deals drugs, but he's got a heart and I've got KILL."

Laurie sighed at the memory of harsher times. "Well, that was a phase in my life. And I'm in a new phase now. I used to hate my body and think I was ugly. For the first time, a man can tell me I'm beautiful and I believe him, because I can look at my body and *see* it's beautiful. I think the fresh rose, barely opening up, is me. Am I crazy to want the tattoo?"

"When you first walked in, Laurie, my initial reaction was like Roger's," I said. "Now, I understand why you want it, and if you're sure of your decision, go ahead." As she left, I added, "I probably would have vetoed a skull with a snake crawling out of its eye."

Pat was in the waiting room area and watched Laurie stride happily out. "Your patient's looking good, Vince," she observed. "New, shorter hairdo, form-fitting jeans. Is she going out to look for a husband this weekend so that she can fill your conception of the well-adjusted woman?"

"Oh, she'll be engaged in something a bit more original," I confided. "She's going to get a tattoo. A pink tea-rose. Right here." I patted my nonformfitting trousers at the approximate location.

"A rose? Tattoo?" Pat echoed incredulously. She seemed utterly shocked to discover that a patient of someone whom she perceived to be so rigidly conservative could do something so outrageous, so independent, so . . . liberated. The way Pat was looking at me, you'd think I had said "a skull with a snake crawling out of its eye."

# 2

**D**ID HE REALLY SAY *TATTOO?* A *ROSE TATTOO?* HE SEEMED
actually pleased about it, for God's sake! Pin Bellino down and he'll
probably say his patient is defying hollow conventionality, finding
and expressing her true identity, *liberating* herself. Which is
bullshit, because all his neurotic patient is doing is grasping at one
more pathetic way to turn men on . . . she even seems to be
turning on her stodgy old shrink in the process. It's bad enough we
women have been painting our faces and staining our tresses for
centuries, shaving and plucking out hairs, not to mention the more
modern horrors of submitting our bodies to surgical knives for face-
lifts, nose jobs, and silicone deposits—now we can look forward to
transforming our hides into permanent walking picture galleries to
give our precious males one small extra measure of titillation.
Okay, I grant that Revlon and Estee Lauder get their regular rake-
off from my meager pay check, but as far as altering my body,
nothing sharper than my Lady Remington shaver is going to touch
it ever—that includes everything from scalpels at the local infirm-
ary and body shop to needles at Salty Sal's Coney Island Tattoo
Parlor.

Men! Take us as we are, as nature intended—unpainted,
unshaven, unadorned—take us or leave us! They always do *both*,
actually, don't they? The fattest, sloppiest, craziest women that I've
treated somehow find a man to complicate their wretched lives
further, and the prettiest, trimmest, most devoted women get

abandoned. Like Sue. I wondered what Dr. Bellino would have to say about *her* case.

There was no need to wonder, actually, because I could confront Dr. Bellino with Sue's plight in our weekly supervisory session. Not that I could expect to learn much from my eminent leader and would-be preceptor, but since clinic policy compelled me to spend a continuous hour in his presence every Tuesday, I might just as well put the time to good use by attempting to raise his consciousness level, even if the task were comparable to surfacing the *Titanic*.

The supervisory sessions had been instituted by Bellino, who classified psychologists and social workers among the educable retarded and charged his doctors with the herculean task of giving them expert guidance in carrying out the psychotherapy they were expected to administer thirty-odd hours a week while the doctors scribbled prescriptions, made astute diagnoses of conditions for the psychologists and social workers to treat, and read their newspapers.

The basic idea of psychiatrists providing supervision in psychotherapy for us lower-salaried professionals is a highly dubious one. Look at the crew of alleged mentors Bellino shanghaied for our floundering craft. To start with, there's Harry Chong. Harry's concept of psychiatric conditions is that if they're diseases, we have a pill or shot to cure them; if the pill doesn't work, the patient is a malingerer who never had a disease to begin with, and shouldn't be wasting a doctor's time.

Then there's Iderlina Feliciano, another newly hatched specialist, whose exclusive province is children. Her physical development never quite matched her intellectual growth and, at the age of thirty, she's shorter than most of the preadolescents. Maybe she's tall enough to drink from the water fountains in her native Philippines, but here she seems to be in constant fear of getting stepped on. She won't get within five feet (which is more than her height) of an adult client, unless it happens to be the mother of a small child.

There's the Princess, Sharon Schaeffer, who would rather see a supervisee, I'm sure, than a patient—though she'd rather see her hairdresser or manicurist most of all, if given her choice. Sharon is probably a very bright woman with a sharp, analytic mind under those golden curly locks, according to some; on the other hand, some of us contend that years of inhaling nail polish fumes and the slow seepage of peroxide through her skullbones have rendered her incapable of doing much more than she does, which is sit around looking terribly bored with the whole clinic.

Ilse Krumpel has been practicing psychiatry for so long she refers to Harry Stack Sullivan as "that young upstart." Far too lethargic to cope with the competitiveness and fiscal management inherent in private practice, she's knocked around a variety of agencies that would hand her a regular pay check without her having to ask for it, including state hospitals, courts, the school system and, in the past decade, the not so placid world of community mental health. I should acknowledge that Ilse did raise three children, and I suppose there was a time when a few hours a week in a steady job was the best she could manage. But she's a grandmother now with little to do except eat, sleep, and come to her job, and unfortunately, she seems to confuse the first two activities with the last. She is continuously adding to her prodigious bulk with the assortment of candy, cookies, and more substantial delicacies she keeps in her desk, pausing only to take a nap or go out to lunch (she's been known to become absentminded and eat lunch twice in the same day) unless we manage to foist a patient on her.

Dimitri Niarhos probably hasn't got much to teach, since he must have cut every class and lecture he could manage, if his attendance here is any indication. Dimitri is the kind of guy who shakes hands with you, after which you count your rings—correction: in his case, better count your fingers. Even though he's working in a clinic setting, Dimitri routinely knocks a few minutes off every patient's session just so he doesn't get into bad habits which might cost him money if he reenters private practice. He'll give you an honest day's work—only it takes him three days—and he's left more jobs under fire than an arsonist.

The one remaining shrink, Diego Martinez, was initially an enigma to me. He was a paunchy but energetic fellow in his early fifties, born in the Dominican Republic, trained in a top American medical school, with numerous past distinguished faculty positions at outstanding medical centers and a list of published books and articles that made his competitors look like cases of writer's block complicated by writer's cramp.. He proved to be an exuberant, indefatigable clinician and, as the only Spanish-speaking shrink on staff, he saw more patients than Dimitri, Frau Krumpel, and the Princess combined. The only problem was that none of us could figure out why a man with his background would accept the lowly position of staff psychiatrist in our nonacademic, underpaying, slum-centered establishment.

Vince was so desperate for a Spanish-speaking shrink that he would have hired Pancho Villa out of an approved residency program and was not about to veto a candidate on the grounds of overqualification, poor career judgment, or potential for insurrection. Maybe Martinez was an independently wealthy adventurer who thrived on a variety of experience and wanted to balance his years at the academic summits with some time in the pits. Who knew? I, like Dr. Bellino, was not about to look a gift horse in the mouth, though the horse seemed as Trojan in origin as Hispanic.

With the possible exception of Dr. Martinez, I really couldn't see that any of these medical marvels were equipped to add to my expertise in psychotherapy. I had supplemented my more-than-adequate education at Berkeley with a three-year program in a psychoanalytically oriented training institute and had taken several other courses in analytic theory and practice at the New School for Social Research and the William Allenson White Institute, whereas the medical marvels had probably covered Freud in three lectures and everyone after him in one lecture somewhere between the slide show on postmortem changes in senile psychosis and the combined free lunch-drug lecture on minor tranquilizers sponsored by the country's richest drug company. Yet, I was expected to sit dutifully in the presence of my supervisor each week and have him pass judgment on my therapeutic errors and oversights.

I didn't mind entering Dr. Bellino's office as much as usual that particular June day, since the blast of cool air that greeted me reminded me how his air conditioner expended its energy in refrigeration whereas the machine in my office, which was apparently constructed from parts of an army-surplus B-29 "Superfortress" engine, was mainly geared to the production of noise. Vince added a less welcoming blast of his own: "It's ten minutes past the hour, Pat. Can't you ever come to these sessions on time?"

"Sorry, Vince," I murmured. "I would have been on time, only I was out front talking to a lady who demanded to see the director because her child had been referred here by a teacher who didn't appreciate his urinating in her desk. I persuaded her that she'd profit more from a scheduled appointment with a child psychiatrist. Next time I'll send them in to you, and be sure to keep your desk drawers locked."

"All right, let's get down to cases," he grunted.

I shrugged helplessly. "I don't know where to begin, Vince. I've got about forty active cases. How much can we possibly cover in one session?"

"Obviously, we can't discuss them all. But this is *your* hour, Pat. You're free to use it any way you want, to deal with whatever you feel would be most productive. . . . Where are you going?"

"Oh," I said, having risen to my feet, "I thought I'd call the welfare center for Mrs. Haynes. She's been having a problem . . ."

"Would you please sit down!"

"Sorry. But you *did* say I was free to do whatever I wanted with the hour, and it would be *very* productive if I could get Mrs. Haynes's mess straightened out."

"I meant, as if you didn't know, that you can do whatever you want in the context of supervision," he explained. "Why are you so resistant to this? Are you so threatened by constructive criticism?"

"No," I said, feeling defensive nevertheless. This whole scene bugged me. Vince was less than three years older than I, yet he always came on like my daddy—and not just in supervisory sessions, either. He acted as if an M.D. degree automatically conferred maturity and wisdom otherwise unattainable. Maybe he felt he had to be that way to keep the staff in line, but, frankly, I suspect Vince was born at the age of 50. If he ever was young, I'm sure he wasn't any good at it. "I'm always willing to hear out someone else's opinion, even if it differs from my way of doing things. It's just that right now I don't have any cases that stymie me."

"All right," he conceded. "Then talk about some case that particularly arouses your feelings—positive, negative, mixed. You do have feelings for your patients, I trust?"

I nodded. "Funny thing you should say that, because I had a very disturbing session with Sue this morning."

He sank back into his leather swivel-chair, clasping his hands beneath his chin as if praying that I would present him with a problem worthy of his talents.

"She called me at nine sharp," I began, "sobbing hysterically, and asked if she could come in—which is why I cut out of conference early, having five other patients and a meeting with a guidance counselor already on my appointment schedule."

"Does she do this sort of thing often?" he asked disapprovingly. "Demanding immediate attention, and all?"

"Not Sue! Never calls between sessions or tries to change her appointment time. Speaks frankly, explores her feelings, has picked up insights . . ."

"What brought this supremely competent woman into therapy in the first place?" Vince asked skeptically.

"Depression, for want of a better word," I said. "The kids were getting older and didn't need her as much, and she felt life was passing her by. She had dropped out of college in her junior year to support her husband—under the influence of that old philosophy, 'education is important to a man, but not to a woman, who will probably get married and stay home and raise kids' and all that other stuff you men always say."

"I say no such thing," Vince protested. "I'll thank you to stop projecting on me all your grievances about alleged male prejudices. If I were against higher education for women, I wouldn't be sitting here sharing my expertise with you. Proceed."

"All right. But some men, like Sue's husband, are not as enlightened as you, most worthy guru. He led Sue to believe he would always support her and any children they might have, so how could he or even she take her education that seriously?"

"But Pat, didn't this woman go back to college?" Vince interrupted.

"Yes, she did," I confirmed. "Her husband did agree to pay her
way when he realized how important it was for her to go back. I
think that's why what happened came as such a blow to her."

"What came as such a blow?"

"I'm coming to what came," I explained. Resuming my often-
interrupted reconstruction of that fateful therapy session, I reported, "First, Sue just cried, and finally, between sobs, she began
to speak. 'Well,' she said, 'last night after I put the kids to bed, I
went into the bedroom, as I thought I'd call my sister to see how
she was feeling. You know I told you last week that she had a very
bad cold. Maybe it was flu. It had started with a mild sore
throat . . .'"

"Pat, what in the world has Sue's sister's cold got to do with Sue's
emotional crisis?" Vince demanded.

"Nothing. That's been one difficulty I've had in working with
Sue. She's always so obsessive," I explained. "Each and every
detail of her life she recounts as though it had major significance."

"I can understand that quality in Sue . . ." he said.

"It's a defense mechanism she uses to protect herself against the
onslaught of various strong emotions," I elucidated.

"I am glad that you have such a sound grasp of the psychodynamic significance of obsessive-compulsive defense mechanisms," Vince said, a tinge of sarcasm in his voice. "However, I
wish you would guard against that same quality in yourself when
reconstructing therapy sessions, and limit yourself to the essen-
tials."

"Oh," I said, perplexed. "I thought you wanted me to try to
recreate the session exactly as it progressed."

"Within *reason*, Pat!"

"Okay," I recommenced. "That's when the phone buzzed."

"Someone called Sue?"

"No, Dolores was buzzing me in the office." Vince reacted with
an impatient glare, so I hastily said, "So I had to interrupt the
session to deal with the guy who took his penis out in the intake
interview room, and then Sue said . . ."

"Wait a minute!" Vince yelled frantically. "Back up a minute. You had to deal with what?"

"Just an exhibitionist. It had nothing to do with Sue's session, so I'll get back to that."

"Pat, how can you say the two things were not related?" he protested. "Do you mean you went back to that session in the same frame of mind after confronting a man who was exposing his . . . organ?"

"It was no big thing, Vince."

"I'll be the judge of that," Vince insisted. "Go back to where you were interrupted by the intercom."

"Dolores said the cops had just brought in a man they picked up at the IRT station exhibiting himself," I related. "Apparently they felt this was the place he needed to be seen . . . for treatment. Dolores said the address he gave her was outside our catchment area and she didn't want to open a chart on him, but I told her as long as he practices his perversion at *our* subway station, we might as well accept him, since he was sure to repeat his behavior and talk his way back here again.

"That settled, I hung up the phone and got back to Sue, who had stopped crying and now had to tell me about putting away her laundry before she could call her sister."

"Pat, you're getting bogged down in trivia again," Vince warned.

"You want me to get to where Sue's big crisis occurred?" I asked.

"I want you to get back to the guy who the cops brought in!" Vince said.

"Oh, I did," I reassured him. "I heard this agonized scream, and there was poor Dolores cowering practically outside my door, shaking and actually in tears. She said that while she was taking information from the patient, he began to play with himself."

"Play with himself?" Vince echoed, like a disciple of Carl Rogers.

"Figuratively speaking," I clarified. "Actually, it was only with a portion of himself."

"Understood. Then what? Did you notify the cops who brought him?"

"They were long gone by then, off to fight crime in more exotic locations than the IRT station or the mental health clinic," I reported. "Besides, what good would they have done? The police brought him to us because of his exhibitionism, so how would it help for us to give him to the police for the same reason? So, I just marched into the intake interviewing room . . ."

"Alone?" Vince gasped.

"Oh, sure. Dolores wouldn't have been of any use; she was terrified."

"Ironic, isn't it," Vince mused, "that a woman who wears a see-through blouse and a skirt slit up to her acetabulum would be so frightened of an exhibitionist."

"Next you're going to blame Dolores for provoking him into jerking off in the intake room, I suppose. It's attitudes like yours that result in rapists going free to walk the streets . . ."

"There you go, projecting again! *You're* the one who brought up streetwalkers," he maintained. "Can we get back to the guy who was showing off his symptoms?"

"Well, I remembered having read how exhibitionists, unlike rapists, are generally not dangerous and behave as they do because they feel inadequate and insecure in their relationships, so I decided to take a firm approach. I looked him straight in the eye . . ."

"Which probably wasn't easy to do under the circumstances," Vince commented.

"And I told him," I continued, ignoring the interruption, "'if you want to come here, you've got to do things by our rules. You'll have to learn to express your conflicts in words, not act them out. So, put it away or I'll have *you* put away.' He looked at me like a little boy caught with his hand in the cookie jar and—zip!—he stopped doing his own thing and was meek as a sheepish lamb."

Vince was shaking his head in disapproval. "Why didn't you call me when the problem arose?"

"You were at the hospital talking to administration this morning, remember?" I replied. "Besides, there was no need to bother you with it."

"You should have called the security guard," he persisted. "Or one of the male therapists. There was no need for you to handle it yourself."

"He was handling it, not me," I protested.

"Damn it, Pat, be serious!" he snapped. "It was a situation for a man to take charge of. Why do you always have to take things into your own hands?"

"Are you making jokes or was that a Freudian slip?" I asked.

"It was neither a joke nor a Freudian slip!" he informed me angrily. "It just came out that way."

"Just came out, huh? Why, Vince, you're blushing! Listen, would you rather I discuss this particular case with Sharon or one of the other female shrinks? If you find it embarrassing . . ."

"Listen, I am perfectly comfortable with discussing any problem that comes up . . . arises . . . *occurs* in this clinic," he fumed. "I find *your* denial of the implicit threatening sexual elements here a bit inappropriate, I must say."

"What's so threatening about a little old penis, for crying out loud?" I demanded. "The first time you walked into a gynecology clinic, did you run around screaming, 'Eek, eek, a vagina!'?"

Vince momentarily laid his head on the desk as if he were about to cry, but he rallied and shook his overgrown hair for a few seconds as if to clear his memory, then commanded, "All right, once more then."

"After I got back to my office and apologized to Sue for the interruption, she began to discuss calmly how she put away her laundry, without the slightest trace of emotion. I figured she must be furious at me for walking out of our session at such a critical time but couldn't deal with this added source of anger and was just retreating further into her obsessiveness. So, in an attempt to break through, I just blurted, 'What happened when you talked to your sister?' Well, that did it, because she burst into tears again and sobbed, 'I never talked to Martha. I picked up the phone and Bob was on the extension upstairs, talking to Diane. He was saying that he loved her and that he would tell me that night he was leaving me to live with her.'

"It turns out Diane is her husband's secretary. As Sue described her, she's a woman with an IQ under one hundred whose only dream has been to quit her job, stay home with a husband, and have children. You know the type, a woman who knows her place—as a servant to man."

"The kind of woman Sue used to be, huh?"

"Deep down, I suppose so, though I hate to admit it. Sue claims, of course, that Diane represents everything she never wanted to be—silly, simpering, not a thought in her head beyond what to wear for tonight's date. Sue says she and Bob used to laugh over how immature Diane was, more like a teen-ager than an adult woman."

"Did your patient show any emotion at that point?" Vince asked.

"Yeah, as soon as she added, 'And now Bob is leaving me for her. I don't believe it.' Then she really broke down; crying loudly, 'I hate her. I hate him. If I ever see him again, I'll kill him!'"

"She was finally in touch with her anger," Vince understated. "Then what happened? Did she confront him?"

"No, she didn't have the nerve. In her words, Vince, 'I can't live without him. He's my whole life.' How's a therapist supposed to cope with a patient's loss of her 'whole life'? In her value system, I suppose it's true. She had an unhappy childhood, fell in love with him instantly and completely at eighteen, married him at twenty— had never been involved with another man, not even in a close friendship. And if the guy were a total rat, it might have been easier to take, but he did seem genuinely supportive when she was so depressed and came into therapy, did support her in her decision to return to school and pursue a career. So, what good did all that do if now he's leaving her for a woman who wants only to stay home and spend the rest of her life pleasing her man?"

I felt my own anger rising, first in my churning stomach, then coursing upward through the arteries in my neck till I could feel my face burning. "I guess it's the 'in' thing today for men to say they believe in women's lib, but you see how it's only lip service to the idea of women being free and pursuing their own interests, other than the subservience of motherhood and . . . wifehood? . . . wifedom? . . . Oh, hell, call it what you want, it's still a stinking situation to be in.

"Here Sue seemed to have acquired increased confidence in herself as a person; she was able to cope with any and all stresses. Now look at her—just because her man is about to leave her, she's on the verge of hospitalization, more depressed than when she started therapy over six months ago. It almost makes me ashamed to be a woman. What is it your friend Freud said? 'Anatomy is destiny.'"

"Objection!" Vince intoned, raising his hand. "How come ninety percent of the time I'm accused of being a pill pusher who wouldn't know an Electra complex from an electroshock box and now suddenly I'm charged with being a couch-fellow of that dirty old Austrian?"

"Oh, it doesn't matter what your psychiatric credo is," I snarled disrespectfully. "You male shrinks are all brothers under the male chauvinist pigskin. God knows, there are plenty of middle-class, well-educated women who are paying forty dollars a week to have one of you tell them their problem is failure to adjust to their feminine role, that they should be more passive and accepting. What's assertive behavior in a man becomes ball-busting and castrating in a woman, right? She should be looking for a nice man whom she can marry and raise a family with—and then the bastard will probably run off and leave her for his secretary, the way Sue's husband did!

"Well, Doctor, you wanted me to talk about a case I've got some feelings about, and I guess I did. Now, do you have any solutions?"

"Just a comment for now," he said. "I think there's one thing you may have lost sight of. When Bob married Sue, he made a commitment to a woman with a set of goals and values. Recently, Sue drastically changed those goals."

"As usual, it's the woman's fault, huh?" I grumbled.

"I'm not trying to find fault," he said. "I'm just trying to point out that Sue's new personality is as much a violation of the old contract as Bob's attentions to his secretary. If he can't accept Sue on the new footing . . . well, you'll have to help Sue realize what price the continuation of the marriage would exact from her own self-development, and help her decide whether or not the sacrifice would be worth the marriage. Actually, I think Sue's gone too far to turn back and Bob has already tried to go along with her and failed. If I'm right, the marriage will dissolve, but perhaps that's the best of a batch of unsatisfactory solutions."

"Another victory for women's lib," I said cynically.

"Well," he sighed, "if Bob does drop out of Sue's life and she goes on living—as I'm sure she will—she'll have an individual identity for the first time in her life. Not all victories can be by a score of seventy-three to zero."

Here's to the winners—wherever they are. God knows, we don't see many of them at the clinic. And the losers in the game of life, from the looks of our waiting room, the triage center for sorting out the casualties, are the women, despite Dr. Bellino's contentions. Sure, he'll haul out his infallible statistics that show the male-female breakdown of our patient rolls is just about fifty-fifty, but start breaking down those stats and Bellino's contentions break down right along with them. First, about a quarter of all our cases are children and adolescents, and in this sizable subgroup, little boys far outnumber little girls. Does this mean there's more misery among boys? Not at all. It simply means boys are allowed to raise more hell and when they become a bit too enthusiastic in their disruption of classroom and neighborhood peace and order, they get referred to us. Meanwhile, their female classmates, behaving themselves like the ladies they were taught to be, suffer unnoticed in silence. Then, there are the alcoholics. Still far more men than women, though the gap is closing. Again, though, the men do their drinking in bars and on the street, where they come to the notice of the authorities and are pushed into treatment, while the women drink secretly at home, their livers shrinking without the benefit of concurrent head-shrinking. So, the remaining cases, the classic therapy candidates, are predominantly women, for among the nonalcoholic men we find mostly far-gone psychotics who wouldn't have been caught dead asking for psychiatric help in their slightly healthier days.

Macho men don't cry, not even for help. Now, women are mares of a different color—judging from the number of depressives, I'd say predominantly blue. They're used to regarding themselves as helpless and provide us with a stream of unsteady customers. Step right in, ladies—take a number. We have a 300.4, that's depressive neurosis. Or 296.0, involutional melancholia. What's that, ma'am? You're normal, but just unhappy with your life? Let me check the American Psychiatric Association's *Diagnostic and Statistical Man-*

*ual (DSM,* as we affectionately call our bible), but I'm afraid that sort of thing isn't covered. Have to go by the book, you know; the state of New York frowns on funding agencies that spend money treating people without legitimate APA-certified mental disorders. This one might fit you, though—307.3, adjustment reaction of adult life. Has a nice respectable ring to it, doesn't it, ma'am? What's that you say, you also have phobias? No, I'm afraid we can't give you *two* diagnoses, the state only provides enough blank spaces on its forms for us to give one number to a customer; however, we will make a note of it in your record and try to get around to treating that, as well.

Suppose *what?* Suppose we get a patient whose condition doesn't fit any of our preexisting classifications? Oh, that would never happen—we use a diagnostic principle that we modified from an ancient Greek invention; we call it the procrustean couch, a sort of psychoanalytic variation of the old bed you might have heard tell about. What, you've actually been *in* it? Oh, society put you in it and said you didn't measure up as a woman, so they sent you here to improve your measurements!

Maybe someday I'd come to my senses and just treat my female patients as I saw fit without trying to enlighten my chauvinistic chief, an endeavor about as rewarding as trying to sell a cannibal on the idea of vegetarianism. Maybe I was just trying to convince myself that I was leading these patients of mine somewhere worth going, that there was light at the end of the tunnel, that there was at least an end to the tunnel.

Basically, I was lost down the same rabbit hole as the rest of them, looking for adventure, finding only abuse and madness. Ultimately, like Alice in Wonderland, you stop looking for adventure and just try to find a way out. How did Alice ever get out, by the way? I remember her tumbling down, down, down, but not how she ever got back . . . oh, yes, she woke up. Cheap writer's trick, make it all a nightmare. Won't work in real life, though. The nightmare is reality and if you want to find your way out of a bad place, the safest course is to go back the way you came, retrace your steps. Sounds like psychoanalysis, doesn't it? I know where *that* goes—certainly not out into the sunlight, only back toward the womb. I know not which way liberation lies, but it lies not on an analyst's couch; I could be in intensive psychoanalysis five times a week for the next twenty years, given the time, energy, and money—which neither the clock, my body, nor Dr. Bellino are about to increase—and never really be liberated, not even from my past.

Not that my past is all that dark; compared with the deprivation of most of the women I treat, my past wouldn't even qualify as shady. In my middle-class home, Father went to work daily, Mother did not, but Mother's staying home to take care of the children would scarcely get her indicted as an unfit mother for not making her daughters more career minded. Actually, while my patient Sue was discouraged from going to college, *my* parents stressed the importance of higher education. They still expected me to get married, but they really did value education. Up to a point. A woman, I was told (rather indirectly, since I don't remember any exact words) always has to be prepared to take care of herself. I've never quite understood why I was expected to marry yet not completely depend on a man, considering how thoroughly dependable my father was and how dependent on him Mother was.

If there had been a son in the family, maybe they wouldn't have been as enthusiastic about sending me off to college, but there wasn't and they did, and I left home with the goal of acquiring something more than a proper husband. "Education is something that no one can ever take away from you"—I do remember my father saying that, more than once. Money, friends, lovers can come and go—boy, can they come and go!—but education, like a diamond, is forever. And so, I have been accumulating education ever since, with the voracity with which some women accumulate diamonds; since the age of five, there has never been a point in my life when I wasn't taking one course or another, even if it was something as pedestrian as getting better photos with an Instamatic.

That's the horror of my life—I'm still viewing it through an Instamatic. Limited focus, limited control. Nobody sends a son off to college telling him that someday he'll make a fine assistant professor or physician's assistant. It would be like telling a Little Leaguer to work toward becoming a great minor leaguer someday. Yet, I'm sure I was given only two career choices, the only acceptable professions in which a girl could "take care of herself": nursing and teaching. How's that for a shot at the Hall of Fame? How many nurses have made it big, once you get past Florence Nightingale? Maybe Clara Barton, who started the Red Cross, but no one since the invention of Blue Cross.

Nursing was out from the start anyway. I hated biology in high school. My teacher was a two-hundred-pound spinster who kept six dogs at home and consequently smelled worse than the specimens. She paired me with a boy who could have passed for her son, just as heavy but four inches shorter, who looked like the poster child for the National Acne Foundation. There now, isn't that a great way to choose your life's vocation? If my lab partner had been our school's all-state halfback, the then man of my dreams, I would have gone on to medical school and discovered the cure for cellulite.

So I chose teaching, the other acceptable calling for a girl. (We women let ourselves be called girls back in those dark days of limited options and consciousness.) I lasted one year. I found myself trying to teach the difference between nouns, verbs, and adjectives to kids whose vocabularies consisted chiefly of nondictionary words that functioned as every conceivable part of speech at the whim of the user. I might have persisted in trying to teach them grammar if I had been more successful with English literature, but trying to convey the joys and beauty of poetry to kids who hadn't had breakfast and were looking forward only to lunch was like teaching gourmet cooking to Ronald McDonald. My Waterloo was Edward Arlington Robinson's poem, "Richard Cory," the one about the rich, dapper guy who put a bullet through his head. I might as well have read them Tolstoy in Russian. They could not think of one possible reason why a man who was rich would commit suicide. If you had money, how could you possibly have problems?

So, that's how I got into social work. I don't think my parents were very happy with my change of vocation, even though social work is still basically a woman's field—not as menial as ditch digging or as ambitious as medicine. You don't get your hands as dirty or as bloody, but then you don't generally get to associate in the course of your work with the better class of people. It's a rather radical idea to want to shake up the existing social strata, even though very few of my clients have really climbed into the rarefied middle-class atmosphere of regular pay checks and Master Charge cards, the lifestyle I seem to be frantically striving to climb out of. But what's beyond that, Bellino's world of country estates and stock portfolios that I constantly put him down for?

Well, I'm far from being despondent over learning that a million dollars won't bring happiness, being more than nine hundred fifty thousand dollars away from my first million and not likely ever to reach it, dedicated as I am to the idea of social equality. That's a rather curious credo for a nice middle-class WASP girl from California who spent every summer on the beach getting a good tan, took ballet and piano lessons on Saturday, and never belonged to an organization more subversive than the Girl Scouts. The closest I ever came to poverty was not having enough money to buy a wardrobe of miniskirts when they became the latest fashion rage, but then at Berkeley it was chic to be poor and wear patched dungarees, so the consequences to my social life were minimal.

How did I get here, I ask myself as I sit in this stifling closet, listening to the roar of my air conditioner heating up the air with its internal propellers, until 5 P.M. when I can finally leave for the IRT station, where our exhibitionist is probably hanging out waiting to get even with me. Masochism, that's the root of it all. Identification with the underdog. Following the implied parental dictate of feminine underachievement. Name three Hall of Fame social workers, Pat! One, Dorothea Dix, who campaigned for the rights of mental patients. Two, Jane Adams, who founded the first social-recreational center. Three . . . strikes you're out. Is that really what I aspire to be, a spinster do-gooder, devoting my whole life to changing the world? A portion of my life to changing a portion of the world? Hell, I don't even make a good spinster. Not that I can't give up men—I've done it dozens of times. (Hmm, I'm starting to sound like an alcoholic.) Maybe someday I will find a really

modern, liberated one who can accept a woman who is into doing
her own thing, even if that dreadful thing is fighting against the
injustices of the world that are foisted upon the poor, especially us
poor women. Trouble is, it's the damn women who run the
traditional homes we all come out of and raise the men who are
threatened silly by liberated women, and I don't mean just the ball-
busting dyke types, either—I mean even warm, considerate,
empathetic types like me. Well, I am what I am, as that great
existentialist Popeye said, so love me or leave me. And they do,
they do!

Connie had already left the reception desk, so I knew without
looking at my watch that it was after five. The waiting room was
deserted except for one young woman, who rose to meet me.

"Hi!" she said pertly, giving my hand a tight squeeze. She was a
beautiful kid with straight, golden hair extending halfway down her
back, a light, even tan broken only by a spattering of freckles on the
bridge of her tiny nose, and pale, wide blue eyes. Her well-
endowed chest was tightly encased by a T-shirt bearing the images
of Mickey and Minnie Mouse, with the bold legend above and
below, LOVE IS . . . WALT DISNEY WORLD. (So *that's* what it is! No
wonder I've had so much difficulty finding it in California and New
York.) Her long shapely legs, revealed by a pair of denim shorts,
were as tanned as her face, and she reminded me of the golden
girls of Malibu that I had left behind on the Pacific surf nearly a
decade ago.

"Hi," I said, returning her smile, which was infectious despite its
fixed, vacant quality.

"Can I help you?" she asked. Funny, I thought that was my line.
She was perceptive enough to pick up my quizzical reaction. "Can I
get you some coffee? Bring you some supplies, or anything?"

"No, thank you," I replied. "Are you here to see somebody?"

She nodded. "I saw Dr. Krumpel today. Yesterday, too." Frau
Krumpel had left over an hour ago. The girl must have been
aimlessly hanging around the waiting room most of the afternoon. I
wondered if someone had screwed up at the front desk, telling her

to "wait a minute" before they checked out her prescriptions or logged her next appointment and then forgotten all about her. It's been known to happen.

"Are you waiting for something now?" I persisted gently.

She gave me a timid smile. "No, I just like to stay here. There's no one home now, and I hate to be alone. I'm frightened. My father will be home soon, though. He works at the main hospital."

Then I knew who she was. Dr. Krumpel had done the intake yesterday, and even the great Dr. Bellino had shown an interest in the case. She was the daughter of the chief of the medical lab, and Vince had asked me to make sure she was assigned to one of our "better" therapists, whatever that means. I suppose he didn't want her to wind up with one of the "greenies," like Chris, though practically everyone we'd picked up was on his or her first job. Funny, when I read the chart, I had pictured her as a lot older than this adolescent.

"It's after five," I pointed out.

"Thank you," she said. "I'll go now. You're very kind." She caught me by surprise by standing on her toes to throw an arm around my neck and planting a hearty kiss on my cheek before departing.

I looked at the log book, stopping my fingernail at one line. That's her name, I think. Stacy Cunningham.

I felt uneasy about her walking home alone, even though it would be daylight for hours yet. Her clothing was, to use an unliberated term, provocative and she seemed to be in a clouded state of mind from which she would respond to any greeting or invitation without regard to the possible dangerous consequences to herself. Not all the males in our community were as innocuous as our exhibitionist.

It was with a measure of relief that I found Stacy back in the waiting room when I got in the next morning. She was wearing the same shorts, but had changed the Disney T-shirt for one with the image of Raggedy Ann, bearing the magic word LOVE. She greeted me with a big wave.

"Good morning, Stacy," I said, my smile belying my underlying concern. I made a mental note that a proper disposition for this patient would be the first order of business after morning conference.

Wednesday at 9 A.M. was the time for the one weekly conference where the staff had the opportunity to interact in a free-wheeling give-and-take discussion of any problems troubling the patients, the therapists, or the clinic as a disharmonious whole. There were at least two other regularly scheduled conferences a week, but those were more structured, with one clinician designated, according to a formal schedule, to present a patient or topic of particular interest. Wednesday was anything goes, and while many conferences were unproductive, when no one was feeling cordial or optimistic enough to share anything but brooding silence, we were often able to cut through the bullshit and regroup our forces in cases where patients had managed to convert our best laid treatment plans into something that resembled a script for *Laverne and Shirley*.

I sat at the left hand of the master, placing my coffee mug with the blue peace dove and the word for *Peace* in twenty-three languages (I took most of the words on trust; the cup might have said *Fuck You* in Swahili or Mandarin Chinese, for all I knew) beside Bellino's ornate china cup bearing the Bellino family crest that he had brought home from his annual pilgrimage to the land of his ancestors, with stopovers in Paris, London, Athens, and other suburbs of his home town.

"May I have the floor?" I asked our chairman politely.

"If you promise to scrub it and return it tomorrow," he growled, kicking one of yesterday's cigarette butts across its scuffed surface.

"This morning," I announced, squaring up three charts on the table before me, "I want to discuss the Rossman family, Pearl and her two children, Lynn and Gregg."

Carl Brock moaned and slapped his huge paws down on the table as if recovering a fumble, rattling everyone's coffee cup in the process.

"I'm not taking on any more Rossmans," he declared. "I've already got Porky, and I'm not taking on any more of Purple Pearl's screwed up kids."

"I'm not asking you to . . . yet," I said. "I want to work out a treatment plan for the family this morning, and I'm not sure at this point what's the best way to proceed."

"Who's involved with the family now?" Nunzio Scaglione, our chief psychologist, asked.

"I've been seeing Pearl for nearly a year and a half," I reported. "Carl picked up Gregg last September on referral from the school guidance office, though I'd been after Pearl to bring him in for months after she complained that he's never stopped bed-wetting."

"How old?" shot Nunzio.

"Eight and a half," I answered. "Then, about four months ago, Pearl asked me to see Lynn, who's now fourteen and has been posing some behavior problems, including truancy. I picked up Lynn, but I think it was a mistake."

"The kid doesn't need treatment?" Vince asked.

"Heresy!" shouted Dave Goldman. "*Everybody* needs treatment."

"Speak for yourself, Dave," Dr. Bellino said into his coffee cup.

"Of course the girl needs treatment," I affirmed, retaking the floor. "But she should have had a different therapist, not her mother's. I explained to Pearl that if I saw Lynn, whatever Lynn and I talked about in therapy would have to be confidential. Pearl agreed, but ever since then, all she wants to talk about in her own sessions is Lynn—how impossible she is, how Pearl never knows what she's up to, what should she do to discipline Lynn, all obviously calculated to get me either to share what Lynn's told me or to undermine my relationship with Lynn."

"How old is the mother?" Sandy Silverstein, our third social worker, asked.

"Thirty-six," I said.

"And trying for thirty," Carl snickered cynically. "You've seen her in the waiting room, I'm sure. She usually has a fat little kid with her who's always knocking over wastebaskets and ashtrays. Purple Pearl always wears bright purple slacks and has purple eye shadow on, even early in the morning. She's got dark hair, piled high on her head, and usually wears high-heeled sandals."

"What was the mother's presenting problem, Pat?" Chris asked.

"Depression," I said, harking back to the distant past. "Feeling overwhelmed by the kids, disappointed in a series of affairs, unable to control her weight, difficulty sleeping at night."

"Couldn't sleep and screw at the same time, huh?" Carl needled.

"Sit on your inkblots, Carl," I suggested. "Pearl is a very dependent person, and in therapy it's been difficult for me to foster a sense of autonomy in her when she wants to cling so much. But we *have* made some progress. She works part-time as a waitress now, and her interpersonal relationships have been a little more stable. But now that Lynn is becoming . . . mature, the main family conflict has switched from Gregg to Lynn."

"Has Gregg shown any change since starting treatment?" Vince asked.

"He was reevaluated by Dr. Feliciano last week," I said, scanning his chart, which I then skimmed across the table toward the seat where the Lilliputian Filipino was trying to hide herself between the beefy carcasses of Carl and Dennis Boyle.

Trembling, she reached for the chart and read in a quavering voice, "Patient is eight-and-seven-twelfths-year-old boy, finish second grade . . ."

"Just your findings and recommendations will be okay, Iderlina," Vince interrupted, in an effort to circumvent an acute anxiety attack in his child psychiatrist.

She flipped a page on the chart and waggled her index finger downward as she summarized, "Marked exogenous obesity . . . hyperactive child . . . reluctant to separate from mother . . . uncooperative in interview . . . shows low reading level for age . . . complaint of enuresis, four to seven times week. Diagnosis: behavior disorder of childhood, hyperkinetic reaction."

"Sounds exaly like what I wrote a year ago," Carl said discouragingly.

"I increase the Tofranil from ten to twenty-five milligrams at bedtime and also prescribe the Mellaril, ten milligrams t.i.d., for control hyperactive symptoms," Dr. Feliciano announced triumphantly.

"Any improvement in symptoms thus far?" Vince asked.

"Well, he's kept the bed-wetting down to once a night," Carl reported.

"All right, can we try to get together on a plan today?" Vince said sharply. "What I've heard thus far is that Gregg has not improved and Pearl is slipping. Where's Lynn at?"

"Usually out on the streets until two A.M.," I resumed. "Acting what we would have called boy crazy in a less enlightened era. As Pearl puts it, 'She wants to do the same things I do.'"

"There's a strong element of competition with her mother, then?" Chris said.

"Absolutely," I replied. "It's a two-way thing, too. Have you noticed the way Lynn dresses? She always wears these scanty little skirts that don't even reach midway down her thighs."

Carl nodded. "Pearl always dresses seductively, too. Tight purple slacks, plunging necklines."

"Right," I said. "Never skirts, though. See, Pearl's an attractive woman, but her one weak point is her legs. She has terrible varicose veins and she's very self-conscious about them. So, you can imagine the effect Lynn's micro-miniskirts have on her."

"God, yes!" Dave expostulated histrionically. "Pat, you should have known better than to try to treat Lynn simultaneously. It never could have worked out. The Oedipal rivalry in a case such as this is particularly traumatic, since you're dealing with a narcissistic mother with severe oral dependency problems herself, and an adolescent child who is basically a borderline personality with incipient psychotic decompensation manifested by a pathological identification with the more regressed portions of the maternal psyche. Why didn't you give the daughter her own therapist from the outset?"

"Oh, kiss my assignment pad, Dave!" I snapped.

"Pat, the problem seems not to be who the therapist is, but getting a separate one for Lynn rather than having her share one with mother," Nurse Jackie said, lifting her head from the afghan she was crocheting.

"You want her?" I asked testily, reaching for my assignment pad.

"Hold it, Pat," Dennis Boyle interjected, looking very serious for a change. "Have you considered family therapy?"

"You mean seeing them together?" I asked. "In addition to all the individual sessions?"

"Maybe not all," he said. "Look, there are obviously a lot of pathological family interactions that have to be dealt with. They're sabotaging the individual therapy, which doesn't seem very effective at this point."

"Pearl won't like it," I said warily. "She's very dependent and isn't going to like giving up her individual sessions."

"Of course she won't like it," Dave said. "But you've got to be firm, Pat. Just tell her that it's the decision of the clinic that the family be treated as a unit. Uh, providing that is the decision of the clinic. Dr. Bellino?"

Vince cast a sideways look at me. In response, I shoved three charts toward him, nearly tipping over the Bellino family crest and immersing the Rossman family in coffee in the process. The prospect of abruptly terminating a long-term relationship with any patient, and especially one as dependent as Pearl, distressed me. Okay, so I hadn't worked wonders with the lady and Lynn's problems were added boulders on the road to therapeutic progress—still, I've dealt with tougher patients without being yanked in the middle of the game.

But Bellino seemed oblivious to the obvious hazards as he parceled out charts like an enthusiastic kid trading bubble gum cards, getting Pete Rose and Reggie Jackson for Fred "Chicken" Stanley and Joe Zdeb.

"Okay then, it's settled?" he verified. "Dennis, you'll see the three of them as a unit?"

"I think an adolescent girl needs a good female role model," Dave groused. "Maybe you should have a female cotherapist, Dennis."

If they expected me to team up with a novice like Dennis Boyle after usurping my therapy case, their judgment was even worse than it had seemed up to this dismal point. On the other hand, it was important to put the patients' welfare first and lay aside our pride. Okay, this once I was prepared to make the sacrifice, and overworked as I was . . .

"How about it, Jackie?" Dennis asked.

"What sign are you?" Nurse Jackie asked.

"Huh?" he responded. "You mean what school do I follow?"

"No, no," she said, shaking her long red hair. "Your birth sign!"

"Oh, you mean stars and things?" Dennis said, scratching his head. "It's some naked guy spilling a jug of wine."

"Aquarius," Nurse Jackie confirmed.

"Yeah, February twenty-seventh," Dennis said.

Nurse Jackie dropped one of her knitting needles. "No, no, then you're Pisces!"

Bellino slammed his fist on the table. "What in the name of God and little fishes does this have to do with mental health . . . or the Rossmans . . . or anything at all?"

"Well," stammered Nurse Jackie, nervously smoothing the outrageous orange-and-black dress she was wearing, "it's just that I'm a Cancer and I don't work well with Aquarius. Scorpio's best for me, but I think I can relate to a Pisces, even though he's close to the cusp."

"I really appreciate your cooperating this way," Bellino snapped. "Would you like me, perhaps, to check the patients' birth dates to see if their signs are compatible with yours?"

"Hey, yeah!" she beamed, the chief's sarcasm utterly wasted on her. "I'll draw up their charts before the first session."

"Their charts are right here!" Vince said, indicating the stack.

"I mean their *astrological* charts," Nurse Jackie explained.

"Look," Vince commanded, shoving the charts toward Dennis and away from his star-struck nurse, "just see this family and skip the celestial mumbo jumbo."

"You must be a Libra!" Nurse Jackie declared. "Practical, obsessed with order, judgmental, businesslike . . ."

"No, I am a Cancer," Vince confided, "the same sign as yours. That alone should indicate how little stock we can place in drawing correlations between the stars and personality."

"A crab! I should have realized," Nurse Jackie acknowledged, her faith unshaken.

I was still seething inwardly as I returned from the conference to the waiting room, wondering whether I should have insisted on keeping up Pearl's individual sessions or even opposed the idea of family therapy altogether. If a female cotherapist was essential as a role model for Lynn, I couldn't understand their picking Nurse Jackie who, with her flaming hair, tall and gaunt frame, and affinity for surrealistic garb, looked more like a Druid priestess or an apprentice witch than a registered nurse.

Someone clutched my arm as I stood rapt in thought at the reception desk and I jumped as though I'd just encountered a coven of witches . . . or registered nurses. I whirled around, almost mashing my chin into a head of golden hair.

"Sorry, Stacy," I apologized when I realized who had touched me. "You startled me."

"You look worried about something," the kid said. "Is something bothering you?"

I forced a smile. "No, everything's fine, Stacy—I was just thinking about something, that's all."

"You looked sad," she observed, and seemed to be ready to burst into tears herself. "It's a terrible thing to be sad, isn't it? I know what it's like. If you'll be my friend, we can be sad together and it won't seem so bad."

"I'll be your friend, Stacy," I said, "but I don't want you to be sad—together or alone."

"Alone is worse," she said almost in a whisper, those pale blue eyes now staring off as though she could look right through the waiting room wall at the crumbling neighborhood outside. "Together is sadness sometimes, alone is always sad. Will you stay with me?"

I wasn't sure what she was asking—or even, the way she was looking past me, whether she was really talking to me. "I have some work to do now, Stacy, but we'll talk later if you like. And one of the doctors will see you now, okay?"

She bit her lower lip and nodded. Then she suddenly gripped me in a tight embrace, her arms around me at mid-spine, holding me desperately for a few seconds then just as suddenly releasing me.

"Thank you," she said. "What's your name?"

"Pat."

"Thank you, Pat, for being my friend."

Had it not been for Stacy's approaching me, I would have forgotten my intention to do something about her right after the conference that had me so unnerved. Reawakened to Stacy's plight, I knocked and entered Frau Krumpel's office, hoping she wasn't yet busy with her first patient. My hopes were realized; although she had consumed a bacon-and-egg-on-toast at the conference, the doctor was still breakfasting, working on yet another cup of coffee and slowly eating her way through a box of cinnamon buns.

"Good morning, Pat, have a bun," she said in one breath.

Remembering my last traumatic encounter with a scale and wishing I had a picture of the doctor to tape on my refrigerator door (though I don't have the type of wide double-door refrigerator I'd need), I declined with a sylphlike wave and got down to business. "Dr. Krumpel, I wanted to talk to you about Stacy Cunningham, the young girl you evaluated two days ago. I've been observing and speaking with her in the waiting room and I wonder if she might not need hospitalization."

Frau Krumpel gave me an apologetic smile, which plowed laboriously across the fatty layers of her jowls. "Ach, she was already in a hospital. Five days at County, nearly three weeks at State. It did no good. Her father insisted on taking her out after she was apparently molested by one of the male patients, a dangerous fellow committed for homicidal behavior. These hospitals today, with their crowded wards and their inadequate staffs, they perhaps protect us from the patients, but I fear they do little for the patients, particularly one such as this girl." She reached into a drawer and plunged a greedy hand into a red cardboard box. "Raisins," she said, with a touch of pride. "Satisfies the craving for sugar without too much starch. Want some?" Again, I declined. Before she had swallowed the raisins, she was reaching for another cinnamon bun.

"Ilse," I persisted, "the state has a rather good adolescent facility. Small ward census, good staff, even three-month stays or longer. Couldn't we get Stacy in there—she'd pose no real management problem and would be an excellent therapy case."

But Dr. Krumpel, her cheeks bulging like a chipmunk's under a walnut tree, was shaking her head disconsolately. "No, no, no," she mumbled through the crumbs. "This woman is twenty years old— far too old for an adolescent unit. They would never accept her."

"I keep forgetting!" I said with consternation. "She's so childlike. Almost like a retarded person."

"Humph, she's certainly not that," Frau Krumpel said. "An honors student she was, both in high school and at college. President of her senior class in high school, I'm told. Very, very different from the regressed person you see now."

"What happened?" I asked. "Were you able to learn anything from the family?"

"Yes, I spoke to the father. He said it was drugs. Took some LSD or perhaps angel dust and became acutely psychotic. The hallucinations and panic responded quickly to phenothiazines, but as for the rest. . . . Well, you've seen for yourself."

"But a drug couldn't have such a long-range effect on a patient!" I argued. "Once the acid or whatever was out of her system in a day or two, there wouldn't be any long-term consequences."

"As a *direct* effect of the drug, no—although with the way kids pop anything they can find down their throats these days, who knows?" She gulped another handful of raisins. "But, no, I think we have here a schizophrenic girl who decompensated during the period of drug intoxication and never reconstituted. She is like a five-year-old now. Perhaps she is guilty over disappointing her father by taking drugs and wants to be the loved good child again. Maybe she grew up too suddenly and wants to go back." She shook her head again, then added hopefully, "I have increased her medication again—she now takes sixteen milligrams of Trilafon four times a day."

"She doesn't seem like the type who would be into drugs," I said. "Seems like the very straight, all-American type. How did it happen?"

"Her boyfriend got her to try them," Frau Krumpel explained. "You know how these youngsters are—anything for a thrill."

"She went along, huh? And you said she was a leader, a class president."

"That is popularity, not leadership," Frau Krumpel said philosophically. "Children—and perhaps we adults, too—look up not to the strong and independent but to those who please, in their actions and appearance. Stacy is pleasant and pretty and thin. That makes for popularity, not strength." She eyed my body very carefully. "Are you sure you won't have a cinnamon bun, Pat?"

I almost took it, then lost the courage to go all the way. "Just a few raisins, please," I compromised. Frau Krumpel gave me a sympathetic smile and poured a sticky mound of them into my bony palm.

I hadn't given up on the idea of finding a suitable hospital for Stacy, but right now she needed a therapist. I had such strong feelings for her that I wanted to give her the very best we had. The morning's conference notwithstanding, most of our personnel, despite their relative inexperience, personality quirks, and out-bursts of irreverent rebellion, were well-motivated and competent therapists and, with the exception of a psychiatrist or two, none were real losers.

I finally decided on Dr. Scaglione. Nunzio was the only one of our psychologists with a Ph.D., and I respected his advanced age— he was nearly sixty, though he'd gotten a late start in the profession. He'd been a medical corpsman with the Italian Army in World War II, before I was even born. He'd made up his mind to go to medical school when the war ended but he never quite made it, and after finishing college as an American immigrant, supporting himself with part-time jobs over a number of years, he went on to graduate school in psychology, raising a family in the process. Even though Nunzio devoted most of his time to our child patients and we needed his fluency in Spanish, his third language, for our Puerto Rican clientele, I decided he was the best choice for Stacy. I reached for her chart, wrote "*Pt. assigned to Dr. Scaglione,*" and deposited it in Nunzio's mailbox in our record room.

By the next morning, I felt better about Stacy, particularly when I got a glimpse of Sally, my ten o'clock patient, in the waiting room. Compared with Sally, Stacy could have passed for a staff member. Sally looked so spaced out that day that NASA would have been eager to probe her. Her matted dishwater-blond hair looked like it had been neither washed nor combed for weeks and, at the other end of Sally, her bare feet appeared equally neglected. She wore a torn peasant skirt and an oversized man's shirt that reflected several days' food intake. I readily identified coffee stains and mustard, but when I got to something that looked like dried blood, I lost my appetite for detective work. Most disconcerting of all, Sally seemed to be talking into the air.

"Come on in, Sally. How are you today?" I asked as I ushered her into my office. I knew how she was, of course, but I wondered if she knew.

"Well, I almost didn't come today," she confessed apprehensively. "Ogla-eye didn't want me to, but at the last minute he agreed to come with me to meet you. Right, Ogla-eye?" She looked timidly toward my left and I turned to look, too, though I didn't expect to see Sally's hallucination. When this sort of symptom recurred, it invariably meant a return trip to the hospital.

"Ogla-eye says I can only listen to him," she continued. "I can't cook for my husband or change the baby; Ogla-eye forbids it. Everything I do must be for him."

Ah, the sense in nonsense. Her hallucinatory companion was functioning as an aid to acting out her negative feelings about her marriage and family. I felt that her psychiatric illness had not so much afflicted her as been *chosen* by her, as her one escape from an intolerable marriage and the unrelenting demands of motherhood with which she could not cope financially, intellectually, and emotionally. The repetitive pattern in her history was amazing, and I gave Freud credit for being right in at least one area: People tend to repeat themselves again and again and again, whether or not we resort to such formidable phrases as "repetition compulsion neurosis" to distinguish such a common phenomenon. The daughter of an alcoholic very often grows up to marry an alcoholic. Sally had been raised by a physically abusive, domineering father, and at sixteen she had eloped with Mel, who soon proved to be her father's match in his harsh treatment of Sally. And now, even her hallucination was a creation who seemed to be an equally dominating and harshly controlling male figure.

"I worship Ogla-eye," she singsonged in a flat chant. "I have no home, and I will follow him to the end of the world. After I leave here, I will begin my voyage."

"Where will you go?" I asked, feeling somewhat captivated by Sally's fantasy. The way things were going in the confines of our community mental health clinic, I just might have pulled up roots and joined my patient, with a promising offer.

"Don't ask!" she commanded, sharply closing me out of her fantasy. Then, dreamily staring into space, she said, "Wherever Ogla-eye wants. He knows everything. He tells me never to take any medicine from the doctor. It would be disloyal to him."

With this last statement, Sally's body seemed to go limp and her hips slid forward on the seat of the chair as her body eased toward the floor. Even though she did not seem to be in any distress, I felt alarmed and cried, "Sally, what are you doing?"

"I'm going to take a nap," she announced, stretching out as far as my office's limited floor space would allow. "Ogla-eye told me to."

Well, I had my own authoritarian demons to answer to and I was sure Dr. Bellino was not about to be overruled by Ogla-eye. And while I could not recall any specific administrative rule against sleeping on the floor of the mental health clinic, it was sure to be only a matter of time before I got into trouble with the International Brotherhood of Hospital Floor Sweepers, Local 141, if I chose to pass Sally off as a living carpet. So, I summoned Dr. Bellino on the intercom to step into my office and over Sally.

"You could have at least waited until the couch arrived from central purchasing before starting psychoanalysis," he chided, looking down at Sally, my human rug. "And here I thought Dave Goldman was our only Freudian. If you take over his province, Dave might have to regress to social work again and start giving patients concrete help with their concerns about food and shelter— and that would play all sorts of havoc with the transference neurosis, wouldn't it?"

"Save the laughs for your depressed patients, huh, Vince. I want some concrete help about getting this sleeping beauty into a hospital today; if anybody needs a bed, she does."

"Will she go as a voluntary?" he asked.

"She needs clearance from a hallucination," I explained. "One that is encouraging her in all manner of obstinacy and obstructionism, as you can see by her position with relation to the door."

"Nuts! No offense, Sally," he added. "Pat, you know we can't get a patient admitted involuntarily unless she's acutely suicidal or homicidal. I don't suppose she came at you with a knife—or threw her shoes at you? Did she try to jump out the window, or do you suppose we could get her to try?"

"I know the problem," I sighed. "In this golden era of community mental health, the mental patients are to remain in the community. Even those who are too crazy or too burned out to have any permanent homes. Don't you think we can get the state to spring for a few bucks to board Sally for a few days, considering the millions of dollars we've saved them by letting them replace hundreds of hospital beds with a couple of dozen chairs in our waiting room?

"I'm really worried about her, Vince. She's in no shape to take care of herself. And I'll bet that after she leaves here, with no intention of returning home to her no-good husband, she'll feel so guilty that her hallucinated male tormentor will suggest something self-destructive to punish her for even thinking about rebelling against her situation."

"Okay, Pat, you win the point," he conceded. "Give me a few minutes to call around and see if I can scrounge up a hospital bed in which Sally can finish her nap." The master doctor, in charge and control as always, left my office with a purposeful stride broken only by the leap required to traverse Sally, still prone to obstructionism.

"Sally," I called, crouching down to jiggle her shoulder. "I think you should go to the hospital."

Without checking with Ogla-eye, she simply yawned and said meekly, "Okay, I'll go. I can rest there."

I breathed a sigh of premature relief. Involuntary hospitalization is, I suppose, a necessary evil in our field, but I've always hated the whole scene. How better to make someone who is already very agitated and paranoid more agitated and paranoid than to bring in the police, complete with guns and handcuffs, to cart him away to an insane asylum! But, what else can you do when a patient is not capable of making decisions for himself, especially when his self-destructive inclinations would counter any choices that would protect him; those in the mental health field have to step in as surrogate parents until he reaches the point where he can manage his own life again—but it's not my favorite part of the job. I'm too opposed to capital punishment, though, to defend any patient's right to inflict it on himself.

"Can Ogla-eye go with me?" Sally asked softly.

Wow, how's that for taking charge! I even outranked Ogla-eye. "Yes," I replied magnanimously, so happy that Sally had agreed to go peaceably to the hospital that I would have consented to her taking along every munchkin in Oz.

And then I made an almost fatal blunder. Knowing that I had two patients waiting, had to call Legal Aid about a rent case and a guidance counselor about accepting a child into a special class, I asked Sally to sit in the waiting room with a mental health assistant until hospitalization could be arranged. I broke one of my cardinal rules: When working with a very disturbed patient, isolate him. The presence of strangers can be very agitating. At first, everything seemed fine. Evelyn Larsen, one of the new assistants, sat beside Sally in an unoccupied corner of the waiting room, chatting casually, as I called my next patient into session.

In less than five minutes, there was a series of loud screams, followed by the thunder of several pairs of feet in pursuit. Sally was nowhere to be seen in the waiting room, but the screams led me to the corridor, where I saw the oversized stained shirt Sally wore fluttering to the floor as Sally raced bareback around the bend followed by two mental health assistants (neither of whom was Evelyn) and the mighty Carl Brock, reliving his glory days when he would nail a pass receiver short of the goal line. Evelyn came sauntering out of one of the offices behind me, too late too catch a glimpse of the fleeting Sally, but not too late to catch a little hell from me.

"Where the devil were you?" I yelled. "You were supposed to sit with Sally until the ambulance came. You know how sick she is."

"I only left her for a minute," Evelyn whimpered. "I just got a call that my son is sick, and someone is bringing him home from school." Her voice trailed off behind me, as I joined the pursuing pack.

I almost crashed into Carl Brock, who had come to an abrupt halt outside one of the doors off the corridor, a door that managed to stop the linebacker whom the entire Michigan State offensive line could not contain.

"She went in the ladies' room," Carl said sheepishly.

"Get a doctor to order a shot for her, Carl," I barked, and entered the no-man's-land. I didn't see her at first, and then I sighted her frightened eyes peering out from one of the toilet stalls. "Come out, Sally," I cooed softly. "It's okay . . ."

Without further coaxing, the stall door clanged open and Sally flung herself at me with a shriek, tugging at my gold chain necklace as if to strangle me. Even as I struggled for breath and saw sparks behind my closed eyelids, my only thought was regret for having worn the only decent piece of jewelry I owned, a gift that had special meaning for me. Fortunately, the necklace broke before my trachea did and flew past my eyes in a golden streak, bouncing behind the trash container.

"Get away from me, Mrs. Patterson," Sally shouted, shoving me against the same container. "I don't want to hurt you!" I was, I admit, somewhat touched, in spite of my aching neck, to see her concern for my safety in the midst of her own terror.

"Calm down!" I ordered, in a less-than-calm tone. "Everything will be all right," I added, in a considerably softer voice.

Sally, the tops of her heaving breasts visible over the edge of her bra, leaned against the wall gasping. "That woman in the waiting room . . . she was looking at Ogla-eye. She started to talk to him. I wasn't going to let her take him away from me. I would have killed her, but she ran out the door when I went at her."

I could hear a crowd gathering outside the door, and as it swung open, I saw a throng that seemed to include every staff member and patient present in the clinic that day. I saw Nurse Jackie's flaming thatch bobbing through the mob, her pale hand holding aloft a syringe filled with Thorazine as if it were Brunhilda's sword. Leave it to Dr. Bellino to maintain decorum by sending only a lady into the ladies' room!

I turned, reassured, to my half-nude patient and said, "The nurse is going to give you an injection now, Sally, to help you feel better."

"She's no nurse!" Sally snapped angrily, looking more agitated than before. "A nurse wears white."

I turned to look, and there was Nurse Jackie dressed in a tight black leather dress and high black boots, syringe in hand, like someone out of an X-rated S-M flick. I didn't expect the doctors to dress like Dr. Bellino, who wore a three-piece suit, white shirt, and solid-color tie regardless of the calendar, thermometer, or prevailing fashion at the discotheques. I could accept psychiatrists in V-neck sweaters, psychologists in jeans, and paraprofessionals going braless in T-shirts. But this outfit of Nurse Jackie's I needed like Custer needed a few more Apaches.

Nevertheless, the sight of this redheaded demon in black leather seemed to mesmerize Sally, who was probably having difficulty deciding whether Nurse Jackie was real or one of Ogla-eye's companions, and since Sally had been considerate enough to remove her shirt previously, Jackie was able to sink the needle into Sally's deltoid muscle with the swiftness and ease of Dracula zeroing in on the sternocleidomastoid.

"Love your outfit," I hissed in Nurse Jackie's ear. "Where did you leave your whip?"

"Chained it outside," she deadpanned, before slinking off like a shadow.

Sally looked after her apprehensively. "The nurses don't look like that in the hospital where I'm going, do they?"

"No, Sally," I assured her. "There's only one nurse in the world who looks like that and we've got her."

What sort of week was it? A week like all weeks at a community mental health clinic, filled with the events that alter one's physiology in the direction of increased blood pressure, decreased resistance, deficient libido, and excess stomach acid. The sort of a week when you wouldn't say, "Thank God it's Friday," because that left twenty percent of the week to go in a thankless world of crisis stress and routine stress. "Thank God it's no longer Friday" was the unique prayer I murmured at 4:30 P.M., as the clinic finally began to wind down. A few stragglers hung around the waiting room to pick up a quick prescription to tide them over the weekend, as the staff members paraded back and forth to the sinks and restrooms to give their struggling house plants a weekly watering or to rinse their encrusted coffee cups. Some exchanged confidences about weekend plans—a bus ride to Jones Beach, a hope-filled singles weekend in the Catskills, or a couple of days at sister's summer shack on Lake Placidyl. Dr. Bellino paused, with his ornate crested cup, at the reception desk to eavesdrop on Dolores's description of a new club she had discovered where the live mambo band hadn't yet been displaced by a speaker system and a stack of LPs and where some of the male habitués were actually single.

"And where are you off to this weekend, Chief?" I asked.

"The Island," he replied tersely.

"Out to the Hamptons, with the other rich shrinks?" I taunted.

"I am going to a place called Patchogue," he informed me, "which is closer to New York than the fabled Hamptons and closer in expenses to the meager means of a community psychiatrist. It is the price paid by those of us who dedicate our lives to those who need our services most, they whose poverty we share."

Connie Rodriguez slammed the appointment book closed on another week and sneered, "Any time you want to share my pay check, dear, I'll split it with you in exchange for half of yours."

"And did I detect a note of snobbery in your alleged equation of poverty with mental illness?" I added, double-teaming him with Connie.

"If you'd spent more time in California reading and less surfing," Vince replied, "you'd know that, according to the classical surveys of Hollingshead, Srole, et al., poor people are more likely to develop severe psychiatric illnesses."

He turned and headed for his office, but I trailed him, objecting, "That's because all the diagnosing is done by you upper-class shrinks. Unfortunately, there's a dearth of psychiatrists who fall in the lower income brackets and who might understand the poor better."

Vince nodded absentmindedly as he packed his attaché case. Undaunted by his indifference, I persisted, "An uneducated housewife comes into a psychiatrist's office upset because her husband just beat her up and left her for another woman. The best rap she can plea bargain for is depressive neurosis, but more likely she'll be railroaded into a round of shock treatment to help her 'forget' her depression. A 'cure' means getting her to become more docile and accepting, instead of expressing her anger, which would really deal effectively with the depression."

Vince scrutinized a Long Island Railroad timetable. "You know, Pat, the next time you ask me where I'm spending the weekend, I'm going to say home. The mere mention of Long Island seems to make you react the way a Palestinian would respond to the Israeli national anthem. Where are you spending your weekend, dressing wounds at the leper colony on Molokai?"

"I am going to a women's conference here in the city," I said, self-righteously. "The topic is: 'Our Poor Sisters: Victims of the Mental Health Establishment.'"

"Well, there's one consolation," he commented. "No matter how badly they're victimized, your sisters will never be as poor as that conference title."

Before I could level him with a brilliant comeback, Maria Sanchez rapped, entered and, looking most concerned and apologetic, said mournfully, "I'm sorry to tell you this, but we've got a real problem."

"Don't tell me, let me guess," I interrupted. "The calendar on the wall tells me it's Friday, the watch on my wrist tells me it's four forty-five, and the sick feeling in my stomach tells me it must be a homeless person." Maria nodded a sad confirmation and slipped backward out of the office.

"How did you know that?" Vince asked eagerly. It was the first time he'd been impressed by something I said all that afternoon.

"Many years of experience in community mental health, dear colleague, have left their tracks on the vast stretches of my imagination."

"Speaking of tracks," he said, looking once again at the timetable in his hand, "I've got a train to catch in exactly one hour. Hate to leave you with a crisis at this late hour, but since your poor sisters won't be convening for their sabbath until the morrow, you're not pressed for time like me. With luck, your homeless victim will be a female and you can add her case to the flames of revolution, along with the rest of the papers they present. See you Monday."

Exit the king. *Exeunt omnes*—save the social worker. Save her ere she perishes in a sea of confusion. Save her for Monday, when the tide rolls in again, depositing the flotsam and jetsam of society into our waiting room. I could see getting deluged with the wretched refuse of our teeming shores and all points inland if I were standing out front with a torch, but I haven't had time to light a match all day!

Too bad Dr. Bellino had to rush off before I could brighten his Friday afternoon with some of the tales told me by homeless wayfarers through years of Friday afternoons. Such as: "The state hospital van dropped me at the subway station with a token and this address on a piece of paper." Or, "When I came home from the welfare center after going there for the last three days to try to replace my lost rent check, the landlord had put all my furniture out on the street and changed the lock on my door." Or (freely translated), "My family sent me from Puerto Rico to live with my uncle. When I arrived, the building was boarded up and no one knew where he had gone or even who he was." The most depressing one was: "My mother threw me out because she complained I hadn't taken a bath since July Fourth. Heck, the next holiday isn't till Halloween. (I don't celebrate Labor Day because I don't work.)" Not only didn't he have a home, but I couldn't use *my* office for two days because of the air pollution.

Alone in the deserted throne room at 5 P.M., I sacrilegiously circled the desk and sank into Dr. Bellino's high-backed, leather swivel-chair. Perhaps some fleeting contact with this seat of wisdom would imbue me with some insight, foresight or, more likely, hindsight, to deal with this recurring problem that defied satisfactory solution.

I pulled Dr. Bellino's dog-eared copy of *DSM* from beneath a pile of unanswered correspondence. Homelessness wasn't even included on the list.

The medical model didn't seem to deal very well with this particular condition but, though I would never admit it to Bellino, I don't know if we social workers do much better. Instead of giving the situation an APA diagnosis, we would conceptualize it as follows: the stated problem—social dysfunction (translation: no pad). Then one would have to make a contract with the patient, analyze the problem, draw up a treatment plan, consider alternatives, and move toward solution. That's the way we were taught to do it. Unfortunately, by the time a homeless person arrives at the clinic's door, he has already considered and exhausted all other alternatives, such as friends or relatives with whom he can crash.

The solution, if unsatisfactory, is actually simple. In the greatest city in the world (that's what our mayor calls it, anyway), there are but two free shelters, his and hers. The men's municipal shelter—known as the Muny to every derelict—is ideally located on the Bowery and is perfect for homeless alcoholics, since the immediate neighborhood provides endless opportunity for much needed social contact and peer relationships; for mental patients, however, who tend to be passive and unsophisticated, the shelter invariably leads to theft of their few remaining possessions, including prescribed medication, and poses a constant threat to their lives and limbs, a situation nonconducive to the improvement of paranoia.

Females may be able to avoid the Muny's sister-house if they are fortunate enough to qualify as abused. We have a nearby battered women's shelter, which goes by some unrecallable euphemistic title, something on the order of The Center for Prevention of Violence in the Family. Unfortunately, homelessness and subjection to verbal threats are not sufficient to qualify for admission; the victim must demonstrate bruises, or preferably fractures. I unequivocally reject Dr. Bellino's proposed solution to this dilemma, which is "take her into one of the back offices and rough her up a little," even though I appreciate the need to work within the system.

I rose from the director's chair no wiser and no less weary and determined that I would be out of this place by five thirty. Whoever the unfortunate client was, he or she would be brusquely informed, "I'm afraid the only available place for you to stay is the city's men's (women's) shelter. Here is the address." I would even give the patient a subway token (never give cash—you can still get a glass of beer for fifty cents in our community's intimate cocktail lounges) from my own depleted coffers and then exit for the weekend with a clear conscience.

But the best laid plans of mice and social workers often turn out to be bad lays. Even after many years in community mental health, I was unprepared for the homeless person awaiting my services. She was all of three years old, with dirty blond hair, wearing a tattered dress, and looking very forlorn standing in the middle of an empty waiting room.

"What's your name, honey?" I asked. No answer. She just looked at me with big, frightened blue eyes.

"Maria, where did she come from?" I asked my assistant.

"You know my patient Mrs. Luciana, the one with the sixteen-year-old son who is always beating her up, and who received double food stamps last month and none this month?"

"Yes, I think I remember her vaguely."

"Well, she was coming back from visiting her daughter and found this little girl sitting on the subway steps, crying. She didn't know what to do, so she brought the child here," Maria explained.

"Where is Mrs. Luciana now?" I asked, looking around frantically.

"Gone," Maria said simply.

"But why, of all places, did she bring the child to a mental health clinic?" I demanded.

"Mrs. Luciana says we're the only place that ever helps her," Maria testified, with a touch of pardonable pride. "She says all the other places she goes give her the runaround, we're the only ones who really care about patients, whatever problems they got, sickness or nerves or welfare or family court . . ."

"Okay, okay," I sighed, "I get the point. This clinic is now the designated panacea for all man's ills. I mean *people's* ills—forgive me, Maria, I must be getting tired."

I offered the child my hand and took her into my office, lifting her into a chair. Probably lost, I speculated, and most likely hungry. Oh, where was Frau Krumpel with her portable mess hall now that I needed her! "Would you like a candy cane?" I asked, remembering some I had left in my desk from last year's Christmas party. She accepted the cane and started to suck on it eagerly, ignoring my questions about her name, age, and family.

I had decided to call the police to learn if they had any reports on lost children when I noticed a piece of paper sticking out of a pocket in her dress. Pulling it out, I saw it was a note, written in a shaky handwriting: TAKE CARE OF PAT. I CAN'T ANYMORE.

What an eerie coincidence, like something out of a dream! Of course if this were a dream, I'd be expected to come up with all manner of symbolic significances. The child was a reflection of my own ego—rejected, wandering, unable to articulate its needs. The child was a superego's reproach, chastising me for shamefully neglecting the other goals my parents set—marriage and mother-hood.

But this was a real child with a real problem. "So, your name is Pat," I said. "That's my name, too." At the word *Pat*, she seemed to become more attentive. She definitely knows her name, at any rate, not like those primitive kids raised by wolves you read about in the social work literature, though I'm sure a wolf would never abandon her cub on a flight of subway stairs.

I reached for the phone and called the local precinct to report an abandoned child.

"Where did you say you're calling from, lady?" the authority figure asked, after I'd recounted my story.

"The St. Dymphna Community Mental Health Clinic," I repeated.

"Yeah? And what do you want us to do?"

"The child needs a place to stay, at least until her mother can be located," I said, explaining the obvious. "The Bureau of Child Welfare will have to make some sort of arrangement. You'll have to bring the child there, then look for her mother."

"What's the mother's name and address?" he said impatiently.

"I don't know!" I said, sharing his impatience. "The child either doesn't know or won't tell me. Look, just send someone to pick the child up. We're at . . ."

"Listen, you're a social worker, right? So *you* take care of it. This ain't no crime, it's a social problem, and I don't have no men available to baby-sit. I got two cars out at that waterfront fire, three on medical emergencies, two breaking up a gang fight, and a couple being repaired in the garage. Besides, we're changing shifts now." He slammed down the receiver before I could begin an appeal.

Next, I dialed the Bureau of Child Welfare, a city agency whose function is to provide temporary and long-term care for abandoned, abused, neglected, and unwanted children. After recounting once more my encounter with little Pat, the worker at BCW asked, "Does she have any friends or relatives she can stay with?"

"Listen," I replied, "we don't even know who she is, much less her friends and relatives."

"How old is she?"

"I'd say she's about three."

"I'm sorry, the children's shelter does not accept children under four."

"I made a mistake, she's four."

"Hmm. I don't know if they have any vacancies at the shelter."

At this point, I was almost ready to take little Pat home myself for the weekend, until the plodding social agencies reopened and set their snail-powered machinery in motion again on Monday morning. But give me a break! I'd only seen ten patients today, including a paranoid who thought a handyman had come to crucify him; an eighteen-year-old mother with three children, aged one, two, and three; and a married couple who spent their whole hour expressing their hatred for one another, and then walked out hand in hand saying that seeing me for therapy was a waste of time. Besides, taking a patient home was against professional ethics. According to the Freudians, the failure to maintain proper distance from one's patients will prevent the analytic transference from developing. I was having trouble enough initiating verbal therapy, since my patient still had not uttered a word.

Finally, after fifteen minutes of cajoling BCW into taking some responsibility for the care of the child, I threatened to call the Channel 11 Action News team to report their ineffectiveness. Faced with the prospect of having to smash television cameras or pretend that the New York City bureau had moved elsewhere, the caseworker agreed to a compromise. Since he was on duty alone for the rest of the night and had to minister to all the child welfare cases in the entire city, he claimed, he would arrange placement if I would personally bring little Pat to the agency. When I opened my office door, I perceived that I, too, was alone. All of the mental health assistants had vanished, one of whom I had hoped to persuade with the lure of comp time (compensatory time off) to accompany little Pat to the BCW office.

And so, as Dr. Bellino boarded the Long Island Railroad for his summer weekend on the Island, I sat on a crowded subway train on a hot summer evening, with little Pat beside me sucking a candy cane in stony silence.

# 3

**G**OOD MORNING, PAT," I GREETED MY COORDINATOR. "HOW'S the kid?"

"I am not a kid, I am an adult woman," she informed me coolly.

"Not you, you aged hag," I clarified respectfully. "I was inquiring about the abandoned child you took to the shelter last Friday."

"The one you missed seeing in your eagerness to reach the starting line and beat your medical colleagues in the great train race to The Island?" she asked scornfully. "As far as I know, the child is fine."

"I'm sure you know as well as anyone, since you visited her after work, so the grapevine tells me."

Pat shrugged. "In case the grapevine didn't inform you, follow-up is part of my casework."

"Of course," I agreed. "That's why you could have gone during working hours. I would have okayed it."

"Sure, and who would have handled the crises here?" she scowled.

"Oh, that's right!" I agreed. "It must really be tough to be so indispensable, never able to take a sick day or a vacation, knowing how the clinic would be reduced to rubble by the time you got back, with only us incompetents here to run it."

"Don't overestimate my dedication," she warned. "I'm taking my vacation time even if the John Birch Society threatens to construct a local chapter on top of the rubble that remains. Even if I don't go anywhere on my vacation but Jones Beach and Central Park."

"Not quite the Riviera or the Champs-Elysée," I conceded, "but a definite improvement over this demolition site. Central Park is a nice place to take a kid on a pass from the children's shelter."

"That's *not* part of my job," she snapped. "Vacation time belongs exclusively to me."

"So do the evening hours," I noted, "and you chose to spend a few with a kid you hardly know. So, now that you know her a little better, maybe you'll want to spend a few hours more with her. Careful, Pat, your heart is showing!"

"It's tough enough to withstand the exposure," she reassured me.

"Oh, I never doubted that, despite its maternal inclinations. But, you know, single parents seem to be all the rage these days."

"I have no desire to be an unwed mother, thank you," she said. "My patients more than meet my need for dependents, and if you'll excuse me, I have a few to see now." Pat looked over my shoulder, and her annoyed expression changed into a diabolical smile. "Looks like you've got somebody to see, too—there's your patient Kate sitting in the corner of the waiting room, and she is as *high* as the dose of Valium you prescribe for her."

I looked across the expanse of waiting room at the dark-haired young woman slumped in a chair and said, "She didn't get that way on Valium."

"Oh, how silly of me!" Pat exclaimed. "How could anything a doctor prescribes be bad for a patient? Really, Vince, you're so gullible where women are concerned—she'll probably talk you into a month's supply of Tuinals to 'help her sleep at night.'"

Ignoring my nonmedical associate, I strode over to my semi-comatose visitor just as another would-be minister of mercy approached from Kate's left. By the time I reached Kate, a beautiful blonde girl was kneeling beside her, clutching Kate's limp hand.

"What's wrong with her, Doctor?" the blonde asked. "Is she very sick? Will she need an ambulance?"

I recognized the volunteer nurse as Stacy Cunningham, who had been living in our waiting room for the past week. Those gentle blue eyes of hers were enough to make me forget for the moment my annoyance at Kate for her present state, but Pat's crack about my susceptibility to young females made me reply more sharply than I would have otherwise. "It's nothing serious, Stacy. I'll take care of it."

As Stacy backed off, still watching apprehensively, I commanded Kate to come into my office. Gripping the sides of the chair for support, she slowly rose to her feet and swayed for a moment before lurching forward to begin an unsteady march to the office.

My session with Kate was a standoff. She refused to enter a hospital to undergo drug detoxification and I refused to supply her with any tranquilizers or pain medications.

I followed Kate out of the office and immediately came eyeball-to-wide-blue-eyeball with Stacy, who had been hovering outside like an expectant father in the pre-Lamaze days of childbirth. "Is she going to be all right, Doctor?" Stacy asked.

"Yes, Stacy, just fine. Please don't worry," I said with more than a trace of aggravation. Stacy pressed my wrist gratefully, then trailed Kate by a few paces as she went to the desk to get her next appointment logged.

I retreated back to the office in flight from frustrating females, but before the door could swing shut, Pat blocked its arc with a swiveling hip and pursued me into my lair, precariously balancing a stack of about a dozen patient charts like a Chinese waiter serving a family dinner for four and attempting to prevent the shrimp with lobster sauce from sloshing over into the moo goo gai pan.

"What did Kate get off you this time, Vince?" she asked smugly. "A little Seconal?"

"Not a damned thing!" I snapped. "She was high, all right."

"She's *always* high," Pat asserted. "I've never seen that woman when she wasn't flying."

"Look, I know she's got a history of drug abuse," I conceded, "but you can't condemn her every time she walks in."

"Or staggers in. I'm not condemning her, Vince, I'm just being objective."

"And I'm not?" I challenged.

"Oh, you're too trusting," she said, with the sort of patient smile you'd give a child. "If some scroungy looking guy asked you for Valiums or Miltowns, you'd throw him out on the spot, but if Kate bats her big brown eyes and swears she's clean and needs 'just a little something' for her poor nerves, you flick out your Bic."

"When you finish medical school, Ms. Patterson, I'll let *you* prescribe the drugs in this clinic!" I answered. "Meanwhile, I wish you'd attend to your own prescribed duties, such as arranging patient care. What are you doing about that Cunningham kid?"

"Stacy?" Pat asked innocently. "Nunzio's seeing her in therapy."

"Well, he's not seeing her now," I informed her. "What's she doing here? Every time I look in the waiting room, she's here. We ought to charge her rent."

"We can't ask her to leave," Pat said. "Her parents work and she has no other relatives, and after that bad drug trip, she doesn't trust any of her old friends."

"Can't you get her into a day center?" I asked. "We have access to the one that the state hospital runs. Let her hang out there."

Pat shook her head. "I wouldn't send her *there*. It's like a back ward. All the 'chronic' patients that they discharge within a month of admission under the new, enlightened system get shunted into the day center. Besides, Stacy had a very scary time when she was in the state hospital and I don't want to risk exposing her to another trauma."

"All the same," I decreed, "we can't keep this up indefinitely, having her around every day like a clinic mascot. Can't you adopt her or something?"

"What good would that do?" she objected. "I'd still have to come to work during the day. *You* adopt her, and leave her home with your domesticated wife."

"Even if Stacy followed me home, which she is not unlikely to do," I replied, "I don't think my unliberated wife would let me keep someone who looks like *that*."

"Well, I have enough problems looking out for myself," Pat declared, "and they've yet to construct a shelter for abandoned social workers."

"Are you just going to throw up your hands?" I said accusingly.

"Not till I get rid of these," she said, pointing with her chin to the stack of charts that continued to encumber her. "Here!" she grunted, heaving the paper mountain on my already cluttered desk with a loud thud.

"What's all this?" I reluctantly inquired.

"Patients who need therapy," she explained. "All new intakes."

"So, assign them to therapists," I advised.

"I have already abided by your wisdom, master," she said with a curtsy. "I have assigned them to Carl Brock and Dennis Boyle and Ramon Montalvo and Chris Pappas, our worthy psychologists."

"Then why are these charts now sitting on my desk instead of with one of the secretaries for the sending of appointment letters?" I asked suspiciously.

"Because the psychologists all gave them back to me. They claim they're too busy to take on any new cases," she informed me.

"Too *busy?*" I shouted. "They *can't* be too busy to pick up new patients. How come you and I were able to absorb intakes like a Scott towel back when there were only four of us handling the entire clinic and now people who have been here only a couple of months are overloaded? I want to know what they're doing that's taking up so much of their time!"

"Don't ask me," she said. "Why don't you speak to General Scaglione? They're *his* troops."

"The hell they are! Nunzio no more commands the psychologists than you command Dave Goldman or Sandy Silverstein. I, my faithful lieutenant, am the top-and-only-ranking commander here."

"You be sure to explain that to Il Duce at his next staff meeting— if he'll invite you to attend," she suggested. "I don't know whose side he was on when he fought in the battle of Anzio, while you were still playing with tin soldiers, but he seems to be presently conducting a rather independent campaign."

"Okay, I'll talk to him," I sighed. "Meanwhile, return these charts to their respective returners."

"If you so command," she said reluctantly. "Good luck with your *paesano*, Nunzio."

I walked down to Nunzio's headquarters—make that office— where I found the aged veteran sitting in what appeared to be a toy shop. Tiny doll families congregated on bookcase shelves, futuristic edifices constructed from Tinker-Toy and Erector sets sprang up from every available flat surface including the floor, and even the air above was cluttered with marionettes swaying giddily from curtain rods and wall hooks. Nunzio sat at his desk, which was covered with a profusion of psychologists' toys, the red-and-white cubes, the drab yellow jigsaw puzzles, and the colored pencils used in the testing processes. He had cleared away a long, narrow space to hold an eighteen-inch sandwich, so packed with filling of assorted colors that I didn't know how he expected to get his mouth around it. He was taking a swig from a battered, burlap-covered canteen as I entered, a container that matched the rest of his uniform, which consisted of a dark green loosely fitted shirt, its heavy material and long sleeves more appropriate to a military base in Greenland than to a sweltering New York office; pants of the same green material, tucked into the tops of short leather boots; and a heavy garrison belt with a belligerent eagle on the buckle.

"Hey, Vincenzo!" he called, greeting me with a hearty wave. *"Come va, cumpari?"*

*"Tutti va* into da ground," I said glumly. "What's the matter, Nunzio, don't we pay you enough to buy your lunch around here so you don't have to make your wife get up at dawn to prepare your noontime feast?"

My chief psychologist flicked his chin with the back of his hand in a gesture of disdain. *"Ma,* where you gonna get a sandwich like this around here? You know what's in here?" He hefted the buffet-on-bread like a clean-up hitter approaching home plate.

"It would probably take less time for me to list what's *not* in that torpedo," I observed.

"It's got salami, *coppacola, mortadella, prosciutto, provolone,* tomatoes, pimentos, *pepperuncini, caponata, giardiniera . . ."* he enumerated.

"And a partridge in a pear tree," I warbled. "I hope you included a couple of Alka-Seltzer tablets at the far end of that loaf."

"Sheesh!" he scoffed. "With an Italian masterpiece like this, you don't finish off with Alka-Seltzer. It demands Brioschi!"

"And just what does it demand in the way of a beverage?" I asked, casting my suspicious gaze on his canteen and the tiny beads of purple liquid clinging to his bushy moustache. "Nothing that would strike terror in the hearts of our AA members, I trust?"

Nunzio gave me a skeptical look and brushed some crumbs out of his whiskers with the back of his sleeve. "You wouldn't expect me to defile a magnificent sandwich like this with a can of soda pop, would you? If your poor alcoholics had learned, as I did at the age of seven, to drink and respect the honest blood of the grape instead of building devil's machines to distill out foul, sterile chemicals, they wouldn't be doomed to a hopeless choice between physical ruin and spiritual deprivation. Here, try this and tell me what you think."

I warily took the proffered battered canteen and took the sort of tiny sip you employ after the waiter has just uncorked a vintage bottle and poured seventeen cc's into your glass. It was a strong, musty, thick wine, quite unlike the smooth valpolicellas I usually ordered. "It has a few rough edges, but it's impressive," I critiqued.

"It's my own," he said proudly. "I will bring you a bottle."

"I don't mean to interrupt your lunch," I apologized, although the doctor went right on gnawing away like a beaver intent on transecting a tree trunk before the Disney cameraman got bored shooting footage, "but Pat seems to be having trouble getting your . . . *our* psychologists to pick up new cases. They don't seem to have room in their schedules anymore."

Nunzio looked at me aghast, his mouth agape to reveal its unappetizing contents. "Aw, no! Vincenzo, you just give those children's charts to me, and I assure you I will find therapists for them. We have just this very week begun an expanded intake evaluation procedure . . ."

"No, I am not talking about children," I interrupted. "I am talking about full-grown men and women with mental problems. Look, I appreciate what you've done with our children's services here . . ."

"Ah, it's nothing," he grinned modestly. "And I have even better things in store. We'll be using the marionettes for a variety of psychodrama." He reached up, pulled a string, and elicited a friendly wave from a sad-faced hobo-clown dangling beside him.

I looked at the stringed ensemble swaying around us. "Where did you get the money for these?" I asked, knowing how the hospital's purchasing department moved so slowly that all our present child patients would be more interested in contraceptives than toys by the time our requisitions were filled.

"I make them myself at home," he said, "like my wine. Most of the toys you see here are from my workshop. Most of the children we treat are very poor, and they have never seen toys like these."

"Truthfully, I haven't seen toys like these. The workmanship is superb. I feel like I'm in Papa Gepetto's toy store."

"Well," he smiled, "you can't do too much for children."

"I feel like a reindeer hunter on Christmas Eve," I said reluctantly, "but the fact of the matter is that maybe we *are* doing too much for the children. Preteen kids make up only about fifteen percent of our total patient enrollment and we can't neglect the other eighty-five percent. I mean, it's great how you've been organizing remedial education groups and parents' groups and so forth, but we can't do the board of ed's job for them. Not when we've got psychotic and severely depressed adults to treat."

He raised his hands in an elaborate gesture of helplessness. "Ah, I hope you don't think I tell anyone not to accept patient assignments. I have nothing to do with running the clinic here, I am just a worker like anyone else."

"Now, that is not true," I said, laying a friendly hand on his shoulder. "You are a very dedicated and exceptional therapist. As you've probably noticed, I've been happy to let you limit your work to the children. But, inspirational though you are, I can't afford to let your troops employ the same selectivity."

"Inspirational?" he exclaimed. "*My* troops? Bah, you're talking nonsense. I never was more than a corporal and never will be. I have no desire to lead . . ."

At that moment, a light rap on the door made itself barely audible and Chris Pappas intruded her pretty head. "Oh, sorry. I didn't know you were busy," she apologized.

"Come in, Chris," I beckoned. "We're just chatting."

Chris thereupon introduced the rest of her body into the room. She wore a pair of green army-fatigue pants, her cuffs rolled several times to correct for the excessive length of the legs, a tan unadorned shirt, and a pair of thick-soled Earth Shoes. She handed Nunzio a neatly typed report and left without a word, forgetting to salute.

"Now, there's a case in point," I pointed out. "If you had seen that girl when I first interviewed her, you'd never recognize her today as the same person. When she came to us, she had long shoulder-length hair, gold earrings, wore dresses and sheer stockings. She was beautiful, like something out of a Greek Islands travel poster. Look at her now! Her hair is shorter than yours and she dresses like an Israeli WAC who's been caught in a PLO commando raid in the Sinai desert. I ought to have Payroll take a stiff fine out of your next pay check for destroying one of the clinic's few beautiful natural resources."

Nunzio washed down the last crumbs of his marathon repast with a hearty swig from his canteen. "It's just another crazy women's fad," he said. "They're all into military stuff now—even the insignia they wear. My teen-age daughter has raided all my souvenirs to put on her jackets."

"Perhaps there's some truth in that," I said halfheartedly. "But until Dolores swaps *her* clinging cashmere for a flak jacket I'm holding you personally responsible for the defacement of that Grecian ruin. I think it's great that these rookies of ours identify with you and whatever battles you're rewaging in syndicated reruns three decades later, just as long as you give them a three-day pass every week to take care of some of the patients who missed getting help back in childhood."

"Sure, Vincenzo," he agreed. "Of course, I hope you'll be assigning some of these adults to the other staff, too, not just the psychologists."

"At this point," I assured him, "the social workers and Nurse Jackie never even get to see a kid, unless it's a niece or nephew. Since you've been expanding our child services, I've been adding psychologists, in lieu of other clinical subtypes, to the point that

Pat and the few other psychiatric social workers we have are about to report me to the Department of the Interior for making M.S.W.'s an endangered species. You want to have your own meetings—fine. You want to expand the number and type of kids' groups—fine. You all want to go around looking like the cast of *Shores of Iwo Jima*—fine, except possibly for Chris; with legs like hers, she should be dressing more like Betty Grable and less like Audie Murphy. Just be sure you don't all get so wrapped up in your private battles and dreams of glory that you forget your platoon is part of a bigger army and a more widespread war. Roger?"

He nodded glumly. "Roger," he said. And out.

If our army were under one flag, it would have to be that of the United Nations. When we assembled as a group on Wednesday mornings, I felt as though I were chairing a meeting of the General Assembly. Between the difficulty of attracting American psychiatrists to our undistinguished facility and our need for therapists who spoke Spanish, Anglos like Callahan, Boyle, Goldman, Silverstein—yes, even Patterson and Bellino—were the clinic's minority group.

Despite our divergent personal backgrounds, however, we functioned as a unit a lot more harmoniously than the General Assembly, and while we didn't have Cambodia and Palestine to deal with, we did have the Rossman family.

"How about a progress report on the Rossmans?" I daringly ventured. "Is family therapy under way?"

"We had our first session," Dennis Boyle reported. "Pearl was stage-center as always and opened things with a glowing account of how well she and Lynn were getting along. Lynn responded to this by making faces, muttering to herself, and shaking her head."

"Gregg, meanwhile," Nurse Jackie contributed, "limited his interaction to asking if he could leave the room, and turning off the lights. Lynn finally decided to bring him directly into the discussion by mentioning his bed-wetting, whereupon he walked over to her and punched her in the arm. Pearl tried to control things by shouting at both of them, whereupon the two of them closed ranks and sat silent for the rest of the session. Pearl then abandoned her happy report of family harmony and began complaining about Lynn's past hostile behavior toward mother's boyfriends, saying that Lynn only wanted to see her lonely and miserable. Pearl made some vague threats, as she has in the past, about placing Lynn in some sort of foster home."

"I know it's tough to get a feel in one session, but do you think family therapy is going to help?" I asked.

Dennis nodded. "In one session, we were able to observe quite a bit of nonverbal interaction. We could see how Gregg's acting out progressed as his anxiety level grew and how the kids seem to turn on each other out of sheer frustration when Pearl takes full control and fabricates a close-knit, loving family unit. I think in time Pearl will be able to pick up some insights and make effective use of them."

"Will family therapy be enough?" I turned to Pat. "Has Pearl attempted to see you in individual therapy since we made the change?"

"Successfully so," Pat confessed. "I saw her Monday."

Dave Goldman let out a loud moan. "She did it again! She manipulated you," he accused. "You have to draw firm limits with that woman."

Pat leaned over the conference table. "Dave, I can imagine how you would feel if your analyst tried to cut you down to one session a week. You'd get an anxiety attack just thinking about it. It was a crisis and I intervened. That's what we're here for, aren't we—crisis intervention? When some situation comes up that threatens a patient's equilibrium and forces her to take some sort of action to meet the threat, we're supposed to help explore options and find solutions."

"Pearl's whole life is a crisis," Sandy protested cynically. "And she tries to get the whole world to intervene in her behalf."

"Oh, come on," Pat argued. "Pearl's had plenty of valid crises—divorce, unemployment, abusive lovers, the kids' acting out. Not all those things were entirely in her control. Even our sudden switch in policy on her therapy was a crisis."

"I do hope," Dave said testily, "that the crisis requiring an individual session was not our decision to terminate individual sessions."

"No, it wasn't," Pat replied, "although I frankly feel that was worth an individual session or so to work through."

"All right," I intervened, "you did have the session with her, so you might as well share what happened instead of us arguing about whether or not the session should have been held to begin with."

"It seems," Pat volunteered after a long sigh, "that Pearl and Lynn went out on a date together."

"A double date?" Sandy asked.

"No, the same guy, someone Pearl had just met, took them both out to dinner," Pat said.

"Well," Frau Krumpel speculated, "it is not that inappropriate for a man interested in a woman with a daughter to take both out to dinner, is it?"

"No," Pat agreed. "However, after dinner they went back to the Rossman apartment and went to bed together."

"That's it!" I decreed. "Get that kid placed *now!* Enough is enough."

Pat looked at me placatingly. "You know Lynn's had past sexual experience."

"She's very precocious for fourteen," Dennis added.

"I am not talking about maturity or morality," I emphasized. "I am talking about sanity. The idea of a kid and her mother having sex with the same man at the same time is so far out I can't think of an adjective to describe it, although bizarre, inappropriate, and depraved might do for the time being. Do you think any judge would hesitate for a moment to remove Lynn from Pearl's custody after this latest bit of psychotic behavior?"

"I don't think Pearl is really psychotic," Dave interrupted with clinical detachment. "She's a rather classic borderline personality."

"Borderline personality is not in the APA diagnostic manual; therefore, it does not exist," Harry Chong protested. "Besides, such incestuous behavior is definitely schizophrenic."

"Where's the incest?" Sandy asked, as though she'd gone to the restroom and missed the most exciting part of the movie. "She wasn't having sex with her daughter, they were having it with the guy."

"Don't be naive," Dave reprimanded. "The group sex was really a vicarious act of incest."

"Regardless, incest isn't, per se, schizophrenic or even psychotic," Nurse Jackie noted. "You can't declare Pearl schizophrenic because of an unconventional sexual act. By that criterion you could make a case for converting half the summer houses on Fire Island into mental hospitals."

"Pearl's fitness as a mother is not strictly contingent on her sanity," I stressed. "Lynn is a minor, and this sort of outrageous behavior is only going to confuse further her already hopelessly screwed up ego identity, as a child, as a woman, as an individual. Does anybody here really feel we should allow the kind of thing that happened to go on?"

Nobody seemed to disagree with me, but Pat finally made a feeble gesture for recognition. "Vince, I just feel badly about taking Lynn away from Pearl, since this incident was something Pearl herself told me about. I feel it's like violating a confidence to use it against her."

"Does Pearl feel guilty about the incident?" I asked.

Pat looked discouraged. "Superficially, no. In fact, she presented it as an example of how well she and Lynn were getting along, like two buddies sharing a good time together."

"But I thought the incident was the big crisis Pearl had to discuss," Dave said.

"It was and it wasn't," Pat said. "She said she had to talk to me and then proceeded with the 'happy report.'"

Dave nodded supportively. "Makes sense. In spite of her attitude, Pearl knew we'd see it as a terrible crisis and get massively reinvolved with her and the kids."

"Pearl's motivation notwithstanding, we have to protect the kid," I reiterated. "Pat, will you contact the Bureau of Child Welfare and get the wheels in motion on this?"

"Okay," she acquiesced, "but it could take time—you know how tough it is to place a teen-ager."

"It'll take longer if you don't get started," I snapped.

"While on the subject of placement, Vince," Pat said, "I'm still trying to come up with a disposition for Ann Blaydow. We can't leave her in the house with her mother the way she is."

"The mother, Irene Blaydow," I explained to the group, "is fifty-two years old, with involutional paranoia. She was released from the county hospital last week after two weeks of treatment—brought there after slashing both wrists superficially, with paranoid delusions about someone repeatedly robbing her apartment. The daughter is only twelve. Irene's had three marriages, with one daughter, now in her thirties, by the first one, and no other kids until Ann was conceived with the man she persuaded to become her third husband."

"Is the woman still psychotic?" Dr. Schaeffer asked.

"Very much so," I said. "Not suicidal, and talks about her wrist-slashing as just a means to get attention. She refuses to go back to the hospital, but is very agitated, considerably paranoid, and I suspect she's not taking medication. She feels she can't properly take care of Ann but doesn't know what she wants to do with her."

"Who did the child stay with when the patient was in the hospital?" Sandy asked.

"With the patient's brother, who lives in the same building," I replied. "Part of the problem, though, is that Irene is delusional about the sister-in-law, claiming the woman is insane and out to hurt her, which means she wouldn't consent to letting Ann live there."

"I really can't see placing the girl in a shelter at this point, Vince," Pat said, "especially the ones that specialize in delinquents. There's a possibility of her going to live with the older sister, who's in Michigan. But maybe Irene will improve sufficiently to be able to keep Ann with her."

"Irene's supposed to be in this morning, right?" I asked. "We'll reevaluate her and take it from there."

An hour later, Pat came in with Irene Blaydow's chart. "She's in a mood, Vince," she warned. "Hasn't been taking her medication and is only consenting to see you, after a ten-minute debate with herself, because she's afraid you'll report her to the hospital and have her carted away if she doesn't comply."

The first two minutes with Mrs. Blaydow convinced me I couldn't have her carted away. She was haggard looking but neatly dressed, and while obviously nervous, she was able to remain in her chair throughout the interview, unlike an earlier visit when she repeatedly rose to pace the room.

"How do you feel compared to when you were in the hospital?" I asked.

"A lot better," she assured me. "I had a lot of worries then. Funny, I was convinced Ann had been in a terrible accident. I also thought people were taking things out of my apartment. Since I've had the lock changed, I'm not worried about that anymore."

"What *are* you worried about?"

She glared at me defensively. "Just the things I ought to be. Whether I'm giving my daughter enough attention. What my crazy sister-in-law will do against me next. Whether people will say I'm crazy because I was in a hospital and come here. Whether I'll ever be able to find a job again."

"You haven't been taking your medication. Is there a problem with it?"

She flung a full vial of Mellaril tablets onto my desk. "You should know! This stuff's slowly poisoning me. Dries up my mouth, makes it hard for me to move, slows me down." Her voice trembled with anger. "You damn doctors, always locking people up, poisoning their systems. I'm fed up with coming here."

"I'll change the medication, Irene, but you have to take it," I said firmly. "I want to treat you on an out-patient basis, but you've got to cooperate. Now, you admit you're still nervous and concerned, so please try the new pills. I'll give you something with it to control side effects, and if you're still uncomfortable, we can try further modifications. Okay?"

Mrs. Blaydow grimly accepted my prescriptions for Stelazine and Artane and agreed to come back the following Friday.

"What did you think of her?" Pat asked later. "She's not that badly depressed, is she?"

"If you mean suicidal, I'm sure she's not," I answered. "She's angry, and that's a good sign. She was able to direct it at me, and as long as she can keep from turning that anger inward against herself, there won't be any appreciable suicide risk. I'm more than willing to serve as a target if it keeps the anger mobilized until the medication works."

"What's the real source of the anger?" Pat asked. "Her own inadequacy?"

"Yes, plus a lot of hostility toward Ann that she won't confront. The delusion that Ann was in an accident was an unconscious wish that harm would come to her daughter. Ann was scarcely a wanted child, and facing up to aging and isolation is hard enough without a daughter emerging into puberty to make demands on you and remind you of the difference between youth and middle age. Her guilt over not taking proper care of Ann is motivated, to a large extent, by her rejection of the child. Well, we'll work with Irene, and as long as we can keep her angry instead of depressed, we'll have some leverage."

Friday morning, Irene Blaydow did not come in. Pat was in my office at nine fifteen with a very perturbed look on her face. "Vince, I got a call from Irene Blaydow's brother just now. She's dead—a suicide. He wants to bring Ann in to talk to us. He's concerned about how it will affect her."

I sat there with a rock where my stomach usually lay. "Sure we'll see her, though I don't know what to say. Are they sure it was suicide? What was it, an o.d.?"

"No. She threw herself out the bathroom window into the courtyard—four stories down. Sometimes you just can't predict these things."

I clenched my fist and rapped it on the desk. "It just doesn't figure, Pat," I said, my voice coming out in a hoarse whisper despite my efforts to speak louder. "I know things like this are bound to happen despite our efforts, but damn it, there's got to be *some* logic to our attempts. She was angry, she was paranoid, but *not* that depressed and not suicidal."

"Vince, you've said it to me and the staff more than once," Pat said, in that soft, maternal voice she can summon up with such effectiveness at dark moments. "You can only evaluate a patient's mental status at any given moment; you can't predict what they'll be like an hour or even five minutes later. We're not fortune-tellers or divinities."

"I know, Pat," I said. "Still, I was so sure about this one. And so wrong!"

# 4

I KNOW HOW IT FEELS TO LOSE ONE, BUT I DIDN'T KNOW WHAT I
could say to Vince to soften the feelings he was experiencing at that
moment. When my patient Ken, a twenty-two-year-old homosex-
ual, was found dead in his basement apartment over a year ago, I
had at least the dubious consolation of being unsure whether he
had willed his death or whether he had simply underestimated the
effects of the drugs he took that night in an attempt to alleviate the
feelings of isolation and despair through the perilous route he had
traveled repeatedly during six years of drug dependency. With
someone like that, you tell yourself that you can't make yourself
responsible for his refusal to stop indulging in self-destructive
escapism, that you can't expect to motivate a person who won't
commit himself to regular therapy sessions and who stands you up
to sleep off a drug hangover or to pursue the prospect of a potential
love affair; and yet, you never forget that patient, never stop asking
why you hadn't been able to mean enough to him that he would
have called you at the crucial moment when life became unbeara-
ble, never stop wondering if you did him a fatal disservice by not
acknowledging your inability to break through and at least offer
him a change of therapists. We can't expect to cure every
symptom, or to turn every tormented, inadequate patient into a
happy, productive citizen, but it's hard not to feel that after months
of treatment you should at least have inspired enough faith and
hope in a patient that he will think of you and seek your help,
however uncertain your efforts will be. Of course, with the ones

who do turn to you, you say, "They weren't serious about suicide anyway," so that sort of thinking puts you in a no-win situation.

Irene Blaydow had been my patient as well as Vince's, but in her agitated, delusional state, the psychotherapy had been limited. I merely attempted to get her to verbalize her conflicts until Vince could get her on an effective medication regimen to relieve the delusions and make her accessible to analyzing her problems in more depth, letting her explore options in dealing with them. Vince, as the psychiatrist, had the responsibility of deciding whether or not there was substantial risk in treating her as an out-patient, and though he would have run into considerable resistance trying to readmit her to the hospital that had so recently dismissed her, he certainly would have fought the system if he had thought Irene was a strong suicide risk. Honestly, I agreed with his decision and that, as much as being able to shift the responsibility for Irene's treatment plan onto him, spared me some of the anguish he was now experiencing.

"I didn't figure her for a suicide attempt either," I said. I didn't know how reassuring my inexpert opinion would be to him; only doctors, traditionally, are supposed to be involved in life and death matters, though if we nonmedical types scrambled to transfer every case where a death wish or suicidal fantasy crossed the patient's mind, we might just as well get out of the field altogether. Depression extends its dark hand into just about every psyche we encounter, whether we diagnose them as schizophrenic, neurotic, or personality disorders, and where there is depression, death hovers among the possible sources of relief, as much an option as the uncertain course of psychotherapy.

"If I missed something that should have tipped me off, I wish I knew what it was," he said. "Maybe it would save some other patient someday."

"Well, I missed it, too," I commiserated. "Maybe her daughter will tell us something that will explain why she did it."

I wondered, as Ann entered the office, whether she was internally reproaching us for her mother's death. We were, after all, the ones who were supposed to have helped Irene pull out of her psychosis, and you can't fail more completely than a suicide.

You wonder what relatives expect of you, whether they understand that curing a depression or another emotional problem is never as simple as administering an antibiotic for an infection or taking out an inflamed appendix. In my experience, I've usually found relatives to be very accepting of our limitations, probably because to them (and rightfully so) the patient is a person, not a disease, and they would be more surprised at our changing that person's personality and defense mechanisms than our failing to intervene effectively. Even if a patient has only presented with symptoms for a few months, those close to the patient are often aware that underlying difficulties and emotional turmoil have been present much longer, perhaps for all of the patient's life, while the therapist is told, "It started about a month ago."

If Ann was angry at us, there was no sign from her. Her face bore a serious, practically masklike expression, and despite her twelve-year-old body, she carried herself with the steady poise of a much older person.

"We were very sorry to hear about your mother," Vince began. "It came as quite an unexpected shock. Were you there with her at the time?"

Ann nodded and reported in a clear but unemotional voice, "It happened around five thirty. She called me into the bathroom. She had the window wide open and she said she wanted me to look at something in the courtyard—that birds had built a nest in one of the trees. She moved away from the window to let me look out, but I didn't see the nest she was talking about. As I turned around, she was moving toward me, with her hands out, as though she was going to push me out the window. I screamed and ran past her out of the bathroom door. Instead of following me, she locked herself in. I was frightened, but as soon as I realized she had locked the door, I started worrying about *her*. I banged on the door and begged her to let me in. She didn't answer. I ran and got my uncle; by the time he was able to force the lock, she had already jumped."

"I don't think she would have actually pushed you," Vince said.

"No, I don't think so," Ann said, numbly. "She had enough time before I turned around."

"But in her confused state of mind, the guilt over even having such a thought was so overwhelming that she killed herself," he said.

I realized Vince was trying to stress to the girl how ambivalent and weak her mother's homicidal feelings had been. I don't know which is tougher to live with, the knowledge that your mother tried to kill you or that she took her own life because of those wishes. Vince was trying to relieve the girl's guilt on both counts, emphasizing the devastating effect of a mental illness on the patient's whole span of logical thought and action.

"I wish we could have helped her," Vince said. "She was very ill. She refused hospitalization and wouldn't take medication—but that was part of the illness, too. She always spoke with concern about you and never gave us any indication that she was planning to do anything to harm you or herself."

The kid nodded charitably. I asked, "Where are you going to be staying, Ann?"

"With my aunt and uncle right now," she said. "My sister wants me to live with her in Michigan; I haven't decided yet."

"If you do stay on here, I'd like to see you again, okay, Ann?" I said. She nodded and left. There didn't seem to be much more we could say to her at that point, nor did either of us want to until we had time to work through our own feelings.

"So that's what I missed!" Vince said. "Homicidal impulses. Toward her own daughter! Funny, the textbooks talk about homicidal anger in depressives, but this is the first time I've actually seen it. They always repress it from consciousness and turn it against themselves. Suicidal ideas you see every day, but not homicidal ones. The only homicidal patients I've seen were big paranoid guys brought in to emergency rooms by the cops, and even then, none of them had actually tried to kill someone, mostly just a lot of threats and maybe breaking objects."

"Irene ultimately did take it out on herself," I noted.

"Yes, and as badly as I feel about her death, I can't help but feel grateful that she didn't kill Ann instead. Incredible, though, that after she used defenses such as delusions that Ann had been hurt and oversolicitous obsessions about Ann's being raised properly, the homicidal impulses, previously unacceptable, broke through all the defenses," he said.

"That poor kid must have been rejected all her life," I speculated. "Conceived out of wedlock when Irene was nearly forty, motivating the mother to enter a third disastrous marriage. It sounds terrible to say, but Ann may even feel some relief at her death."

"I hope she finds an easier life, wherever she winds up," Vince said, "but I can't honestly wish her a sense of relief. It would just about be impossible to experience that without a corresponding sense of guilt."

"I suppose you're right," I said. "Poor Irene at least felt strongly enough about how she *ought* to respond to Ann as a mother that she couldn't live with the guilt over a homicidal urge she probably never would have truly acted out."

"I don't believe she would have been capable of homicide no matter how psychotic she became. But she was overwhelmed, and a hospital could have prevented this," he said. "How many unnecessary commitments of patients who don't want hospitalization can be justified in preventing one death like this? I wish I had the answer."

I left Vince's office with a numb, leaden feeling in my gut and a sensation of weariness in all my muscles, wondering where I would find the energy to carry me through the day ahead. But I had no sooner raised my head to survey the waiting room than a surge of adrenaline sent my heart pounding and tensed every muscle as though I were coiled to spring at something. That something was a tall, slim, light-skinned black man engaged, near the entrance, in ardent conversation with Stacy Cunningham, who was fetchingly attired in a pink angora sweater and hip-hugging blue jeans. Stacy was lightly caressing his arm, and he was standing so close to her that he was about to emerge from the encounter with the world's first pink angora three-button suit. I had to stifle an impulse to shout a warning across the length of the waiting room, as one would to a baby about to touch a rat or a snake, for the dapper male was the notorious Earl "Sportin' Life" Jackson, the hospital's community organizer, a character who was more of a male chauvinist pig than the wild boars I've seen emblazoned on medieval coats of arms at the Cloisters.

He was reputed to have attempted to seduce every new woman who joined the hospital staff, plus a fair number of the healthier newly enrolled patients. I had even seen him flirting with a fifty-year-old grandmother, nearly twice his age, that week. Maybe that won't bother me so much twenty years from now, but what incenses me is not so much his sexual pursuit and activity, but the exclusion of any other sort of attitude toward women. Maybe Shakespeare and Freud would contend that he subconsciously turns me on, so strong is my aversion to the man: "Methinks the lady doth manifest a reaction formation." Still, I know that Jackson's sweet build-up leads to a put-down of the woman—into the horizontal position—and he really has no interest in the more upstanding woman, whether she's a commanding executive or a pie-making grandma. Dr. Bellino, even with his ingrained m.c.p. attitudes, could qualify for office in the National Organization for Women next to Jackson and his excesses. At least Bellino can accept women in roles other than sexual ones, even though he prefers them to be nurturers, like creators of homemade ravioli, or handmaidens, like nurses who have stayed out of college. Not that such positions for women are particularly dignified, but they are at least vertical.

I was therefore understandably upset to see Sportin' Life in such proximity to Stacy; apparently he was no more happy to see me, for as I took two steps across the waiting room toward them, still undecided about whether or how to intervene, he took one uneasy look at me, gave Stacy's shoulder two quick pats, and slithered out the door like a vampire who had glimpsed an approaching sunbeam. That left only Stacy for me to deal with, a far less formidable challenge. "Hi, Stacy," I said breezily. "Who was that man you were talking to?"

Stacy beamed up at me, more starry-eyed than usual. "Oh, a new friend. That's Mr. Jackson. He's a big executive here at the hospital, and he's very nice and friendly. He said he might have a *job* for me and he's invited me to lunch next Tuesday to talk about it."

"Oh, yes, I've heard of him," I said, not very enthusiastically. "He's certainly a busy man and needs to get around a lot. I hope he'll be able to keep your lunch date."

Stacy's face fell. "Do you really think he might not? Oh, I hope he can. Not just that I'd want a job, he's really very nice. Don't you think he'll keep it?"

I shrugged. "We'll just have to see about it, won't we?"

I sacrificed my belated lunch hour to descend to Sportin' Life's office in the lower regions. The community organizer's office was on the first floor of the building we occupied, a higher plane than devils of Jackson's ilk are generally reputed to occupy.

Jackson's receptionist was a hell of a lot better looking than the three-headed dog said to guard the entrance to Satan's realm. She was an exotic olive-skinned kid, no more than twenty, with a body that just might have insured her staying in Sportin' Life's anteroom beyond the three-month average. Out of all the young women whom the community organizer benevolently guided into available jobs, he always retained the best looking of the lot as his personal showpiece, replacing her whenever someone he deemed even more spectacular came along. It was sort of like a baseball farm system, only the displaced losers in Sportin' Life's private beauty contest often moved out to better-paying jobs in the community when released from the showroom. Of course, after Sportin' Life had been established in his position for a while, it became tough to top the reigning beauty who had won out over months of competition, but the boss was fickle enough to change the feminine decor every so often on general principle. Our own Dolores had been his personal receptionist briefly, and now I understood for the first time as I gazed at this latest trophy how he had managed to pass someone like Dolores on.

I introduced myself to the nubile neophyte and asked if I might see her boss. If he had one of his female interviewees in there, I was not about to wait around, knowing that he would never let one out in under an hour just for the sake of preserving his reputation.

As luck would have it, Sportin' Life was uncharacteristically alone, and he heartily instructed his harem favorite to usher me in.

In all my years at St. Dymphna's, this was only the second or third time I had been to Jackson's lushly upholstered seraglio, and it was my first time there alone. It was dimly lit, with thick red drapes and ebony-stained walls and, of course, the famous casting-couch in black velvet occupying a prominent place in the room. *Playboy* comes to Slumsville!

Checking to make sure that my navy blue dress was buttoned to the top of my voice box and thanking God that I hadn't worn my new white skirt with the thigh-slit that day, I strode in with a professional gait and selected what seemed to be the most Spartan chair, a designer piece of chrome and plastic. I found myself, to my chagrin, booby-trapped, my ass sinking almost to the floor, leaving too much of my legs exposed, to Sportin' Life's obvious delight.

"Well, Pat, this is certainly an unexpected pleasure," Sportin' Life said, scratching one end of his thin pencil-moustache as he sat behind a desk wide enough to double as an auxiliary couch of conquest. "We don't see enough of you around here." He ran his eyes up and down my legs as if to make up for lost opportunities.

"Thank you, Mr. Jackson," I said politely but decorously. "What I want to talk with you about is, unfortunately, rather delicate, and I hope you won't take offense. It's about the young woman you were talking to in the waiting room this morning." He nodded amiably and waited for me to go on. "Her name is Stacy Cunningham. Her father, George, is the director of laboratory services at the hospital." This last piece of information was received with a more pensive nod, but he still offered no comment. "As clinic coordinator and someone well acquainted with Stacy's situation, I feel obliged to tell you that she's having severe emotional difficulties and is particularly vulnerable and impressionable right now. She may appear capable of making rational choices to you, but it would really be very detrimental now for her to get emotionally involved with someone."

"I see," he said softly. "Please understand that I was only having a friendly conversation with the girl."

"She mentioned to me that you asked her out to lunch," I told him.

"I certainly didn't mean any harm by that," he protested. "She seemed to want to talk more, and the only free time I really have is my lunch hour. I figured I'd take her out for a sandwich or a slice of pizza somewhere around here—nothing big. But if you feel she's too much of a nut-job to handle it . . ."

"I didn't say *that!*" I intervened, my anger rising along with my hemline. "Just remember that anyone who comes to our clinic is hurting, and the women usually more so than the men. So many of them have been abused and exploited by the men in their lives, going back to their fathers, if they had any. That's a main reason why the female patients we see are such a depressed lot and feel so negative about themselves. If you take a woman in such a dependent, needy position and make sexual overtures, promising her love and care in the bargain, it's really preying on her vulnerability."

"Hold it a minute, Pat!" he said indignantly. "I don't know what you think of me . . . no, check that, I think I do know. That Earl Jackson . . . Sportin' Life Jackson, that's what they call me . . . screws every woman he can find, loves 'em and leaves 'em, treats 'em like dirt. Funny thing, though, I'll bet you don't hear many of those complaints from women I've actually been involved with. I come on, but I come on straight, and I'm certainly not indiscriminating. Sure, I asked that nice kid to lunch, but I don't generally seek out my companions in mental health waiting rooms. And I don't get my bed partners there."

"I've heard about Noemi Velasquez," I said skeptically. "Are those idle rumors?"

"Did Noemi complain about me?" he asked, equally skeptically.

I shook my head.

"No, I thought not. Noemi's been coming to your clinic less than a year. She and I go back a lot longer than that. Just because she's now registered with you, that doesn't make the lady a defenseless, exploited incompetent. But put your mind at rest about Stacy. I'm no psychiatrist, and if you think my being friendly with her will be harmful to her in any way, I'll bow out. I'd like to help her, but I have more than enough people who come into this office every day who need my help, too."

"Most of them young and female, I'll bet," I said cynically.

"You win your bet," he said calmly. "A big part of my job is to find job openings for residents here in the community. A lot of openings are in offices, for secretaries, receptionists, file clerks. The older women are either burdened down with children or never even learned to speak English. The young ones are ambitious and trainable."

"I don't suppose you've considered filling some of those jobs with unemployed young men?" I challenged.

"Sure I have!" he snapped. "In the first place, if someone says to me, 'I need a girl for my office,' he doesn't want a lecture from me on equal employment practices. Secondly, you've worked with kids, male and female, from this neighborhood, the ones this office sends you every summer during school recess. Applicants for summer jobs run five females to every male, and half of your boys drop out in a couple of weeks. They're more interested in hanging out. The really motivated ones get the hell out of this community and go where the really decent jobs are."

"Leaving the women here to take the lousy jobs?"

"*I* work in this community," he pointed out. "My job is to upgrade it and the people who choose to stay here, not push them to leave. If family ties and the culture keep women here, I try to make their lives worthwhile."

"Professionally or socially?" I taunted.

"Pat, I am leveling with you," he sighed. "I have never said to a girl, no screw, no job."

"Well, it's implied!"

"Is it, now?" he said. "Confidentially, I never patronize hookers. I don't get any satisfaction from sex I have to pay for—either with money or other means."

"You may not think you're buying it," I said, "but I wonder how the poor woman who's broke and desperate for a job views it."

"Am I, then, so unattractive, so dull, so cold that they don't find me desirable?" he asked rhetorically. "Don't try to lay a guilt trip on me, Pat, because I *know* I make these ladies happy. My problems are never with the ones who want out, just those who want to get more into a relationship than I'm ready for."

"Some might say that business and pleasure should never mix," I warned.

"Some must find their work very dull indeed," he speculated. "You can't care too much about what people say. They'll always talk about me, much as they talk about you. It's that way wherever you work."

"Oh?" I said, my interest aroused. "And what do they say about me?"

Sportin' Life emitted a throaty chuckle. "Oh, lots of the same things they say about me. That you're single and free-spirited, and likely to remain both for quite a while. That you're a cool, savvy chick who knows where it's at, that you're liberal enough to shoot convention to hell if it gets in the way of going after what you want. That you're not easy to get close to, but very nice when one does."

"Is that really what *they* say, Earl, or what you say?"

"What *I* say is maybe we ought to get outside these stuffy offices of ours sometime and give the chemistries room to mingle," he purred. "What do *you* say to keeping that lunch date that I'm going to break with your patient?"

"Is that a pass, Mr. Jackson?" I asked demurely, seriously considering the offer.

"Is it a completion, Miss Patterson?" he asked hopefully.

"Maybe I've misjudged you, Earl," I said thoughtfully. "Okay, but lunch may be a problem. Usually some crisis will come along, and I rarely manage to salvage more than a few minutes out of my laughingly termed lunch hour."

"Say no more!" he offered gallantly. "Let's make it a leisurely dinner, then. This way, Dr. Bellino won't have to know anything about it."

"Wait a minute!" I interrupted, my newfound enchantment suddenly evaporating. "What does Dr. Bellino have to do with whom I see or have my meals with?"

"Hey, all I meant was, I didn't want you to mess up your vibes with the boss-man, that's all," he explained. "You know how men get . . ."

"Not with me, they don't get!" I said. "Dr. Bellino has no say in my personal life."

"Okay, don't get sore," he said placatingly. "I just assumed from what I've heard around . . . well, you know!"

"No, I don't know. Tell me what you've heard," I demanded.

"That, like, the two of you have maybe a thing goin'," he stammered. "Like, that would be cool, you know . . ."

"No, it *wouldn't* be cool!" I practically shouted. "It would be most uncool to mix that sort of thing in business, particularly our line of business."

"Okay, but what are you so steamed about?" he asked, bewildered.

"I'm angry that you believed it," I shot back. "Angry that you assumed I couldn't get a position of responsibility and authority without screwing my way into it! You almost had me fooled, Sportin' Life, telling me what you felt I wanted to hear, even though it wasn't the line you give most of your women. All the while, you were thinking I was just another broad, ready and willing to screw her way into a job!"

"Have it your way," he shrugged, "but I'm not about to apologize. See, I'm not all that convinced that you're leveling with me. I know what goes on all over this community, even up there where you work. It's common knowledge that you're quite the little pet of Bellino—that he's even put his own neck on the line for you, more than once. Now, do you expect me to believe that there's nothing at all between the two of you?"

We sat in silence and glared at each other for several seconds. Finally, I said softly, "You know, you're right. Dr. Bellino and I have our differences and our disagreements, but actually there *is* something between us, a *lot* between us—a mental health clinic!"

I stalked out of Jackson's office, seething with more anger than I knew what to do with. I decided to lay off some of it on Dr. Bellino, and burst into his office with uncharacteristic impulsiveness to find him engrossed in a most nonmedical conversation.

"What's the tax write-off on that deal?" he asked into the phone receiver, ignoring my entrance. "Uh-huh. And the anticipated return next year? . . . Well, sure sounds good, go ahead with it."

I waited politely while he finished, remembering from my childhood that good little girls should remain quiet in the presence of their elders, especially men taking care of important business. Besides, I knew better than to try to compete with financial interests, even when I was armed with the second most interesting topic, sex.

He hung up the phone and nodded permissively for me to deliver my news. "Sportin' Life Jackson tried to seduce one of our patients!" I announced.

"Is that all?" he said, rather disappointedly. "From the urgency of your entrance, I thought the Department of Health, Education and Overabused Welfare had just cut off all mental health funds to use the money for a weekend of roulette in Las Vegas in a last attempt to save New York from bankruptcy. Too bad; I would have asked them to place our inadequate budget on red, double-or-nothing, and maybe we'd have enough left over to finance a few in-patient beds if we won."

"Obviously you won't take anything seriously that can't be rung up on a cash register!" I said. "Look, Jackson is a hospital employee, and he picked up one of our patients from right out of the waiting room with the sole purpose of sexually exploiting her."

"First of all," Vince rationalized, "even if he did speak to her in the waiting room, he might have previously met her at one of the local clubs or even a more prosaic spot, like the pizza palace. Most of our patients are nonpsychotic and capable not only of managing their unemployment and disability funds, but even their sex lives."

"The patient was Stacy Cunningham!" I revealed triumphantly.

"Oh," Vince said, somewhat crestfallen. "Not one of our better-equipped patients at the moment."

"But certainly one of our better endowed, which is all Jackson cares about!" I added. "Stacy is about as inconspicuous in our waiting room as a basketball center would be in a jockey's dressing room. Put a staple in her navel and she'd pass for a *Playboy* centerfold. She's got a waist like Scarlett O'Hara before the fall of Atlanta, not to mention a 36D chest that needs no Reconstruction."

"Nor points south vulnerable to invasion by Jackson, and I don't mean Stonewall," Vince pondered with concern. "Maybe we should intervene somehow."

"I already have," I dutifully reported. "I had a long talk with him and I think he'll leave Stacy alone, but I'm not sure about other patients. He admitted to me that he's friendly with Noemi Velasquez, whom I've seen him talking to in our waiting room. I'm sure the old snake-oil merchant told her he could cure her migraine headaches, anxiety attacks, and all her welfare problems with one wave of his magic wand."

"I'm sure most of those legends about him are concocted by Jackson himself," Vince said, "to maintain his alluring reputation. How well do you really know him?"

"Enough to know he made a rather obvious pass at me," I confided.

"At *you*? Jackson tried to seduce *you*?" he squawked. For the first time that day, I had captured his interest.

"And why is that so incredible?" I asked, finding his disbelief distinctly uncomplimentary.

"Well, you're not . . . his *type*," Vince protested.

"Because you can't picture me with a staple in my navel? I may not advertise like Noemi or our own combination receptionist-aphrodisiac, Dolores, but what I don't flaunt I've nevertheless got, and the maintenance has been excellent, considering how the demand exceeds my supply."

"I will personally nominate you for the centerfold of the *Journal of Orthopsychiatry* and pin your image up right beside my life-size poster of Joyce Brothers," he placated. "I wasn't putting you down as a woman, Pat. But, hell, Sportin' Life is *black* . . ."

"Oh, I might have known that would be your objection!" I fumed. "You are really such a bigot."

"Me?" he cried. "*You're* the one who refused to go to bed with him!"

"That had nothing to do with his color," I protested. "I would detest his attitude just as much if he were as white as a bed sheet in a detergent commercial. Physically, I've got to admit he's a damn good-looking man—more attractive than most of the men my work compels me to see daily."

"On behalf of my fellow palefaces, I excuse your racist remark as the sort of ultraliberal statement social workers are expected to make at least once a month to maintain their certification in whatever association monitors bleeding hearts," he retorted. "Of course, having turned down Jackson, you might have to have a quick affair with a Cherokee labor organizer or even dally with an Eskimo lesbian to keep your membership in good standing."

"Joke all you want, but you're more into this racial mythology than us allegedly gullible, seducible social workers," I said. "You're amused and titillated at the notion of this suave black stud making out like an insatiable satyr—provided his partners are cute, brainless little 'darkies' not worth the interest of an upper-class white."

"Pat, I do not condone indiscriminate liaisons (Dr. Bellino never says *screwing* unless he's referring to changing a light bulb)," he protested. "And at the risk of drawing further criticism, I deplore them even more among the lower classes, since they don't have the resources to bail themselves and their partners out of the jams they get into. I don't blame you for becoming outraged when he made a pass at you."

"Uh, that's not what got me angry," I ventured timidly. "It was when he practically accused me of having an affair with you."

Vince blinked suddenly, as if I'd swatted him between the eyes with a copy of *True Confessions*, but he managed to retain his composure. "Well," he said, after an interminable silence, "what do you expect from Jackson? A hungry lion would be incapable of regarding Indira Ghandi or Beverly Sills as anything more than someone's prospective dinner. Certainly you didn't let his predictable impressions upset you?"

"I suppose not. It's just that he said it was common talk around the hospital."

"Do you think Jackson has a monopoly on soap opera mentalities?" Vince said, though looking a bit more uneasy.

"Vince," I fretted, "do you think anybody on the staff here might be saying things like that?"

"Absolutely not!" he reassured me. "If anyone did, someone else would be certain to report it to me, in strictest confidence, assuring me that he or she put absolutely no stock in the vicious rumor but wanted to tell me about it for my own protection. As director here, I have to waste more time with this Machiavellian nonsense, listening to inane gossip and paranoid plotting, just not to insult the well-meaning bearer, who thinks he's saving my life and expects to be rewarded someday accordingly."

"Well, maybe no one would dare say anything," I postulated, "but how do we know what they're thinking? What would stop people here from thinking, like Jackson, that your relationship with me is something more than business?"

"Other than your looks and your disposition?" he deadpanned.

"You're not taking this very seriously, but it could be serious," I persisted. "In this sexist society, nobody will accept a woman on the merits of her work. Her ultimate value is still seen as being some man's plaything!"

"Relax, toy-of-the-month, before you get all wound up," he cajoled. "My overeducated guess is that most of the staff view me as being too straight arrow to even consider an extramarital affair. And most probably view you as too free-swinging to hook up with a guy who's never seen without his necktie and wedding ring. Then, too, you know the psychological need to deny sexual intimacy between Mommy and Daddy, even on the institutional level. Finally, if we were caught flagrante delicto in the conference room, eighty percent of the kooks on the staff would feel bound by their liberal ethics to support our 'getting into our own thing' or would find our conduct as unworthy of their attention as everything else that transpires in the conference room. Now, may we forget about Sportin' Life for a while? We've got bigger problems closer to home. Have you heard about Sandy Silverstein and her junkie?"

I nodded glumly. "Yeah, it seems to be common knowledge that Jeff O'Malley is living at her house. Of course, that doesn't prove he's screwing her, though she's been seen holding his arm and looking very intimate on the street."

"That alone is enough to require our intervention, isn't it?" Vince said. "Since when is a therapist supposed to have a personal relationship with a patient?"

"It depends what you call personal," I said. "The problem is that Sandy has been 'involved' with other patients before and we've never stepped in. In fact, I think we've been secretly grateful. When old Mary Baczewski was wandering the streets with her shopping bags and wouldn't accept a nursing home, Sandy let her crash with her for over a week till she could talk her into placement. When that sixteen-year-old runaway, Lola, escaped from the home and showed up at Sandy's doorstep on a Friday night, Sandy kept her and acted as an envoy to the kid's parents. There was the old guy who had the stroke whose check was stolen—he was at Sandy's halfway house for a while. Vince, she lives in the neighborhood, and since her mother died, she's got an extra floor in that house. She's a soft-hearted soul, and even if she doesn't maintain proper professional distance, sometimes she solves sticky problems we couldn't otherwise handle quickly within the system."

"And you don't think she's more involved than on a social worker's level with Jeff?" he asked skeptically.

"I don't know, Vince. But I've seen her give an old man a hug or hold a teen-ager's hand and we don't make big things out of that. Jeff is a withdrawn, schizophrenic kid, and if Sandy feels he needs a little physical contact, she'll give it to him," I said.

"And if she feels he needs a *lot* of physical contact? . . ."

"Knowing Sandy, I don't think she finds it easy to say no to anyone," I admitted.

"Will you talk to her with me?" Vince asked.

"Why me? Can't you handle it alone?"

"Yes, but I think she would feel more at ease with you present," he said. "If I call her in alone, it looks like an official reprimand. I'd like to handle it as diplomatically as possible. See if she's free now."

Sandy was. I used to think I was a rebel, but compared to me, this girl was Jefferson Davis. She was wearing a baggy gray sweater that didn't completely conceal her generous endowments, and a pair of faded blue jeans, the kind I would never wear in the city except on a Saturday trip to the laundromat. Sandy was about twenty-seven, but her long, straight brown hair and pudgy unpainted face gave her the appearance of a teen-ager. She was the type who would visit the most decrepit tenement in the most crime-ridden neighborhood without a thought for her own safety, and if an entire gang in leather jackets did not strike fear in her, a shrink in a three-button suit wasn't likely to intimidate her either.

"Sandy," Vince said, "it's come to our attention that one of your patients, Jeff O'Malley, is living at your house."

She nodded. "Yes, he's my tenant. Temporarily, until he finds a place."

"I don't want you renting to clinic patients," he said. "Especially your own. It's impossible to maintain a therapeutic relationship when you're living with someone."

"He's got his own floor," she protested. "Complete privacy. It's not like we have to share the same rooms."

"And he never drops in to visit?" Vince questioned. "Never has a meal or a cup of coffee with you, like a good neighbor?"

"That's not going to harm him," she said. "He needs a little socialization, and he's very shy around other people. Besides, I knew him from the neighborhood even before he had a break-down."

"Then you shouldn't have accepted him as your patient!" Vince said.

"He wanted me as his therapist," she said. "He wouldn't have come here otherwise. Hey, what's the hassle? You never objected when I took Lola on Saturday outings or when I put up Mr. Berkowitz for a while."

"I know," Vince acknowledged. "And I guess I was wrong. Sandy, you've got to limit your contact with patients to the clinic."

"And how am I supposed to keep them away from my door, with an electrified fence?" she snapped. "These people live within a few blocks of me. My address and phone number are in the book. Hell, it's not like I'm charging St. Dymphna's overtime for my services."

"You don't have to let them move in," he insisted. "There are apartments to rent."

"Find them!" she challenged. "Jeff couldn't. A lot of landlords don't take welfare cases, let alone mental patients. And those who will take them do it because they know they can stick them in unheated, rat-infested flats and never paint the place or wire it adequately. Jeff is a brilliant, talented guy, a top musician. I'm not going to throw him out into the street or put him in the Muny with a bunch of drunks."

"I'm not asking you to throw him out," Vince said. "But you will have to relocate him if you want to continue working here. Pat, can you get Pablo Suarez, Amos, and some of the other assistants to scour the neighborhood and see what they can come up with in the way of a suitable place?"

"Sure," I said. "Sandy, they're really very good at coming up with apartments or furnished rooms. They have a lot of contacts who don't spend money on advertising."

Sandy grunted reluctantly. "Well, I'm going to check out the place myself before Jeff makes any moves."

"Okay," Vince agreed. "It shouldn't be more than a week or so before the assistants come up with something. Now, in the future, I want you to tell me immediately about any contacts you have with patients after working hours, even phone calls. I know it's difficult to avoid them, but the potential problems can be very serious. Also, who's your supervisor? Dr. Krumpel? Make sure you discuss Jeff fully with her."

"Jeff's not a problem case for me," she pouted.

"Well, you may pose problems for him," Vince countered. "Don't you feel that living in the same building with a young therapist of the opposite sex may engender some sexual feelings—if it hasn't already? And, so help me, Sandy, if I ever learn that transference feelings are being acted out, you're through here!"

"Don't worry," she said grimly. "You'll never learn about it. Is that it?"

He nodded and she left. "Okay, Pat, get the assistants hopping on this, *stat*—which is medical talk for right now."

The encounter with Sandy that afternoon left me with many disturbed feelings that continued to gnaw at my insides through the afternoon, and they were still chomping away when I returned to Vince's office the following week for supervision.

"Vince, about Sandy . . ." I opened.

"Oh, yes, I meant to talk to you about something," he interrupted. "Don't assign her any more male patients unless they're over the age of sixty or under twelve. No sense putting temptation in her way."

"Don't you think she'll realize that something's missing from her case load? We don't know that she's done anything unethical. As long as our angel of mercy confined her round-the-clock services to the untouchables, those who have been rejected as too crazy, dependent, or hopeless by everyone else, we winked at her breaches of professional standards, even praised them in the name of community mental health. Once she picked up an attractive, seductive male, we started wagging fingers and making judgments."

"Don't you think she's been sexually involved with him?"

"I have no proof, but honestly, sure I suspect it," I admitted.

"So how come you were all up in arms over Sportin' Life romancing Stacy, but it's okay for Sandy? Sounds like a double standard to me."

"Maybe it is," I conceded. "Men are more exploitative. Sandy and Jeff are consenting adults, so I don't consider what Sandy's doing immoral. Stacy, on the other hand, is a potential victim of mind and body rape."

"Hold it, hold it!" he groaned. "Lest we forget, Jeff is as much a psychiatric patient as Stacy, and since we don't even know that Sportin' Life had anything but a budding personal relationship with Stacy and Sandy does have a professional one with Jeff, how does he come off as a mind rapist and Sandy as an angel of mercy? You know why? Because everybody assumes the man always takes the initiative in a sexual relationship, which is about as universally true as saying men hold all the jobs or men drive all the cars. Tell me honestly, Pat, haven't you ever been sexually attracted to one of your patients?"

I stared at him for a few seconds, wondering how much I dared say. "There was one. It almost became a *Tea and Sympathy* thing. Do you remember that movie? I saw it as a teen-ager, only I really didn't understand it back then. It was about an older woman, the wife of a college professor, who has a sexual involvement with one of her husband's students, a boy who has a lot of anxiety about his sexual identity."

"Tell me more about it," he urged.

"It's been so long since I saw that movie that I really don't remember much . . ."

"Not the goddamn movie, your patient!" he exclaimed. "Look, this is a supervision session, isn't it? It's about time we started talking about significant things, like countertransference, instead of your using the hour to lecture me about women's rights."

"Okay," I said, with some misgivings. "The patient, Mark, first came into therapy here about ten months ago. He came for the first time because of a crisis—which is usual for a lot of our intakes. The night before, he had had a terrible fight with his drunken father, one where they almost came to blows. Mark's own rage really frightened him; for one moment, he had thought he could and would actually kill his father. So, the next morning, he came running here."

"What do you remember from that first encounter?" Vince asked.

"I remember being impressed by his height. Mark was tall, very tall. That was probably part of the unconscious initial attraction. I'm sure it was unconscious—at that point, I never believed I would develop erotic countertransference feelings toward any patient, since it honestly had never happened before. I always liked tall men; being tall myself, they made me feel more dainty and feminine. Anyway, I would have rated Mark as quite physically attractive, had I been consciously thinking in those terms.

"Not that Mark was the image of masculine power that day. The poor guy was still anxious from the previous night's encounter. I asked him, with my best supportive but thoroughly professional aura, to tell me exactly what happened. 'My father came home drunk as usual, and, this being payday, at his worst. He called me a no-good bum and said that I would never amount to anything. He said I'd never be able to support myself if I kept trying to be an artist.'

"Wow, an artist, a poor, struggling artist, I thought. Well, I got the picture immediately—a blue-collar father, who was a hard-working laborer, pitted against a son who was a creative dreamer. I've always had a soft spot for artists; the unconventional side of me respects someone who hasn't compromised and sold out to get by.

"Mark tried not to respond to his father because, as he

explained, he'd learned that when drunk, his father was irrational; but when his father continued to berate him, Mark told me, 'I finally saw red. I thought if he leaned toward me once more with that stinking alcohol smell on his breath, I would hit him—I would kill him! I got up from the kitchen table, ran into my room, and slammed the door.' Mark said he was shaking so hard he couldn't sleep for hours. He had never been so upset."

"You said there had been other fights with his father," Vince pointed out. "What was so traumatic about this one?"

"Part of it was the father's putting him down about not being able to support himself, although, actually, Mark did have a part-time job as a hotel clerk at night. I was glad to hear that he wasn't totally dependent on his parents to support him while he pursued his education and his art. I could see that he had some ego strength, that he wasn't someone with a passive-dependent or inadequate personality."

"So why did his father's remarks affect him so strongly?" Vince asked.

"No, that wasn't what got to him. What did it was his father's saying that no girl would ever go out with someone with no income and no interest in anything but artwork he couldn't sell. Then, the father said, 'Maybe you're not interested in girls anyway. Maybe you're queer. You seem to prefer hanging around with that boyfriend of yours from art school.' It struck a nerve, because Mark did have problems with dating and did feel more comfortable with men and was beginning to wonder if he wasn't, deep down, really gay."

"Distinct possibility," Vince commented.

"Hardly," I answered. "Mark certainly had feelings of attraction toward women, especially a girl who was in one of his classes in art school. Mark told me how he plotted for weeks to walk up to her at the end of the class and start talking to her. One day he finally got the courage to do it and promptly dropped his portfolio and all his drawing equipment on the floor. As he scrambled around, picking things up, she mumbled something about being late for an appointment and ran out. The next day, he saw her walking in the hall next to this big football-player type. 'Women just don't go for me,' he said. 'I guess my chances for a romance with that girl are pretty hopeless.'

"I tried to be supportive and give him some encouragement, even though it was an intake session. I pointed out that he really never even had a chance to talk to her. I told him I understood his embarrassment about dropping his portfolio and that maybe she really was late for an appointment. 'And you don't know what her relationship is with the guy you saw her walking with,' I said. 'Maybe they're doing a class project together, or maybe discussing an upcoming exam.'

"'Yes, I know I get so anxious in terms of approaching women I like that I can't even think straight,' he said. 'Girls are so hard to talk to. Men friends are different; you can say whatever you want and it's okay. Girls reject you if you're not super-smooth.'

"Mark, I thought, you have a lot to learn about women. You should only know how many girls sit home every night waiting for the phone to ring, and I don't mean just the acne-speckled two-hundred-pounders. I told Mark that I wasn't so sure that *all* women were hard to talk to or demanded that their men be as smooth as a fresh-shaven eel. I told him that we would explore exactly what goes on when he attempts to relate to women. He was so painfully shy, although he seemed to be so together in terms of his vocational pursuits. And I marveled at how such a personable, attractive, intelligent man could be so fearful of women. At that very moment, I committed myself to a new mission in life . . ."

"Other than raising Dr. Bellino's consciousness level," Vince interrupted.

". . . to help Mark relate more comfortably to members of the opposite sex."

"Well, I wouldn't put that in the same league with bringing peace to the Middle East," Vince said dryly, "but it's more worthwhile than inducing guilt in men for failure to give single women gratification previously sought only under the aegis of marriage."

"My relationship with Mark," I continued, "started out in total innocence and with the noblest of intentions—as many far baser relationships likewise begin. I saw him once a week for several months, and he made swift progress.

"His relationship with his father improved, and his father not only cut down his drinking but even started attending AA meetings. With women, Mark had made tentative approaches and, in fact, even gone out on a couple of dates, to a museum and to the opening of a friend's art exhibit. You might remember my presenting Mark's case at staff conference a while back. Dave, in true psychoanalytic style, even confronted me about my countertransference feelings toward Mark."

"I don't remember the meeting," Vince admitted.

"Probably because I answered Dave's provocative question in a vague, noncommittal way. I said my feelings were positive, but that was because Mark was such a 'good' patient; he came regularly for therapy, talked openly about his feelings, and had good insight into the causes of his conflicts."

"Looking at it objectively now, was Mark really that much different from your other patients?"

"Compared to what we usually draw here? You bet," I answered. "All patients are 'good' in the best of all possible clinics, but here it's refreshing to see a patient who doesn't come only when he receives a letter from the welfare department or who has been suffering from headaches for the last six years but can't see any connection with her six-year-old marriage to an abusive, assaultive husband."

"What were Mark's transference feelings? How do you think he felt about you?"

"I knew he liked me," I said. "He had given me several of his favorite paintings—two of them are hanging in my office. I didn't feel there was anything wrong in accepting them. You know that therapists often receive gifts that have personal meaning from their patients, and even strict Freudians have been known to hang patients' paintings in their waiting rooms.

"I never became aware of anything unusual in my feelings toward Mark until last winter, after I had been seeing him almost six months. I had run into him, quite by coincidence, with one of his new dates outside the opera house at Lincoln Center. I was

struck by how attractive she was—which, interestingly enough, I
never mentioned to Mark when he asked me my impression during
our next session. I remember that I felt vaguely achy and feverish
that night; it was the start of a cold that lingered on for weeks and
weeks."

"You blamed *that* on Mark?" he asked.

"In retrospect, yes," I asserted. "I believe that most illnesses,
even the common cold, have psychosomatic origins. I don't think
that the onset of my physical malaise merely happened to coincide
with my meeting Mark's attractive friend. I really think I was more
a victim of depression than contagion."

"You, depressed?" Vince said, seemingly surprised.

"Yes, successful, attractive, healthy, personable, liberated young
me—strike healthy," I said. "It was the winter of my discontent—
and I wasn't exactly singing 'Winter Wonderland.' Maybe it
was the job, maybe it was my turning-thirty crisis—whatever, I
think I was very vulnerable, which is why I fell in love with a
patient."

"You actually fell in love with him?" Vince said, aghast.

"Would it be less shocking to say I 'experienced eroticized
positive countertransference feelings,' as Dave Goldman would put
it?" I asked. "Well, I didn't have any fantasies about keeping house
for him or even his keeping house for me, but looking back, I was
becoming maternally overprotective where his women were concerned or, to be more honest, feeling like a jealous lover. One day,
after he had been feeling confident and optimistic for several
weeks, he came into my office looking very downcast. He had
begun to date a girl he met at the Monet exhibit. According to
Mark, she was attractive, personable, and was a painter like
himself, though she supported herself by designing book jackets.
Mark was quite taken by her and had been able to overcome his
usual anxiety about women enough to date her several times.
When he described her to me, I wondered if she wasn't a bit too
worldly and experienced for him, but as a good therapist, I kept
these reservations to myself. At our previous session, Mark had
told me he was going to her apartment for dinner; it was about time
for a bedroom scenario, so when he later came in looking so upset,

I figured it was the result of that weekend's encounter. I started the session by commenting right off about how depressed he looked and asked, 'What's up?'

"'Nothing's up, that's the problem,' he said. 'My date with Jane was a fiasco. It seemed to go so well in the beginning. She cooked a great dinner, with one of my favorite dishes: linguine with clam sauce.'"

"God, don't tell me she overcooked the linguine!" Vince gasped.

"There are, for some people, more traumatic disappointments in life," I informed him. (I'm not saying that food has replaced sex as the biggest pleasure in Dr. Bellino's life, but it's rumored that there's a mirror on the ceiling above his kitchen table.) "No, the dinner went fine, capped off with a bottle of sparkling white wine. Mark said, 'After dinner, we moved onto the couch—which also served as the bed in her studio apartment—and I was kissing her and touching her all over and I felt so good, not anxious at all. We were just about to do it . . .'"

"Do what?" Vince asked, his mind probably still on the linguine.

"Make love, of course," I translated. "Poor Mark was too embarrassed to say it, let alone *screw* or *fuck*" (like some psychiatrists avoid). "And then the phone rang."

"Damn!" Vince exclaimed. "Just when things were getting interesting."

"She jumped up immediately to answer it. It was an old friend of hers—male—who was in town for the week and wanted to see her. Mark said he tried not to listen, but of course he was right next to her—and I can just bet he wasn't about to seize the opportunity to take a quick shower. Jane talked to the guy for a few minutes and finally said she'd call him tomorrow. 'After that call, I was finished,' Mark said. He was blushing as he told me, 'I couldn't perform at all, and that was it. Oh, she tried different ways, you know.'"

"What ways?" Vince pursued.

"Oh, for heaven's sake, use your imagination," I replied. "Mark couldn't even look me in the eye with the limited description he gave me."

"That's one of the difficulties when therapists pick up patients of the opposite sex," Vince observed.

"I notice that most of *your* patients are female," I pointed out. "Why haven't you passed them on to female clinicians?"

"No need to," he asserted. "Women have virtually no shame. Never mind, though. What *was* he able to put into words?"

"Just that he hurriedly put on his clothes and left. He didn't attempt to see her or call her after that. Too embarrassed, besides which he felt she probably never wanted to see him again. So, I told him in my most supportive manner, 'I wouldn't be too sure about that. Many first sexual experiences aren't perfect, despite what romantic novels might lead us to believe. I can understand your feeling let down . . .'"

"Pardon, your Freudian slip is showing," Vince interrupted.

"I'll try to raise it," I snarled. "I asked Mark to try to recall his thoughts and feelings that night, and he said, 'The minute that other guy called, I knew she would much rather be with him than with me. I'm sure *he's* super-smooth, probably with a lot of experience, and really knows just how to turn a woman on. I feel like a kindergarten student when it comes to women. Do you realize I'm twenty-one and still a virgin?'"

"Is that punishable by law in California, by the way?" Vince asked.

"It wasn't *that* exceptional, even in California, when I was his age, though now there are probably more twenty-one-year-old whooping cranes than virgins. Of course, even though only bad girls had gone 'all the way' by that age back in the dark Victorian era of my youth, men were another matter. Men, we girls fantasized, *never* had been virgins. It was as though they had somehow acquired sexual experience prenatally—or at least well before their adolescent attempts at seduction. Even Mark seemed to believe that was the natural order of things. 'Now, how do you know that she would rather have been with him than with you?' I said to him. 'It seems to me that you're always comparing yourself with other men and feel you're coming up short.'"

"Gave him the old 'slip' again, eh?" Vince needled.

"Listen, I didn't create our sex-crazed language, I just speak it. I told Mark that people aren't born with knowledge about sex—it comes with experience, and rather naturally, beginning when you feel like being close to a certain person and making contact with them. 'It seems you put too much pressure on yourself, in terms of A-plus performance,' I said."

"Spoken like a true sex therapist," Vince applauded. "You sound like Dorothy Johnson after she got her Masters."

I jumped my narrative to the evening following Mark's session. "That night I was very tired by the time I arrived home. Thinking I must be coming down with cold number five hundred eighty-four of the season, I even went to bed early, which I have rarely done since making a vow at age eight against premidnight bedtimes and spinach once I reached maturity. The telephone woke me up right in the middle of a dream—and it was about Mark, one that was *very* sexual and not set in my office. My 'unconscious' attraction to Mark had broken rather abruptly into consciousness. With the phone ringing away, I looked at the clock and saw from the illuminated dial that it was only eleven, although I felt I had been in bed for years. I finally fumbled for the receiver. Guess who? 'Pat, it's me, Mark,' he said."

"*He* calls you Pat?"

"Oh, lots of my patients do," I said casually. "Don't any of yours call you by your first name?"

"Not unless you count 'Doctor,'" he said haughtily. "No wonder you have transference problems! Never mind, what did your patient want?"

"He apologized for bothering me at home, but said he couldn't wait until tomorrow to talk with me," I replied.

"Had you given him your home phone number?"

"No, he just got it out of the phone book. That's why so many of you shrinks have unlisted numbers, I know. Strangely—or maybe not so strangely—I didn't mind Mark calling. I was just a little embarrassed thinking how groggy I must sound. Mark said, 'I decided that you were right, maybe I *was* too sensitive about what happened between me and Jane last Saturday. I called her up, but she sounded very brusque and not interested. After I hung up, I felt too restless to study or read, so I went out for a walk. I went over to the Art Students' League just for something to do. I was getting so agitated just staying in my apartment.' By the way, that was another sign of the progress Mark had made—finally being able to separate from his parents, who had such an undermining effect on him, and moving into his own place. Mark said that when he got to the League, there was Jane, walking in, arm-in-arm and looking very happy, with a very handsome man. Mark said he tried to hide in the shadows until they went in, and he didn't think she saw him. Afterward, he was so upset that he didn't know what to do and even contemplated 'a one-way trip to the bridge.' Then, he decided to call me. He said, 'You always listen to me, and I feel so good after I talk to you.' I asked him where he was. Even as I asked, I wondered why, whether I was actually thinking of seeing him. When he said he was calling from a pay phone on a street that I—and probably he—realized was only two blocks from my apartment, I considered, for a brief second, meeting him at the corner coffee shop, thinking how much easier it was to be supportive and encouraging in person."

Vince looked at me with apprehension, obviously trying not to be judgmental but silently rooting for me to make the "right" therapeutic decision, as one pulls for the good guys in a movie melodrama. I quickly put him at ease. "Are you crazy, Pat, I thought. You know you have the hots for this patient. Just the memory of that dream had me blushing. I gave myself a quick mental lecture; I couldn't even justify a sexual encounter with him under the guise of helping him. Mark was, after all, as every patient, in a very vulnerable position. I would be as evil as Sportin' Life Jackson; Mark was really needy and he trusted me. So, I wound up talking to him for about ten minutes, telling him how I understood how very discouraged and upset he felt about being so obviously rejected for another man, and assuring him that there would be other women with whom he would be able to have a more positive relationship. Then, giving to a point, I told him I could see him at nine the next morning. That was it, Vince—my big countertransference crisis. At the crucial moment, I decided that *Tea and Sympathy* was a movie, *not* reality."

Vince sat quietly for a long half-minute, apparently disturbed by my confession. Finally, he said, "Pat, do you mean you might have actually had sex with the guy?"

"It was something that I would have really liked. It was on my mind for a fleeting moment—and longer than that, if you count dreams. Of course, I didn't follow through on the temptation, as I just told you."

"But you made it sound as though you came close," he said, with a perturbed frown. "Meeting him at a coffee shop in the middle of the night is one thing, but going to bed with a patient is a far different thing!"

"Is it, Vince?" I said with placid skepticism. "In both cases, you're going outside the bounds of the therapeutic relationship to meet the desperate needs of the patient. Just to play devil's advocate, if a few hours with him could have restored his confidence in his masculinity, why would it be preferable to wade through months of weekly therapy sessions instead?"

"Amazing audacity!" he gasped. "If a male therapist did that with his female patient . . ."

". . . and you know it happens . . ." I added.

". . . he would be denounced in the vilest terms as an unscrupulous libertine, exploiting a patient for the gratification of his own lust."

"Agreed," I agreed. "Which is what stopped me—the realization of my own desires and vulnerabilities. Maybe Sandy Silverstein does give herself out of sheer concern for her patients, and if that's the case, I'm not sure she's wrong—certainly, in this case, my motives were far from strictly altruistic."

"The countertransference was out of control," he analyzed.

"I'm not sure I want to invoke that sterile rationale," I replied. "Countertransference, like the term *transference,* implies that the therapist is relating to the patient in a neurotic way, based on the recreation of some unresolved conflict with an earlier significant figure. But Mark is handsome, intelligent, and sensitive, the kind of man I would naturally find highly desirable. My relationship to him as therapist doesn't lead to these feelings—if anything, it inhibits them. In any good therapeutic relationship, erotic feelings are inevitable, and if only the patient has them, the therapist must be made of stone. I don't think they're all that dreadful."

"I don't care what the books say," he protested. "If the therapist maintains his or her proper distance, the patient is no more likely to develop strong erotic feelings toward the therapist than toward his or her professor or dentist or butcher. It *can* happen in any of those other relationships, but it's far from 'inevitable.' And, believe me, therapy goes a hell of a lot more smoothly if you can avoid transference or libido or romantic infatuation or whatever the devil you want to call it. Just recently I almost had a patient of mine stampede out of therapy in a panic simply because she had an erotic dream about me."

"Oh?" I said, eager to learn how my distinguished supervisor confronted such challenging matters. "Who was it?"

"It's not important, Pat," he mumbled, probably regretting he said as much as he did.

"Can't you tell me about it?" I urged. "I'm sure I can profit more from your firsthand experience than by reading or hearing about textbook abstractions."

"It was Terri Ryan," he said. "I don't know if you're at all familiar with her."

"I've seen her in the waiting room," I said casually. Oh yes, Vince, how could I miss that dark-haired young beauty of yours who can draw every eye toward her even when Dolores is gyrating around the front desk.

"In her dream," Vince recounted, "we were in the office together and I took her in my arms and started kissing her. She thought about how both of us were married, and said to me, 'This isn't right.' And in the dream, I replied, 'But it's what you wanted, isn't it?' The dream particularly threatened Terri not only because it suggested that she was unhappy with her marriage, but also because she feared becoming too dependent on me. She even considered dropping out of therapy for fear the time would come when she would never be able to. If she had followed through . . . well, you can't do too much for a patient who is no longer there."

"You sound almost guilty about it," I ventured carefully. "Aren't dreams of this type pretty common for patients to have?"

"For you glamorous types, maybe," he grunted. "Not for a chunky, rumpled sort like me, who would be typecast as Paul Newman's manager or Robert Redford's sidekick, the one Ann-

Margret pecks on the forehead before the closing clinch with her leading man. Still, if the books are right, looks and age have nothing to do with it—transference works better than fairy god-mothers when it comes to turning frogs into princes. Somehow, I couldn't get myself to accept it as mere coincidence that the only patient of mine to report such dreams happened to be my loveliest and most favorite. For all my dispassionate professionalism and conscientious weighing of words, I had been seductive enough to upset Terri's developing equilibrium and possibly the therapeutic apple cart as well."

"All that disaster from one sex dream?" I asked skeptically.

"If you call a lousy kiss a sex dream!" he replied. "If her dream had been captured on film, it wouldn't have gotten a rating spicier than PG—not like the X-rated countertransference dreams *you* have about your patients. Terri could have at least waited until we got around to the R stuff before her superego censored the dream. Then again, maybe it's Terri's modesty that draws me to her. She grew up like my sisters and cousins—Sunday morning Mass, no movies during Lent, no touching below the neck on dates. She's one of us."

"Terri *Ryan?* A member of the formidable Bellino mob? I mean, clan?"

Vince grinned. "Before she married an Irish bartender, she was Theresa Venturi, a working-class, third-generation Calabrese kid who knew the difference between *calamari* and *caponata*, and who didn't know wine came in any color besides red until she went to a wedding at eighteen where a cousin married outside the faith."

"Ethnic prejudice, Vince?" I chided. "How undemocratic."

"We assign black patients to Mosley and Jeanne Ellis, don't we, because we feel they understand the patient's lifestyle and provide someone for him to identify with," Vince said. "We try to provide the Puerto Ricans with Spanish-speaking therapists, even if the patient speaks fluent English. Besides, my liking for Terri goes beyond the ethnic—she's straight arrow, and that goes beyond being Italian or Catholic. Still, I suppose she sensed that she was special to me, and that's what confused and unnerved her so.

"It would have been so easy for me to fall back on basic

interpretation number one, the old transference lecture that explains how patients tend to invest in the therapist qualities carried over on an unconscious level from previous significant relationships. That would have thrown the onus on Terri and left me as detached as in her fantasies about me. No, I had to tell her straight out that I did admire her values, her concern for her relatives despite their often inconsiderate treatment of her, her devotion to the kids she does volunteer work with, and her faithfulness to her husband."

"Did you ever stop to think," I warned, "that in so doing you might be interfering with her options to disown her relatives, have an affair with the exterminator, and tell the world where to place its axis?"

"We could always reopen those possibilities later in therapy," he explained, "but not if the therapy ended abruptly because of that damn dream."

"Vince, what exactly is Terri's problem?" I asked. "What are you treating her for?" (Besides for the lift she gives your Tuesdays.)

"She came to me about nine months after she had been hospitalized, without too much success, for severe anxiety and obsessions about being possessed by the devil," he recounted. "She wasn't exactly delusional, yet the intensity of these disturbing ideas about demons terrified her, especially at night. The one significant change in Terri's life at the time of her breakdown was being told by her gynecologist that she had an underdeveloped uterus and would never be able to have children. Terri had been holding down a low-paying clerical job and feeling inadequate even at that; her husband had lost his job, and she was the sole breadwinner. Her husband had become depressed over his inactivity and started spending his days at the racetrack and his evenings in the local tavern. While he was basically responsible and considerate, Terri began to wonder how eager she would have been to marry him right after high school if her home situation had been better.

"Terri's parents had split when she was only six, and her mother was aloof and undemonstrative. As a kid, Terri idolized her older brother, Bill, and for a time, he had shown her the kindness and affection her mother had never provided. But when Terri reached puberty, Bill's brotherly kisses began to linger in unbrotherly fashion, and one night she caught him peering at her through her bedroom door while she was undressing. So, Terri fled the one supportive relationship in her life, and when her husband came along with his vows of love and the chance for her to escape from that tension-packed household, Terri chose escape. Escape to what, though? She was ill prepared for marriage, for sex, for work, for the world. I think the one thing that kept her going was the hope that within a year or so she wouldn't have to get up from a bed where she had spent so many sleepless, frightening hours to go to a noisy office with its meaningless chores. Once the baby she and Jim wanted so much was born, she could stay home securely all day, safe in the peaceful world of motherhood. When her hopes for a baby were crushed by the doctor's verdict, Terri's only available escape was a mental one."

"Through insanity?" I asked. "Delusions of demonic possession? Doesn't sound like much consolation, does it?"

"Terri had friendly spirits as well as devils," he revealed, "and they were what really fascinated me. Demons are so common to the mentally ill, of course, that they were acknowledged in biblical times to be the cause of insanity. Terri only experienced the devil in the form of nightmares or fears, not in the more psychotic form of delusions or hallucinations. Her friends were a more unique phenomenon. They weren't delusions or hallucinations either, yet they were more vivid than fantasies. To Terri, they were best described as a 'presence,' both reassuring and intensely disturbing."

"What are they like?" I asked.

"They're a bunch of rather exotic types—Terri won't or can't be very specific about most of them. Except for the *Star Trek* crew. They're often with her. I can see why she turned to them. They might have understood her, the crew of the Starship *Enterprise*. Their mission, after all, was to go to worlds never before explored." He chuckled. "I can imagine Captain Kirk's crisp unwavering

voice: 'We are entering the atmosphere of Terri Ryan's unconscious, terrain uncharted, inhabitants unknown. Reduce speed to
warp one. Ready, sensors. Prepare to beam down.'"

"You're a bit of an escapist yourself, aren't you?" I said. "I never
would have guessed it."

He looked at me reproachfully. "Then you're nowhere near as
observant as Terri. I know it's practically standard operating
procedure for every patient to attempt at some point to win the
approval of the therapist by confiding some secret allegedly
withheld from other doctors, but I believed Terri when she said
she had never told the therapists in the hospital about her fantasies.
And the curious thing that gave her the courage to confide in me
was this coffee mug." Vince lifted the mug, which was half-
submerged in his desk's scrap heap of memos, official communica-
tions from the Department of Mental Health, and patients' charts.
It was not the mug he usually brought to staff conferences, with the
haughty family coat of arms, but one absurdly emblazoned with
images of Disney's Alice in Wonderland, the Mad Hatter, the
March Hare, and other members of that irreverent entourage.

"Terri said to me, 'You understand fantasy. If a psychiatrist can
keep something like that on his desk . . .' She never finished that
sentence, but I think it would have concluded, 'he's not threatened.' Terri was frightened by the benevolent Star Trekkers as
much as the devils. That's why she could tell me so little about her
fantasies—because she constantly turned away from them, not
daring to question what they represented, what purpose they
served. And, Pat, I felt the secret of success in Terri's treatment lay
not in dispelling these fantasies but in helping her to confront them
and even accept them."

"That makes sense," I agreed. "But you make it sound like this
fantasy chasing is a special interest of yours. Have you done some
sort of research in it?"

Vince stared at the Wonderland mug still in his hand. "No," he
said softly. "This is rather personal, Pat, and maybe I shouldn't be
discussing it, but I've always been a rather fantasy-oriented person.
Often, characters I encountered in books or movies became very
vivid and stayed with me for weeks or months. I would think about

them, invent new adventures that I could share with them, even talk to them in my imagination."

"Lots of kids have imaginary playmates," I said in my best supportive fashion. "It's quite common."

"I had imaginary playmates at age twelve, sixteen, even later," he confessed. "Most of them came and went until, somewhere around the eighth grade, I got hung up on a medieval maiden from a French storybook, a very bold, devoted girl named Nicolette, whose personality I matched to a totally unrelated illustration in a book of Arthurian legends, a redhead with a slim, graceful body and the most enchanting trace of a quizzical smile. In the beginning, the fantasy was well under control. Someday, I would meet a girl as lovely and resourceful as Nicolette. Later, the daydreams weren't of being with someone *like* Nicolette, but with Nicolette herself, magically transported across the centuries. As time went on and I became more aware of what *real* women were like, Nicolette changed. She was still the superwoman, but instead of being my devoted sweetheart, she was my nemesis, my tormentor, the heartbreaker who could have any man she wanted—and didn't want any."

"And you became disenchanted with her," I assumed.

"Lord, no!" he exclaimed. "I found this new Nicolette to be more alive, more fascinating than ever. I had pretended I was in love before; now I *was* in love. The more she teased and mocked my adolescent awkwardness and inexperience, the more I clung to my thoughts of her."

"A not-so-harmless fantasy?" I said, filling an awkward pause.

"Well now, here's the really strange part," he continued. "In time, Nicolette actually became a real help to me. I was so determined to escape from her put-downs that I became very self-conscious about my appearance and actions. I lost a few pounds, started carrying a comb, and forced myself to start conversations with girls, just to show her I wasn't as hopeless as she thought. And as I saw what was happening, I came to appreciate my dream girl. I understood that I had somehow created her to give me the incentive that I previously lacked. Even though she was female, she was, to some extent, an idealized self, with the confidence I lacked. We came to terms with one another. If I had been offered a year of free psychoanalysis to rid me of my redheaded demon, I would have spurned it on the spot.

"Well, I guess I've wandered off Terri a bit," he said, looking a little embarrassed.

I'll say he had! I had just about completely forgotten Terri Ryan, so absorbed had I become in Vince's uncharacteristic personal revelations. I thought of our many arguments, the bantering and jousting, and wondered if I hadn't become the eerie reincarnation of his personal demon. "Yes, what about Terri?" I said, relieved to change the subject to a more clinical one.

"The first task I had," he related, "was to relieve her worst fears, to make her understand that she was not hopelessly insane, or even that far removed from sanity. When she spoke reluctantly about her fantasy life, I didn't attempt to drug her into insensibility, but I accepted and even tried to explore the phantoms. 'Try to *see* them, Terri,' I would urge. 'Don't be afraid of them. Listen to them. They're only parts of your own mind, perhaps among the healthier parts.' And, together, we came to know them better, the members of Terri's 'audience.' The more we spoke of them, the less need there was for their presence, since our sessions together were providing Terri with the outlet for sharing her innermost dreams and fears that could previously be supplied only by her amorphous friends. There were buried feelings that once would have distressed her more than the most hideous of her night devils: anger at her mother for raising her in an atmosphere of bitterness and superstition, disenchantment over the course of her lackluster marriage, sexual feelings toward her own brother. They all came under scrutiny now; even in the glare of therapeutic confrontation, they were far less threatening than their imagined shapes when she kept them in darkness. Terri became able to verbalize with confidence her desires and her dissatisfactions to her husband, her mother, and other important people in her life. The more she dared, the more she believed herself capable of, and the less bizarre her fantasies and daydreams seemed to her."

"Vince, since you've been so frank with me today—and I do appreciate it—may I ask you a personal question?" I ventured timidly. "Haven't you ever had any fantasies of your own about Terri?"

"Erotic, you mean?"

"Among others."

"I think I can honestly say I've never really imagined getting physically involved with her," he said rather proudly. Then, with less smugness, he added, "I have had other thoughts which might, I suppose, qualify as fantasies. For example, she often worries about how she would survive on her own if something ever happened to her husband; and I've thought that if such an unlikely thing happened, I would like to find her a job with me, in some capacity, to make sure she got along. I suppose, given our similar backgrounds, it crossed my mind that given the right circumstances, I might have married a girl like Terri."

"Really, Vince!" I cried, getting impatient with him despite my intent to respond to his confessions in only the most supportive, nonthreatening way. "Here you were so shocked because I dared to let the fantasy of a sexual act with Mark flit across my conscious mind, and you've actually had fantasies of *marriage* to your patient. Marriage isn't all cooking and laundry, from what I've heard!"

"But it *is* a hell of a lot more than a licentious romp, which is *all* you were contemplating with *your* patient."

"That's unfair and inaccurate!" I shot back. "You know I care a *lot* about Mark's total welfare. In fact, that's why I never took the idea of going to bed with him at all seriously." Vince's pained expression made me realize I had gone much further than I intended in this frank discussion, and I retreated to a more conciliatory position. "I'm sorry, Vince. I didn't mean to imply that you had done anything out of therapeutic bounds with Terri, and I hope you feel the same way about my handling of Mark. I certainly don't presume to warn *you* about the pitfalls of transference and countertransference. I'm sure you know that your feeling of closeness to Terri might make it difficult at times to maintain your distance, especially when the time comes to let her go."

"Of course I know that," he said smugly. "That's why when Terri told me about the kissing dream and her fear of increasing dependency, I dealt with it in a somewhat unconventional way.

Instead of following the classical psychoanalytic route of seeing the patient three times a week to work out the transference crisis in intensive therapy, I suggested we cut the frequency of our sessions in half—to every other week."

"You did *that* to your favorite patient?" I gasped.

"I didn't *do* anything to her," he clarified. "It was something we agreed on together. I'll admit she was a bit leery at first. Then she realized that I actually believed that for her, therapy was a volitional step toward self-understanding and growth, not something she had to do to save her from the loss of control she feared."

"So, what did she say to your suggestion?"

"'See you in two weeks, Doctor!'" he quoted.

"Well, Vince," I said, "I'm going to mark her last appointment on my calendar and keep track of the Tuesday afternoons when she doesn't come in—because I fear you won't be fit company for woman nor beast on those days. I have the feeling that you're going to miss her more than she misses you. What are you going to do when she's not there to brighten your Tuesdays, she and that fascinating crew of imaginary spirits she tows around?"

Vince wrinkled his brow pensively. "You know, that's exactly what Nicolette said to me the other day." He gave the precise sort of impish smile that left me unable to decipher whether he was joking or mad—or, possibly, both.

I looked at my watch and saw we had run well over the hour. "Thank you for a most interesting supervisory session," I said sincerely.

None of us welcomed the Wednesday morning conference that week. By now everyone on the staff knew that one of the patients had suicided, though Irene had been in treatment with us such a brief time that only Vince and I had actually known her. Vince eased his way through an emotionless summary of the case, from the day Irene was thrown on our doorstep, prematurely discharged from the hospital, to the night she threw herself from a bathroom window. Only when he spoke of Ann and her mother's halfhearted homicidal gesture did his voice become hesitant and colored with the pity and frustration he was trying to bury under the dull weight

of a load of polysyllabic chunks of jargon, such as *projection,
introjection,* and *reaction formation.* Since I had not only heard the
story but lived with it for nearly a week, I was as eager as Vince
must have been to have his grim monologue come to an end and
put poor Irene finally to rest.

I don't suppose Vince spoke for much longer than fifteen
minutes, but I kept looking at my watch, though I wasn't sure
whether I was afraid the time would run out before he'd finished or
afraid the conference would never end. Just when the fifteen
seconds of reverent quiet following the conclusion of Vince's
presentation had lulled me into a sigh of relief that the ordeal was
over, psychologist Ramon Montalvo opened his mouth for the first
time ever at a staff conference and said, "Have you spoken to any of
the relatives about the patient's relationship to her daughter before
her psychosis?"

"What's the point of rehashing all this, now that the woman's
dead?" I intruded testily.

"No, maybe we should explore it further, Pat," Vince said softly,
with a quick appreciative smile for my effort at terminating the
matter. "We still have the daughter to deal with."

"Ah . . . I found out late yesterday," I volunteered hesitantly,
"that Ann went to Michigan to live with her older sister,      ·all."

With that, the case slammed shut. A nod from Ramon ι.      ;d
he was withdrawing his question. Vince launched the conference
precipitously on a new course by saying sharply to Nunzio
Scaglione, "How are things going with Stacy Cunningham?"

Nunzio shifted his pot-bellied bulk in his chair, stroked his gray
moustache, and rotated both hands in the air as if cranking up his
motor prior to starting his report. "Beh!" he shrugged. "The girl
herself, she's not talking too much about specific things in her life.
I talk to her father, though. It seems Stacy's mother died when she
was fourteen years old. The woman was known to have cancer at
least a year before her death, but nobody explains this to Stacy—
she knows her mother's sick, of course, but she's not suspecting the
mother's going to die. Toward the end of her life, the mother was
very irritable, sometimes even violent. They think maybe even the
cancer spread to her brain—who knows? She and Stacy, they don't

get along at all then, and Stacy even went to live with her grandmother the final months of her mother's life, because she couldn't study at home with all the mother's yelling and demands.

"When the mother died, Stacy was a little angry at her father and other relatives because they didn't tell her the mother had cancer; she felt she would have been more tolerant and spent more time with the mother if she knew. But Stacy didn't stay angry; she sort of took over the house, cleaning it, cooking meals for her father, going to games or on car rides with him on the weekends. About the time Stacy was finishing high school, the father began seeing the woman he's married to now. Stacy went off to college someplace in Ohio, and, though she did well, she didn't go back for the sophomore year. She told her father she wasn't sure what she wanted to do, and, rather than waste time taking courses that later proved useless, she wanted to take a year off. Stacy took an office job and tried to go back to the old routine of housekeeping and cooking for her father. He admitted to me he was often torn between wanting to spend time with his girlfriend and staying home with Stacy, who was making such determined efforts to take care of him.

"Well, he solved the dilemma by marrying the woman, who then moved in with him and Stacy. The stepmother and Stacy tolerated each other pretty well. According to the father, Stacy was never really friendly to her, but not cool or hostile either—*mezzo-mezzo*, you know. Pretty soon, Stacy begins going out more, having lots of boyfriends. She's a nice-looking, popular girl. Comes home a little late once in a while, but what the hell, she's over eighteen, you know, and she never stays out all night or comes home drunk or high on drugs. Then, bang! One night her father gets a call she's in the emergency room. Bad drug trip. They give her Thorazine, they keep her almost twenty-four hours for observation—her father, he works at the hospital, you know, so they try to do as much as they can for her there. But when she remains very anxious and disoriented, they send her to County Hospital for psychiatric treatment. You know the rest."

"What does Stacy talk about in sessions?" Vince asked.

"Mostly about how inadequate she feels," he said. "She claims she's never felt sure of herself, even in high school. College frightened her, work frightened her, men scare her. Now, she's terrified about being alone anywhere. Says she feels like a three-year-old who is in the middle of a crowded street and looks up to find her mother gone."

"Does she talk about her feelings toward her father and stepmother?" Dave Goldman asked. "Sounds like there's quite an Oedipal situation there."

Dave would see Oedipal triangles in a geometry book. In this case, I had to admit, he had a good case.

"She says her father is the only person she's got who she really cares about," Nunzio said. "She calls the new wife by her first name and, of course, doesn't feel they have any real relationship."

"Don't you feel that this combination of childlike and seductive behavior she's manifesting," Dave interpreted, "is an attempt to win back the father's attention?"

"The girl is definitely schizophrenic," Harry Chong interrupted. "Regressive behavior is very common in schizophrenic psychosis—it is a variation of the primary symptom, autism, as described by Bleuler. She is probably not being adequately medicated."

Frau Krumpel, who had been medicating Stacy, bolted down the large chunk of prune danish she had been placidly masticating, nearly asphyxiating herself in the process. "She is taking sixty-four milligrams of Trilafon daily!" she pronounced. "I would not call that an inadequate dose." She hurriedly bit into the danish again to compensate for the loss of oral gratification the premature swallowing of her previous mouthful had caused.

"The fact her psychotic behavior was not improved is proof in itself that her psychosis is inadequately treated," said Dr. Chong, holding firm. "Maybe she is not taking it as prescribed. Maybe you should switch her to intramuscular Prolixin."

"Schizophrenia or not, I don't think we can ignore the psychodynamic implications," Nunzio said. "I quite agree with David that there is some goal direction underlying her regressed and seductive behavior, no matter how psychotic she is."

"I think we've been through this before," Sandy Silverstein drawled sleepily over her coffee cup, "but what's intrinsically psychotic about seductive behavior? Should we put you on

Thorazine, Nunzio, because you persist in growing and grooming a moustache that serves no purpose other than to make you sexier in appearance?"

Despite the chuckles of appreciation she was accorded, I wasn't about to join Sandy's side in the eternal battle for freedom of sexual expression. My libido was not yet fully recharged after the drain of the Mark & Terri supervision session. Vince, however, was not about to let Sandy's challenge go unbattled, especially when he had his own battle ax to grind. "Ms. Silverstein, there is, I contend, a difference between the exhibitionistic dress and promiscuity espoused by a growing number of modern women and the childish, indiscriminate touching and clinging with virtual strangers that Stacy manifests. I grant you, that difference may be a subtle one, but I am inclined to invoke psychosis in Stacy's case and amoral hedonistic nihilism in most of the other cases."

"I still think Prolixin would curb this inappropriate behavior," Chong proselytized.

"What Prolixin cannot curb perhaps Dr. Scaglione can," Vince said. "Nunzio, did you see what she has on in the waiting room this morning? And if you didn't, I don't blame you, because there wasn't that much of it! She's wearing this skimpy pair of shorts that barely covers her gluteal folds in the back and a knit jersey, bare in the back except for the strings, that clings to her chest, with no intervening bra, as though she had been hosed down with water . . . Ramon, sit down! She'll be out there the rest of the day, I assure you."

Montalvo grinned sheepishly. "I was just going to pull a chart. I have a patient I was going to discuss next." He resumed his seat reluctantly.

"She's not seven years old anymore," Vince resumed, redirecting his remarks to Nunzio. "If she persists in dressing that way, it's only a matter of time before some guy jumps her."

"Yeah?" objected Sandy. "If I got raped wearing a tight jersey and shorts, you'd say that's what caused it, huh?"

Vince appraised her critically. "In your case, no. In Stacy's, yes."

"Do you honestly think," I asked, attacking his flank, "that just because Stacy is wearing . . . what's she's wearing that it would put thoughts of *rape* into the head of the average man?"

"If such thoughts cross the mind of a law-abiding, married psychiatrist approaching middle age," he answered, "I shudder to think what goes on in the head of the average man."

I gave Vince a long, studied look. "Gee, Nunzio," I then said, "maybe you'd better get Stacy to do something about her summer wardrobe."

"Speaking of carnal malfeasance," Vince said, glaring at me, "how are you progressing on finding a placement for Lynn Rossman?"

"Uh, that would be Pearl Rossman's daughter, right?" I stalled, hoping a fire-drill bell would ring as it used to in grammar school. I sneaked a look at my watch in case we had fortuitously run overtime so I could claim I had my ten o'clock appointment waiting, but I was better off, I realized, waiting for the fire alarm.

"Yes, the very one," Vince said impatiently. "The adolescent who still sleeps with her mother—and any men who also happen to be in the bed, remember?"

I was not saved by a bell, but a Boyle, as Dennis kindly saved me with a fire alarm of sorts. "It seems, Vince," he said, "that there's a new crisis in the Rossman household. This time it's Gregg. He started a small fire in the living room."

Nurse Jackie added, "Pearl smelled the aroma of smoked hickory wood and came in from the kitchen to find that Gregg had a fire going on the seat of her rocking chair. Gregg said that he was only playing with his toy Indians and was making a small campfire for them. Gregg stuck to the story when we saw them, but fire-setting's too dangerous to mess around with. We recommended hospitalization, at least for observation."

"No wonder the kid's frustrated," Vince muttered, "with mother and sister having all the fun in one bed and him left alone in his, with nothing to do but wet it. Did you get him admitted?"

Nurse Jackie and Dennis stared incriminatingly at Dr. Feliciano, who slumped fearfully in her chair so her tiny head barely cleared the edge of the table. Trembling like a rabbit in the midst of a pack of hounds, she squeaked, "I write letter yesterday for mother to bring to County Hospital, ask admission for a fire-setting. Also call up late afternoon, but resident not yet make up mind to admit little boy. I call right away after conference, make sure he's in hospital."

"If he's not, he may have burned mother and sister to a crisp by now," Nurse Jackie said ominously.

"At least *something* in this case will have wound up well done!" Vince snapped. The meeting adjourned, and Dr. Feliciano ran off to call the hospital while Ramon Montalvo ran to the waiting room to look at Stacy Cunningham. "You're not off the hook," Vince hissed in my ear as I gathered up my stack of charts and empty coffee cup. "We didn't know about this fire-setting until this week. You could have started working on a placement for Lynn right after last Wednesday's conference, like you were supposed to."

"Oh, I got backlogged," I alibied. "And once you get much past Thursday noon, there's no point trying to do anything with city agencies, especially in the summertime, so I decided to hold off until Monday. Just as well, don't you think? I don't think Pearl could bear having both children removed from the home at the same time. And I understand from Nurse Jackie that there's been no more mother-daughter dating; in fact, Pearl's been practically celibate herself all week."

"I'd find that hard to believe," he scoffed, "even if she'd sat on the rocking chair Gregg set afire while it was still blazing."

My first patient that morning was Lucy Nunez, a thirty-eight-year-old unmarried mother of seven, four of whom were in foster placement. Of the three children at home with her, two were ten months old, a pair of undernourished twins whose combined weight just about totaled the desirable weight for a single child their age.

"What am I going to do, Mrs. Patterson?" she wailed. "I feed them, I really do, but they just don't want to eat. What am I supposed to do, shove the food down their throats?"

"I know you're concerned about the twins not gaining weight," I said gently to her. At that point, she seemed to relax, the hostility draining from her face. With four children in placement, she was forever the target of attacks on her maternal adequacy by well-meaning social agencies, which led to her developing an unrelenting defensive attitude toward all. I wondered how many of Lucy's critics, so preoccupied with her failure, had attempted to zero in on the anxiety and guilt she must have felt watching her children starve rather than accept the nourishment she offered.

"I'd like to visit you tomorrow," I said suddenly. "Maybe I can offer some suggestions." Just me, who knows as much about child care as raising giant pandas! They certainly didn't teach that in Casework Practice IV and, even more certainly, I haven't had any personal experience. Yet, I found myself saying, "So, I'll see you tomorrow, Lucy, about noon." It was like throwing ten dollars to a drowning man because you can't swim but nevertheless feel you should do something.

Bellino was even less enthusiastic about my proposed home visit than I was. "It's setting a bad precedent," he fretted. "A certain amount of outreach is necessary in this business, but we have the assistants to meet that need. If you go out to Lucy's house, next week somebody at the hospital or one of Lucy's neighbors may want me to send a social worker somewhere else. How can Dave or Sandy refuse when the senior social worker is doing it? Once you've got the professionals trapped, it's only a short step to asking us to send doctors into the home. Face it, we can treat three or four patients at the clinic in the time it takes to see one at home, not to mention the reimbursement hassle over undocumented outside visits. As long as I'm director, the policy of this clinic is that professionals do not make home visits. Particularly the clinic coordinator."

"Whose duty is to stay home and watch the house and kids, right?" I said. "Okay, then I'm going on my lunch hour tomorrow. You can't stop me from that. I can do whatever I want during my lunch hour, even if it's a quick screw with my lover, as long as I'm back by one o'clock." With that I strode out of his office, leaving Dr. Bellino slightly embarrassed and more than slightly flustered.

The next noon, with a prayerful heart and fasting stomach, I climbed the four dimly lit flights to Lucy Nunez's flat, guided only by the eerie glow of the spray-painted FUCK YOU graffiti on the walls. The ubiquitous legend reminded me of the clinic, where the same phrase appeared in three-foot-high letters beside the door, magically and faithfully restored any morning following the hospital's infrequent attempts to remove it. It was the only sign on or near the door. ST. DYMPHNA MENTAL HEALTH CLINIC had originally been stenciled in gold on the glass door panes, but the glass was shattered at least once a month by the community's equivalent of a neighborhood redevelopment committee, the same group that included the spray-can calligraphers. Glaziers apparently work faster than sign makers and the redevelopers usually got to the new panes before the sign makers, so finally the hospital decided to leave us anonymous, somewhat like a Prohibition-era speakeasy. Every time I would say to a prospective client or visitor on the telephone, "There's no sign on the door," I was tempted to add, "but it does say *fuck you* in big white letters." But then again, they might confuse the clinic with the butcher shop, public school, police station, and First Methodist Church, all of which were decorated with the same greeting, rather like the way everything within fifty miles of the Pedernales River in Texas bears a likeness or the name of Lyndon Baines Johnson.

Lucy lived on the top floor of the decaying tenement. The one-time owner of this venerable structure had long ago retired to sunny Florida and the City had reclaimed the building for back taxes. Most of the hallways' twenty-watt bulbs were burned out, there were pools of water in the halls whenever it rained for two consecutive days, and when the temperature dropped below freezing outdoors, it often did the same indoors.

After the dingy, dirty halls, Lucy's apartment looked surprisingly bright and airy. Of course, the absence of blinds or curtains on the windows and the sparseness of furnishings certainly contributed to its open look. Lucy lived in what would have been advertised as a two-and-a-half-room apartment—if slum dwellings were advertised. Realistically, it consisted of one twelve-by-twelve room, a narrow entranceway, three feet of which contained a two-burner hot plate, a rusty sink, and a Hollywood-style refrigerator, the kind that Beverly Hills dwellers have in their bars to make ice cubes and store orange juice for screwdrivers. And, of course, there was the bathroom, complete with leaky toilet and corroded bathtub. Where the paint was peeling from the apartment's walls, you could see the shades of pink and green with which they had been previously painted, in years long past. Ah, maybe the twins have lead poisoning, I thought with clinical detachment as I noticed pieces of paint crumbling from the wall. There was no furniture in the room except for a bed in the corner, where apparently Lucy, six-year-old Sonia, and the twins all slept. Clothes seemed to be stored only in a variety of boxes.

"Thank you for coming, Mrs. Patterson," Lucy sighed. "Here, have a seat," she offered, pointing to one end of the bed. I gingerly sat down after making sure that the roach which had started to make a beeline for the proffered seat had finally decided that the feeding-ground might be better on the floor. God, I thought, I hope I don't see any mice or, worse, a rat. I knew that Lucy had them. Once, she had told me, she awoke to find a rat as big as a cat staring her in the eyes. If there's one thing I'm afraid of, despite years of poverty as a struggling social work student, it's a mouse.

"Here's Sonia," Lucy said, introducing a frail, sad-eyed waif. "She's six."

"Hello, Sonia. What school do you go to?" I asked by way of making pleasant pointless conversation.

The question was more barbed than I had realized, judging from the pained, apprehensive look on Lucy's face as the kid replied waveringly, "I don't go to school."

"And these are the twins, Jose and Carlos," Lucy interjected briskly, eager to change the topic. She pointed to two very tiny infants lying huddled together on one side of the bed. God, they were small!

"Oh, how sweet!" I cooed supportively. "Which one is Jose?"

My second seemingly innocent question seemed to distress Lucy even more than the first. Wringing her hands, she stammered, "Um . . . uh . . . the little one."

That was about as helpful as designating one of the Gabor sisters as "the sexy one." Noting my perplexed look, Lucy added, "Jose weighed two ounces less when they were born, so I always call him the little one." After an awkward silence, she snapped, "Sonia, show Mrs. Patterson which one is your brother Jose."

Sonia shuffled reluctantly from the spot against the wall where she had been cowering. She stopped six feet from the bed, peered at the bony bodies huddled together, and said timidly, "That one, near the wall." Then, almost inaudibly, "I think."

"Lucy, there must be some way you can tell them apart!" I protested. "Isn't there?"

She shrugged disconsolately. "I used to pin their names to their undershirts," she explained. "Then the hot weather came, and they didn't wear undershirts. I thought it was okay, because Carlos had a birthmark on his shoulder. Or maybe it was Jose that had it. Well anyway, the birthmark disappeared. But Jose had a bruise on his back from the time Sonia dropped him . . ."

"Not true!" Sonia wailed. "He got the bruise the time *you* dropped him. The time I dropped him, he fell on his head, remember?"

I was beginning to experience unpleasant childhood flashbacks of the Duchess's kitchen when Alice in Wonderland heard her singing, "*Speak roughly to your little boy and beat him when he sneezes . . .*"

"Well, he's okay now," Lucy hastened to assure me. "Even the bruise is gone." The last observation was made with an air of regret for having lost a valuable landmark.

"Well, Lucy," I pressed, "if you've really lost track of which baby is which, the hospital has footprints on record. They'll straighten it out for you."

"Sure," she scoffed. "Then, they're going to say, 'What kind of a mother don't even know her own children?' They give me enough trouble with the kids' weight. Right now, I got to get them to eat. If they don't grow up, what do they need with a name anyway?"

"They don't care what their names are, lady," Sonia chimed in. "See, they're too little to understand. But I can even spell *my* name: S-O-N-I-A. My neighbor taught me." She gave her mother a furtive glance as she reassured herself that she was in no danger of anonymity even if Lucy was as negligent about remembering her name as those of the other children.

At this, the twin closest to me, the one tentatively identified as Carlos, began to whine and squirm restlessly. As the whine progressed to a full-spirited howl, I cautiously reached for the squalling infant, hoping to quiet him before he roused his oblivious twin. I felt an ominous trickle down my arm, which was sheathed in a new suede jacket. I jerked the baby a few inches away from me as Lucy hovered anxiously by, eager to discover how a scientific expert would deal with such a crisis.

The child's crying had now progressed from routine howling to frantic screaming, definitely not a favorable endorsement of my child-handling techniques. What was the problem? I thought babies were supposed to *stop* crying when you picked them up. Ah, I deduced, perhaps it's because he's wet.

"I think we should change him," I shouted to Lucy above the piercing, insistent screams.

"I don't have any diapers left and my check doesn't come until tomorrow," she said morosely. Faced with the dismal prospect of sleeping on a poor man's version of the water bed, she cast a desperate glance about the room. "But wait," she said excitedly, "there's Sonia's piggy bank."

Ah, see how resourceful my patient was, contrary to what her previous social workers all claimed. Moments later, we had counted twenty-four pennies, an obsolete fifteen-cent subway token, and a tin coin bearing the likeness of Millard Fillmore. (Probably all the Lincoln and Kennedy coins wound up in cereal boxes shipped to the Upper East Side, while the kids in our community got Millard, James K. Polk, and Rutherford B. Hayes.)

Sonia mournfully witnessed her "donation" of her life's savings to her little brothers' health and welfare. "Give them this at the bodega downstairs for a small box of Pampers and tell them I'll make good tomorrow when I get my check," Lucy commanded.

It was hardly a time to give Lucy a lesson in basic economics, but it was a splendid example of how the poor get screwed. The bodegas, neighborhood groceries and shops, were sure to charge

Lucy fifteen or twenty cents more on the diapers than the supermarket, and buying a large box at the chain store would have ultimately saved her . . . oh, how the hell would I know what diapers cost, but it would have been a substantial amount. But, of course, only the bodega extends credit the eve of check day, and Lucy couldn't afford even a small box on a cash basis, a situation they never covered in Economics I.

As Sonia ran down the tenement stairs, twin number one continued to cry nonstop, while twin number two slept, as though in a comatose state, at the opposite end of the bed. Uneasily, I watched the sleeper's chest and abdomen for signs of breathing and decided to refer him, at the first opportunity, to the pediatric clinic's audiology division to have his hearing tested. Desperate to stop the wet one's howling, I considered an alternate approach to the problem while waiting for the rescue pads. "Do you think he's hungry?" I asked Lucy.

"I don't know," she responded blankly. "I tried to feed them this morning, but they didn't eat much."

That's just the problem, I thought, but withheld comment. "Do they take solid foods yet?" I asked. "Like cereal?"

She stared at me skeptically. "You mean like Cheerios, and Captain Crunch, and that chocolate vampire stuff?"

"Good grief, no! *Cooked* cereal, like farina or oatmeal."

"I tried that once a long time ago," she said listlessly. "They didn't want it."

"Maybe you should try again," I urged. "What other foods have you tried?"

Lucy squinted, trying to concentrate despite the distracting howls from the baby. "Ah, you name it, I tried it. Rice, beans . . ."

"You tried to feed *beans* to the babies?" I gasped.

"Oh, I mashed them up first!" she assured me. "I wouldn't give them whole beans. What kind of mother do you think I am!"

*"For he can thoroughly enjoy the pepper when he pleases,"* Lewis Carroll's Duchess rasped in my memory.

"Strained fruit," I suggested expertly. "Have you tried that?"

She looked at me placatingly. "I gave them bananas," she ventured cautiously.

"Oh, Lucy, that's excellent!" I said encouragingly. "Bananas are very easy to digest."

"Easy to fix, too," she added, with more confidence. "You can mash them with a fork."

"Of course!" I beamed. "And babies are almost never allergic to them."

"I heard somewhere that they give good nutrition!" she said happily.

"They do, they do," I agreed. "How often do you feed the babies bananas?"

"Never," she said, crestfallen. "They don't like 'em. I have more luck with mashed beans."

"Let's stick with milk then, Lucy," I said. I thrust the noisy infant into her reluctant arms and marched into the kitchen area. There was a dirty-looking bottle on the counter, half filled with curdled milk, which I emptied into the rusty sink and swished under lukewarm water from the tap. It certainly wasn't sterilized. I wondered if that was important for a ten-month-old, my knowledge of infant care being woefully close to Dr. Bellino's assessment of it. One didn't learn much about babies in such courses as "Art of Western Civilization" in college, and in high school all I learned was how to prevent them. Going back to my more distant past, in seventh grade home ec, I had learned only how to make chicken à la king at 9 A.M. (unfortunately, I had home ec first period).

Well, there was no great trick to filling a baby's bottle. I stooped to open the dwarfish refrigerator and spied an almost empty milk carton bearing yesterday's date.

"Lucy," I admonished, "this milk is a little old. Don't you have anything else?"

"There's a bottle of *malta* in there," she volunteered.

I looked at the amber bottle and shuddered. "You wouldn't give *beer* to your babies?"

"'Course not!" she stiffened. "*Malta* ain't like beer. Well, maybe a little, but it don't got no alcohol. Hey, Mrs. Patterson, what kind of mother you think I am?"

"I'm sorry, Lucy," I apologized. "It's just that I never had any experience with *malta*." I rose to my full height, tired of posing like

the catcher in the rye in front of an underdeveloped and under-
stocked refrigerator, with my knees becoming frostbitten.

She nodded. "That's okay. It's really good stuff. Builds up your
blood, gives you energy. Better than vitamins. Go ahead, you take
it."

"Thanks, Lucy," I demurred, "but maybe the baby should have
it."

"Aw, he won't drink it," she grumbled. "Try the milk. Unless
you want me to mix up a batch of Kool-Aid. They'll drink that
sometimes."

"Lucy, you can't give them Kool-Aid!" I protested.

"No, it's okay," she reassured me. "I know it ruins kids' teeth,
but they don't have any yet."

Resuming my crouch, I grabbed the milk container. What the
hell, with all the preservatives around these days, some were
bound to have gotten into the cow, if not the container, so I poured
the milk into the bottle.

"Never fear, Lucy," I shouted hearteningly, reaching for the
unhappy child. "Quiet is on the way." At first, the baby resisted.
Trying to push the bottle out of my hand, he cried all the more.
Lucy gave me a see-what-I-mean look as she complained, "The
children just don't want to eat, and everybody is blaming me for
not feeding them."

My father always said I had a stubborn streak in me. I guess I
never was easily discouraged. When at first I couldn't ride a two-
wheeler, I took that darn bike out every day all summer regardless
of other demands and enticements from family and friends until I
could, albeit shakily, ride it. Approaching twin number one with
the same attitude I had adopted toward my bicycle, the more he
fought the nipple, the more I persisted.

Lucy watched attentively this little drama, which I sensed had
been played more often at the Nunez household than *My Fair Lady*
on Broadway. Finally, probably due more to his fatigue from the
struggle than to my maternal skills, twin number one began to
suck, first cautiously and then more eagerly, on the nipple. Now I
felt I understood better why the twins were so malnourished. I'm
sure that Lucy had made minimal attempts to feed them, but they

were "fussy eaters" and Lucy was too depressed and listless to make the extra effort. She hadn't planned to have any more children after Sonia, and here she was, after placing four others, with two very demanding, helpless infants. And I'm sure the twins had been detrimentally affected by her depression. It seemed almost as if what had begun as simple erratic infantile eating patterns had become full-blown cases of anorexia nervosa. I wondered if, like their adolescent counterparts, the emaciated teen-agers who blithely starve themselves to death, these infant anorexics simply didn't want to mature and grow up in the world they had seen so far. A person's conception of the world is based on his early relationship with his mother. Lucy seemed to be so overwhelmed by internal and external stress that she could not provide much mothering for the twins. Thinking back on Lucy's own history—she was the youngest of a large brood, orphaned in early childhood when her chronically ill mother finally succumbed to tuberculosis—I reflected that one has to have had a good mother to be one.

Lucy struggled with the overwhelming guilt of being a "bad mother"—the worst epithet imaginable—on a daily basis. She reacted with rage to any implication that she did not take care of the children, and ceding any of the ones in placement for permanent adoption was unthinkable, no matter how distant the child was in miles and memory.

"What do you think, Mrs. Patterson?" she asked. "See what I mean about the twins not wanting to eat?"

"Yeah, I know what you mean," I acknowledged. "But he finally did start to eat. I guess all I can suggest is that you just have to keep at it until they come around."

"But I'm so tired all the time, and my asthma has been really bad," she lamented. "Some days I can't even get out of bed. Sonia has to take care of me." (Which is why the kid probably had never been sent to school.) "And now," she wailed, "I don't see how I'm going to manage."

I didn't either. Lucy would manage, as events proved subsequently, the way she always had—by depositing her offspring with some experienced, soft-hearted woman, the most likely unused

candidate currently being a common-law mother-in-law in Puerto
Rico. And then, for the time being, Lucy would be free and
childless—except for little Sonia, her nurse and housekeeper, a kid
whose personal fortune now consisted of a useless fifteen-cent
subway token and a Millard Fillmore tin quarter.

Maybe Dr. Bellino is right about home visits. What did the trip to
Lucy's get me, except discouraged? The clinic, for all its faults,
doesn't leak when it rains, generally has heat in the winter, and has
a security guard. Out in the community, one is likely to encounter
filth, rodents, roaches, decay, stifling heat, bone-chilling cold,
floods, muggers, rapists, and killers. On the other hand, in the
community, unlike the clinic, one will never encounter the most
noxious bane of all—Rosie McGonigle.

Even though I had a six o'clock class in midtown that evening, I
sought out Bellino just before quitting time to let him know just
how strongly I felt about Rosie's harassment. "Every day she's on
my back, especially about the assistants," I complained. "I have to
listen to her bitch about their coming in ten minutes late or failing
to sign out at lunchtime or keeping a chart out of the file cabinet too
long!"

"Don't we all?" he exclaimed, trying to placate me with a good-
humored grin.

"Not anywhere near as much as the assistants!" I said. "Rosie is
always picking on them, because they're the low men, or people I
should say, on the totem pole, probably the most overworked and
underpaid of the whole mental health staff. David took a two-hour
lunch to see his analyst for one of his more severe daily emotional
crises; Jeanne to take her sick child to the doctor. Who got hassled
for taking care of personal business on office time? Jeanne, of
course. With David, everyone except the ever-vigilant Rosie
looked the other way, and Rosie cluck-clucked a few times and let
it lay. Jeanne got called on the carpet, David's offense was swept
under it. Jeanne got an official verbal warning, second in severity
only to a written warning notice, three of which might lead to a
suspension."

"As terrible as that?" Vince said, with a sarcastic smile. "Our disciplinary procedures have all the teeth of a biddy—the female fowl, I mean, not the foul female we've been discussing. Verbal warnings, official or not, aren't worth the paper they're not written on. And the written ones? Even if you collected enough to draw a suspension—and no one seems to know how many strikes it takes in this league—that would amount to little more than an unpaid vacation, which many of our staff, having exhausted their supply of paid vacation and sick days, take frequently anyway. Dave Goldman's a little too sophisticated to be intimidated by stern looks and parental scoldings, but it's more than made up for by the razzing he takes from me and the others over his umbilical attachment to his couch-renter. So, you see, we all pay the price for our sins, even if in different currencies."

"I'd hate to live off *your* wages of sin," I scoffed. "How about the time you put an intake chart for a new patient, Rosa Perez, in the clinic's personnel file, between Carmela Perazzo and Maria Sanchez. Did anyone say anything to you? Rosie gruffled a bit, as always, but nothing was said and everything was forgiven."

"What the hell does *gruffle* mean?" he demanded.

"To act in a gruff manner," I explained. "When you're angry at or irritated by someone, you gruffle at them."

"I do not. There's no such word," he said.

"I just said it, didn't I?"

"You won't find it in the dictionary. It's a neologism."

"Schizophrenics use neologisms," I said, highly offended. "If you persist in making such implications, I'll say a few more words that you won't find in the dictionary, despite common usage."

He raised his hands in surrender. "I've had enough warfare for one day. Anything to avoid another gruffle. Uh, I assume your word may be used as a noun?"

"My words, like me, are ready and able to perform in any capacity thrust upon them, no matter how overworked they already are," I informed him, still somewhat grufflely. "Am I dismissed?"

"Go in peace," he said piously.

"Not until you dismiss Rosie McGonigle," I said.

# 5

**S**HE REALLY GETS TO YOU, DOESN'T SHE, PAT?" I COMMISER-
ated with my coordinator. Although it was already past five and Pat
was apparently eager to go somewhere, she was still too wound up
over Rosie McGonigle's carping to be able to put the clinic behind
her. "Look, Rosie's harmless enough and not worth corroding your
gastric lining over."

"Well, just be sure to keep your bitch on a tight leash when she's
around me and my mental health assistants!" she warned. "God,
what a day this has been! And to top it off, I'll be late for my six
o'clock class."

"Gee, I'm sorry," I said sympathetically. "Maybe you can borrow
one of your classmates' notes after the session."

"Uh, no, Vince," she explained. "I'm afraid it's not one of those
profession-related courses, like 'Medicaid-Reimbursable Psychiatric Diagnoses' or 'Proper Physician-Underling Relationships.'"

"Oh," I said, less sympathetically. "Well, if it's something like
'Erotic Art in the Twentieth Century' or 'Postgraduate Sex
Therapy,' maybe you can borrow someone's drawings."

"It's a course in hydroslimnastics," she said, picking up a bulging
canvas zipper-bag from the floor and slinging it over her shoulder.
"And now, if you'll excuse me, I must run for the subway and hope
that it, too, is running reasonably on schedule so that I can at least
get my feet wet."

I grabbed my attaché case and fell in step beside her as she
pattered down the staircase. "What sort of course is that?" I puffed.

148

"Now, Dr. Bellino," she said with even breath as she strode past the security guard into the steaming street, where water from open fire hydrants gushed into the gutters, "I'm sure that a man of your great intelligence and education knows it comes from the Greek root, *hydro-*, which means water. And I'm sure you know the meaning of *slim*, even if it's not a word that holds much interest for you on a personal basis. Hydroslimnastics refers to a group of exercises which you do in the water, giving you more flexibility and mobility."

"Uh-huh," I nodded. "Did you minor in that at Berkeley?"

"I did not take physical education," she said primly. "But, I'm sure that a great medical doctor like you must know the benefits of regular physical exercise—if only from the books you've read, such as the ones you've got piled all over your desk and on top of your file cabinets and on your credenza in your office, where you sit all day long."

"Yeah, we had to read a lot of books at Columbia," I acknowledged dryly. "See, we didn't have a beach to pursue our education on, like at Berkeley, where once you've read the regulations posted next to the lifeguard's chair, you've pretty much done your reading for the year."

Pat abruptly halted her rapid strides and whirled to face me. "Is that your opinion of education at Berkeley? Sitting on the beach all day?"

"Oh, I didn't mean *everyone*," I deadpanned. "I know a lot of students there sit around in basements and make bombs or lie in the grass and smoke it, or read Mao Tse-tung in Chinese. But it's usually the beach crowd that does postgraduate work in swimming pools."

Pat tossed her long brown hair back over her shoulders and resumed her pace. "And I suppose the varsity swimming team at Columbia straighten their neckties each day, walk to the library, and read about the backstroke?"

"We had a few jocks there," I shrugged, "but none of them made Phi Beta Kappa on his physique."

She cast a disdainful look at my durable, substantial body. "Obviously, that wasn't a criterion," she said. "Don't your friends at the Hamptons have swimming pools, at least to drink cocktails around at five, before taking off for sumptuous dinner parties at eight? No quick dips after champagne brunches or before that one o'clock tennis lesson or tax-deductible seminar on improved fee collecting?"

"Patchogue," I corrected. "No pools. There is a large, stagnant bay, which provides some fairly good crabbing. Crabs are scavengers that thrive on dead things, which may be why the waters are not very pleasant for swimming. I generally leave the crabs alone in their environment, and if I occasionally pull a few of them out, I certainly never intrude my body into their domain. As far as I know, all the nets in Patchogue are employed for catching fish and crabs, and none are stretched across cement slabs for middle-aged people in shorts to bat fuzzy balls into. I drink alone if I'm into serious drinking, and if I'm not serious about it, I don't bother to drink. If I ever become a rich shrink, I may go out to these fabled Hamptons you're always talking about for a look, but I think I'll hate them, especially if they're into hydroslimnastics. To tell the truth, I'm not that crazy about Patchogue. Is that saddlebag you're carrying for your bathing suit?"

She readjusted her burden on her shoulder as we descended the subway stairs. "This is for my towel and my portable hair dryer," she explained. "My bathing suit is in my jacket pocket. See you tomorrow."

Pat is, for all her eccentricities, a rather well-rounded woman, I must admit. Perhaps hydroslimnastics would bear looking into.

I was getting tired of trying to pull together a staff that was forever charging off in different directions. I was fed up with being surrounded by lackadaisical doctors, militant radical social workers, tradition-bound paraprofessionals, impractically theoretical psychologists, and a nurse who came to work dressed to audition for a local production of *Hair*. I longed for the good old days of my residency training on the wards at St. Gerard's, the structure of the rigid hierarchy where the doctor, even a first-year resident, was king and the nurses and social workers were his to command, where the unit functioned with crisp precision because one man called the signals and directed the plays, unlike a playground game where everyone clamors to carry the ball and nobody blocks. And then one day the answer to my prayer came in the form of a resume, a simple sheet of biographical data that managed to conjure up sweet past memories of a peaceful, ordered world. And I knew that while no one person could turn around the chaos of the clinic, perhaps she could at least bring back a ray of hope.

Connie must have suspected something that morning. It wasn't my custom to haunt the reception desk, not even when Dolores was wearing the type of outfit that kept the doctors coming out to the front to pick up and sign their forms without waiting for Connie to fling a batch at them at the end of the day.

There I was, my hips against a typewriter table a few feet behind Connie, where for the past fifteen minutes I had been scrutinizing a log book that was two months old. Actually, I was scrutinizing each visitor who approached the desk over the top of the book. Connie could have seen from my appointment sheet that I had no one scheduled during the next hour and a half, but if my presence mystified or disturbed her, she gave no indication as she went about her routine of collecting appointment cards, logging patients in, stamping forms, and discussing her marital problems with Dolores in Spanish.

At seventeen minutes to ten, I dropped the book and straightened up expectantly. I was sure my stakeout had come to an end. A pert little brunette was hesitantly approaching the desk. "Hello," she said deferentially, waiting until Connie had disposed of a small pile of forms. "I have a ten o'clock appointment with Dr. Bel . . ."

"Miss Scovetti," I interrupted, standing behind Connie's left shoulder. It was more an announcement than an attempt at confirmation.

She nodded and managed to say, "Yes," although my sudden materialization had obviously surprised her. She probably wondered if I intended to interview her right there.

"I'm Dr. Bellino," I said as I circled the desk. "Please come in." I strode toward my office, looking over my shoulder as I uttered this last remark so that she would know enough to follow me rather than wait for a door to materialize at the reception desk as I had.

Thus did I maneuver Julia Scovetti, R.N., into my office with a minimum of awareness by anyone else on the staff. Connie was used to my seeing all sorts of unscheduled people—a hospital employee who was reluctant to be seen in Mental Health for fear that gossip would get back to his department about his visits; a relative of a patient who refused to come for help; a student assigned to do a term paper on some community resource. Miss Scovetti could have been any of these, and there was no way of their knowing that she had come for a job interview unless she herself had volunteered that information—which I prevented by intercepting her so quickly at the desk.

This skulking about was going against the open, honest style that had endeared me to the community. Well, that's the way I'd been up to now—and what did I have to show for it? A staff full of conniving sociopaths, hypochondriacal hysterics, stuffy pseudoanalysts, and belligerent liberals who regarded the clinic as their personal battleground against medical tradition and conventional morality.

Julia Scovetti didn't seem to fit any of the above categories. I watched her settle herself silently into one of the wooden-armed, black leather chairs across from my desk, graceful as a bluebird fluttering down to a nest, crossing her legs at the ankles as the etiquette books directed ladies to do back when people knew what etiquette books were.

Your bearing is proud, Julie, I noted, in spite of your soft voice and your gentle eyes; you carry the dignity of your profession well, despite your small stature. Your cream-colored blouse with the bow at the throat, your dark pleated skirt, the simple pumps beneath your crossed ankles—modest, almost decorous, and yet you are more feminine than Dolores out there, whose every body contour I know as if I had seen her undressed. I thank you for your dignity, your softness, and your modesty, all the qualities I expected of you. And thanks for being beautiful, for the dark, wavy shoulder-length tresses, for those clear blue eyes, and your lithe form—I did not expect that, but I'm glad, Julie, because if I have to throw you in with that pack of vixens—Sandy and Nurse Jackie and

Princess Sharon—I want you to outshine them all in every area. I'll see to it that no one ever attacks your professional capability once I've chosen you, but you'll have to hold your own in the more ancient rivalries women engage in—and it looks like you'll manage that quite well.

"So you're a St. Gerard's grad," I said heartily, pretending to be reading the resume I already knew by heart. "I did my residency there . . . a little after you, I'm afraid." She was twenty-five and already had been working four years—at her age, I hadn't even completed my internship. While we doctors are reading about the unconscious psychodynamics of paranoid schizophrenics, these cherubs are wrestling with wards full of them, trying to get them chemically schlogged enough so that they'll sit tranquilly across the desk from us while we pursue our apprenticeships.

Miss Scovetti's eyes glowed, not merely because she had found a fellow alum or because I was being friendly, as she said, "The Wilson Pavilion? It's a good place."

She said it with conviction and admiration, not worrying whether I shared her high opinion. Wilson had its problems, like any psychiatric service, but it was a solid, if underrated, program. Nurses rarely got more than a few months' exposure to it during their diversified training, and many of those babes in blue sailed through with their eyes shut in terror, expecting to be raped or less exotically assaulted by inmates who had trouble maneuvering a fork at dinner time; on the Thorazine weight-reduction diet, patients were just as hungry but couldn't find their mouths. Miss Scovetti had apparently gone through Wilson with those wide eyes wide open and, like me, she had liked what she had seen, enough to choose day-rooms filled with deranged gin rummy players and "quiet rooms" stripped of all except a mattress and a madman over bloody emergency rooms and soporific operating rooms.

"You've been at Dewey Hospital for the past two years," I said next. "Why do you want to come here now?"

She tensed up slightly, aware that we had progressed from pleasantries into the bowels of the interview. "I've been working at the day hospital there most of that time, as one of the head nurses for the past eight months. I like it, but I wish I could follow an individual patient longer than a few months. I'd really like to try out-patient therapy."

"Aren't there any openings in Dewey's O.P.D.?" I asked, hoping there were not.

She sighed and those shining blue eyes seemed to cloud over, and I wished I hadn't said it, although I didn't know what was upsetting her. "Doctor," she said with a desperate little shake of her head, "this is probably a mistake, but I'm going to level with you." She paused, not really expecting but apparently hoping for some encouragement.

"You won't lose any points for honesty, I promise, Julie," I said. Hell, I hadn't really intended to use her first name at this point and I certainly could have kept it at Julia. Well, she started this intimacy thing, didn't she?

Julie responded to my remark with a grateful smile. "Dewey expanded its O.P.D. to include a community psychiatry division, something geared more toward outreach and crisis intervention as opposed to the traditional hour-by-appointment model. There was a slot for a chief nurse in the program and I put in for it. I really expected to get it—in fact, it had been practically promised to me. When I asked for a transfer to out-patient over a year ago, I was told to wait for the new community psych program. It opened and I was passed over. They brought in an outsider to fill the position."

"Had you been having difficulties with anyone in the administration previously?" I asked.

She shrugged ruefully, as though wishing she could oblige me with a war story or two. "Doctor, I never had a bit of trouble. I assure you my references will all be first-rate." A genuine blush colored her creamy cheeks; blushes are like rainbows—I believed in them, but you don't expect to see them in New York. "That sounds pretty egotistical, I know, but I always put my job first. I'm no genius and I don't try to institute sweeping reforms, but I know how to carry out orders, to train and supervise new people, and to work as part of a team."

"And yet you were passed over," I reiterated. "Do you have any

idea why? I'd be interested in your ideas . . . I already have a few
of my own."

She seemed surprised at my last comment. Knowing I was not
about to reveal my inner speculations without first hearing hers,
she began. "The official explanation was they wanted someone with
more experience—but the woman they hired had less direct
clinical work than I did. Frankly, I suspect they didn't think I was
tough enough for community psych. They seem to choose women
who've picked up their R.N.'s piecemeal from several community
colleges and city programs, raising a brood of fatherless kids and
going through a slew of mates in the process." Her mellow voice
seemed to be choking on something bitter now, and I picked up
the narrative myself without a pause.

"And they look at your record," I continued, "and say, here's a
nice, young Italian girl, educated in Catholic schools, single, white,
middle-class. What does she know about life? How can she
understand the problems of people who don't live conventionally?"

Julie looked at me with a bewildered expression, surprised to
hear her words coming from my mouth. "But is it wrong not to
have messed up your own life? Do you have to drink or take drugs
yourself to help an addict or alcoholic? Do you have to make
mistakes before you can know the right way?"

I shook my head and smiled. "Did they inject you with infectious
tubercle bacilli before they let you treat tuberculosis patients,
Julie? Are you happy with your own life and values?"

"I thought I was," she said quietly. "Until I found they were
hurting my career." Suddenly, she flushed again, this time more in
anger than embarrassment. "But what did I do wrong, other than
*not* doing anything disruptive, self-destructive, or weird? I can
accept just about any values in people as long as they aren't cruel to
others; my values may be more conservative, but I don't force
them on my patients!" This last remark seemed to jar an unpleasant
memory in her mind, as her voice dropped suddenly at the end of
the sentence.

"Something else, Julie?" I prodded.

"Once," she said cautiously, weighing her words as if doubting her own memory, "I had an unmarried young woman who had learned she was pregnant. Everybody was telling her she simply had to have an abortion. She had some deep misgivings about it, and at her request, I gave her some Right to Life pamphlets to read, with all the abortion information other people at the hospital had given her. I know one of the other nurses, a girl who was living with a man, was very angry at me and openly accused me of trying to make this patient feel guilty about abortion. I suppose her criticism spread all over the hospital and didn't help my reputation as something of a prude. Maybe that's what cost me the community psychiatry slot. If it did, so be it—isn't a patient entitled to explore all the options?"

"In *my* clinic she is," I assured her.

"I think I would like your clinic very much."

"It might be a far cry from your day hospital unit," I warned. "I'm sure that as head nurse you have quite a bit of administrative responsibility. Here, your duties will be pretty much limited to direct patient care. You might miss the challenge of taking charge of something more than just one patient at a time."

She wrinkled her brow skeptically. "Me? I'm just a nurse. Sure, I have a degree of responsibility for my unit and I can hold down the fort in a crisis till help arrives, but I don't presume to be more than I am. I'm happy with my profession and I don't aspire to being anything more than the finest nurse I can be. Is that so unusual?"

I sighed at the unhappy prospect of shattering her illusions. "In this place," I explained, "we have clerks aspiring to be mental health assistants, mental health assistants wanting to be social workers, social workers trying to be psychoanalysts, psychologists wanting to practice medicine, psychiatrists wanting to be administrators, and a nurse who wants to be . . . actually, I'm not sure what Jackie wants to be, but I suspect it's Bianca Jagger. If you don't mind my saying so, I find your attitude refreshingly traditional in one so young."

"Well, so far I've never wanted to be the head of anything bigger than a hospital ward or day care unit," she assured me.

"And after that?" I pressed.

She shook her dark hair. "I'm not much on long-range planning. Not the ambitious type, I guess. You know, I went to a private high school, and before they accepted me, I had to fill out a lot of application forms—and so did my parents. One of the questions they asked my mother was about my 'leadership qualities.' My mother, with her characteristic frankness, wrote, 'I don't think Julia is much of a leader, but she can be a very dedicated, trustworthy follower.'"

"And you got accepted anyway?"

Julie's face exploded in a radiant grin. "The principal wrote back, 'We would love to accept your daughter. We already have applications from over a thousand leaders and desperately need some followers.'"

Silently commending the lady's wisdom, I turned our conversation toward more professional concerns. What was Julie's therapeutic orientation? What had she read? How much actual therapy had she been able to do in the course of her job? The answers satisfied me. She was intelligent, sensitive and, if a little short on direct therapeutic experience in the sense of formal sessions with out-patients, she was eager and able to learn. As a head nurse in a day hospital setting, I knew she had considerable experience under fire, whether she had sought it or not, and she looked none the worse for wear.

I looked at my watch, still reluctant to dismiss her. "Do you have any other questions about the place, Julie?" I dallied.

She replied, "No, I think you've answered them all for me. I'd really like to work here. When will you be filling the position?"

That was the polite way to ask when she would know whether she had the job or not. "As soon as I possibly can. A week at most," I said. "Do you have any other jobs in the wings?"

"Two others," she admitted. "Nothing I'm crazy about, and I don't know where I stand yet."

"Well, I'd appreciate a call before you settle on something, if you're still interested here."

"I am and I will call," she promised. "And, best of luck, Dr. Bellino, whatever. I've really enjoyed meeting you." She boldly held out that tiny hand and I cupped my cumbersome paw to make a nest for it as it wafted toward me. I squeezed it as tightly as I dared.

"Same here, Julie. See you again, I hope."

That wasn't an interview, it was a conspiracy, I thought as she departed without even getting the customary tour around the clinic. I didn't want to expose her to questioning eyes; if I had my way, she'd see the rest of it soon enough.

I had been totally seduced. No, wait, that wasn't fair to Julie; I was ninety percent sold on her from that dispassionate resume, a documentation of conservative background, traditional schooling, and minimal experience. I had seduced *her;* she had come in, vulnerable, still hurting from professional rejection, and I had provided the balm in an unctuous excess of concern and supportiveness. Still, she had laid herself open to me, bared her feelings, and at twenty-five, she was old enough to know what a powerful aphrodisiac feminine vulnerability is. So, ultimately, I suppose, we'd seduced each other—two straight arrows, a happily married man and a virtuous young woman who would never dream of exchanging a chaste kiss with one another, but who were on the brink of merging their professional destinies, certainly two entities far more significant and intimate than their respective genitals.

I was sure Pat would have been skeptical of my motives; sublimated libido, pure and simple, she would have probably concluded despite her professed anti-Freudian bent. "Screw the little bitch and have done with it!" she would have said, if she had dared verbalize it. "Save yourself a lot of prudish rationalization and blurring of lines between professionalism and personal eroticism." But then, maybe my imagination couldn't picture Pat as being anything but an opponent of Julie, since Julie was in so many ways her antithesis: the faithful follower, not the rebel officer; champion, not denigrator of physicians; conservative where Pat is liberal, cautious where she is bold, reverent where she is profane. No, it wouldn't be Sandy, Sharon, or Jackie that Julie would have to compete with, it would be Pat. Even now, I was balancing Julie's delicacy against Pat's statuesque grace, Julie's midnight tresses against Pat's cascading lighter crown, Julie's vibrant blue eyes against Pat's pensive, somber brown ones. Pat's labors had sustained the clinic, but our ideological skirmishes were taking their toll on my own morale. Julie was my perfect soul mate, with a resume that could have been designed by a computer to fit my needs and a form that was the materialization of a dimly recalled dream; yet, I feared what the clinic might do to her and I suddenly wanted to protect her from it, as I had never sought to protect Pat.

I didn't have much time to speculate about what Pat's reaction to the new staff member would be, because within minutes of Julie's exit Pat had sauntered into my office, attempting to look unconcerned and failing miserably in the attempt. "Hi, Vince," she greeted me without wasting time by waiting for a response. "Who's the lady who just left your office?"

"Our new nurse," I informed her, trying to look pleased to break the news.

"*Our* new nurse?" she choked. "How come *we* didn't even know you were about to hire another nurse, much less that you'd already picked the winner in your private Miss Hypodermic pageant?"

"Don't let her get under your skin!" I couldn't resist saying.

"When did you interview the runners-up?" she demanded.

"What business is it of yours?" I answered crossly.

"Or weren't there any other interviews?" she persisted.

"I screened other resumes," I explained, not sure why I bothered to. "She was the best qualified and I'm satisfied with the interview. Why should I waste my time, and inconvenience other applicants, if I've made my decision?"

"Do you mind if I see the winner's resume?" Pat practically commanded. "It must be quite formidable for a young kid like that to impress you enough to dismiss all other applicants without even one look! Or was it one look at that dainty little doll that made the impression?"

"Just because she looks more feminine than feminist, don't categorize her as one of those brainless, helpless stereotypes you accuse us men of inventing," I warned. "Miss (not Ms.) Scovetti has been running a day hospital unit very capably, and she trained at St. Gerard's, which I know from personal acquaintance to be one of the finest nursing schools anywhere."

"I might have known!" Pat groaned. "When you're not reliving your days of academic glory at the Columbia medical school, you're wallowing in nostalgia over the mythological clinical greatness of your residency training program. Vince, St. Gerard's is a well-funded, university-affiliated teaching hospital! Columbia is a heavily endowed university. St. Dymphna's is an underfunded, deteriorating ghetto operation that bears no resemblance to healthy academic programs, living or defunct. Do you really think that by bringing in some kid who's treaded the same sacred floorboards as you at St. Gerard's you're going to turn this place into a replica of the well-oiled institutions you left? Stop dreaming! More likely, this clinic will chew up that fragile little nightingale in a week and make her sorry she didn't stay cloistered in the middle-class hospitals she's used to. What does *she* know about community mental health?"

"Enough to get her started!" I assured her. "And I'll teach her the rest."

"Oh, I didn't realize you had so much free time in your schedule to allow you to undertake private tutoring," Pat simpered. "Far be it from me to tell you how to run your business, but if you use some of that free time to skim a few more resumes, you might find an applicant who won't require so much individual attention."

"I've already got plenty of staff who know how to do everything," I countered. "Maybe if I train one myself, she'll know how to do everything *right!*"

"'Right,' meaning *your* way?" Pat argued. "So you can have a little yes-man . . . pardon, yes-person around?"

"I'd prefer to think of her as a lieutenant," I clarified. "I figure every general is entitled to at least one lieutenant, someone beside him in war or at peace, whose only concern is for the chief's well-being. I know if the battle ever gets down to that one last sword, it's lost anyway, but it's a great consolation not to die alone."

"What a charmingly romantic way you have of looking at things, Vince!" Pat cooed. "It must be ever so much more fun than living in the real world, where this clinic happens to be unfortunately located. If I may ask, why haven't you considered some capable doctor like Chong as your lieutenant? I would think there would be more similarities in your training and outlook than you'd find in a young woman."

"Because in the real world, where you profess to be a citizen, I'm still too young to be a mentor to a young doctor, aspiring as he should to replace me soon. I've barely started in this leadership role myself. No, as far as I know, the only breed of creature that ever existed primarily to assist doctors—and I don't see why psychiatrists should be excluded—was a near-extinct species called nurses."

"Near-extinct?" Pat said, looking amused. "I didn't realize that the nightingale in your office this morning was practically a dodo."

"The kind of nurse I'm discussing is practically gone," I explained with bitterness. "The majority of nurses have evolved into some sort of independently practicing, supereducated beings who are competing with doctors for administrative jobs or clinicians' roles. As lieutenants, they're of less use than you master's-level social workers and psychologists—they're worse, since *you* only profess to be experts in psychiatry, whereas they 'excel' in medicine as well."

"What a sad loss of highly trained flunkies!" Pat commiserated. "Especially since women make such perfect lackeys!"

"Don't go accusing me of sexist behavior for having a woman in a subordinate role," I said. "As a medical student, as a resident, I served under women many times and made a damn fine subordinate. I did their bidding as faithfully as any knight who was ever commanded by his queen, and enjoyed sparing them any bit of work or aggravation I could draw onto myself. Maybe five years from now, Julia Scovetti will tire of being a handmaiden and take off in a new direction, but for now, that role suits her, as I once loved playing the knight. We've got too damn many leaders around this clinic now; you can concede me one small follower."

"Since I wasn't consulted in the hiring of your nurse, I don't see that I have a choice in this concession to the appetites of your voracious male ego. I'd have as much chance of dissuading you as I would of telling Sportin' Life Jackson to keep his hands off his next job applicant."

"You're comparing me to Sportin' Life?" I asked in disbelief.

"I'd give you the worst of the comparison," she said angrily. "Getting a woman stripped naked and under him is enough to validate his worth for the moment. *You* want a woman to throw her entire soul into a daily confirmation of your ability. Sportin' Life seems basically kinder to me, reducing as he does the whole ugly arena of domination and submission to a simple physical act."

"*Domination* and *submission* are nasty words, Pat," I replied. "What of the prettier ones, such as *leadership, loyalty, dedication,* and *devotion?*"

"Dedication and devotion to whom? To Vincent Bellino, M.D.?"

"No, to Bellino's concept of decent patient care and clinic administration," I answered. "Julie will be just another clinician with an unwieldy case load, but just knowing she's around will make the battle a bit brighter."

"Now I've heard everything!" she crowed. "Between that philosophy and your new lieutenant, the only other thing you'll need for your glorious battle is a white flag." And she promptly retreated.

Pat's disrespectful exit was followed immediately by a request from Dr. Diego Martinez on the intercom, more respectful in tone but definitely more disquieting in nature. "Dr. Bellino," he petitioned, "I would like to request an appointment with you at your earliest convenience to discuss some urgent matters."

I found his formality very perplexing. While Diego's past employment at university medical schools and distinguished medical centers might have accustomed him to environments where such protocol was de rigueur between director and subordinate, the eminent author-teacher-clinician had, up until now, shown commendable flexibility in adapting to the clinic's free-wheeling, informal atmosphere and there had never been a trace of snobbishness or anything less than warm camaraderie in his interactions with the lowest paid clerk-typist or trainee.

"I've got a few minutes free if you want to pop in now, Diego." I said casually.

"I would prefer a definite appointment," he said coldly. "What I have to discuss may take some time."

"All right," I sighed, scanning my appointment book. "How about eleven thirty this morning?"

"I shall be there, Dr. Bellino. Thank you."

My first thought when Diego entered my office was the fervent hope that the news he bore was not as bad as his appearance. While he had never been exactly dapper, he always conveyed in his dress the impression of the dignified professional he was, tasteful and conservative. Today, he entered wearing a pair of bright green, nearly fluorescent trousers, mismatched to a yellow-and-black checkered jacket apparently manufactured from an old taxicab and sold with matching trousers, vest, and banjo. His shirttail hung over the top of his trousers on the right side, and I noticed he had apparently forgotten to wear a belt. His silver hair, normally slicked back from his chiseled copper features, looked like a bird's nest after a hurricane. He must be drunk, I thought immediately, though only the most inveterate of our alcoholic patients would present in such a state at that early hour of the day.

"Ah, your shirttail has come out, Diego," I blurted, in my impulsive attempt to restore my only Spanish-speaking psychiatrist to some semblance of his former order. With a malevolent glare, he lifted the apronlike end of the semibuttoned shirt from his thigh and wadded it back under the top of his pants, only to reveal a graver indiscretion. "Your, uh, zipper seems to have come open," I said with an embarrassed wave of a flaccid index finger. He rectified the indiscretion, at which point I abandoned any further attempts at restoring him to a more presentable state. He stood behind one of the chairs on the opposite side of my desk, both hands gripping its back as though to anchor himself against being blown away, for his body was swaying like a birch in a windstorm. It was not the unsteady lurching of an intoxicated man I was observing, however; he was in an obvious state of agitation, barely able to keep his feet in one place. A stimulant drug, perhaps, such as cocaine or one of the hallucinogens?

"Please sit down, Diego," I said.

Reluctantly, he circled his perch and sat down, thrusting a chart at me. "Look at that last note," he challenged. "It's a disgrace."

The note had been written by Pablo Suarez, our teen-age trainee. In an oversized childish scrawl, with several words boldly scratched out, I discerned that he had reported: *Made a home visit to patient. He seem very nervis. He say he miss last apointmint because he was to sick. I tole him to come and see Dr. Martinez tomorrow.*

"That note is a disgrace!" Diego declared. "This is an *official* medical document, and that note is careless, slovenly, and illiterate."

"Well, I'll admit it's not great medical literature," I conceded, "but Pablo is only a trainee. I understand that part of the courses the new assistants are taking include basic English skills, sort of a high school equivalency preparation . . ."

"It's not a question of mere education," Diego said fiercely. "That boy is careless and unmotivated. It's a joke to have someone like that involved with the care of patients. I demand that he be fired immediately!"

"Diego, calm down," I said sternly. "I'll discuss this note with Pablo, and even have Ms. Patterson check future notes he writes, but let's not blow this out of all proportions."

"Dr. Bellino, you said yourself that the Department of Mental Health is going to be conducting an investigation next month," Diego reminded me. "You told everyone at the staff meeting to make sure their charts were in order."

"Sure, Diego," I agreed. "It's just a routine audit, something they have to do under the terms of our contract."

"Don't you realize the potential repercussions if they see this chart?" he shouted, snatching the document from in front of me. "We would not pass the investigation. We would lose our license and our funding! The clinic would be shut down, and all of us will be out of jobs!"

Diego rose to his feet and began pacing the narrow confines of my office, gesticulating wildly. He was not engaging in mere rhetoric; the man actually believed what he was saying and was genuinely frightened, although I could not understand why even the threat of such a virtual impossibility would so unnerve him, since a man with his credentials and expertise would never go jobless. He had somehow taken on the responsibility of the entire clinic—*my* responsibility. Perhaps his experience in his native Dominican Republic or Latin American hospitals, in other countries where strict government control and authoritarianism prevailed, had colored his judgment.

I vainly tried to reassure him. "The City would never close us down. If we weren't here, over one hundred thousand people would go without mental health services, because the only resources would be private doctors out of their financial range. The Department funds us and knows the limitations we work under."

"*They* will fire this boy!" he predicted.

"No they won't," I said. "If they ever tried to get rid of a handpicked Puerto Rican kid, the community would send an angry delegation to raise enough heat to warm the entire South Bronx for the month of January. We could have used Pablo's stipend to hire a lit major from Yale, but that's not what community mental health is all about and no one knows that better than the Department."

"If you insist, I have no choice but to yield to your authority," he said sullenly. "I hope future events do not make you sorry you ignored my warning. I now leave you with this. I need an answer this week." He thereupon presented me with a bulging manila envelope. Before I could ask what it contained, he pivoted sharply on his heel and marched out, his shirttail once again flapping in the breeze he created.

The envelope contained a resume that rambled over eight single-spaced typewritten pages accompanied by a bibliography of nearly one hundred books and papers written by Dr. Martinez. Most of this was a duplication of material Diego had submitted at the time he was first employed at the clinic. Resting atop this formidable chronicle lay a freshly composed letter addressed to me, which commenced with a lengthy preamble extolling his past achievements and honors, more than adequately documented in the enclosed manuscript. He then went on to say that he had received an offer to join the faculty of a prominent medical school (name unspecified) and might have to leave, with deep regrets, St. Dymphna's unless certain inducements were instantly accorded him; to wit, an increase in salary and some sort of title in recognition of his superior qualifications and contributions. The letter was appropriate enough, though verbose and overpadded with self-acclamation. From a man of lesser achievement, I'd term it grandiose, but Diego Martinez had a record of which he could be justifiably proud and he was in the position of having to make a hard sell. Even a truly superlative job offer did not warrant the sort of psychic turmoil he had shown in my office that morning, but at least it helped me understand him a little better. He was apparently in the throes of an increasingly popular and common psychiatric condition termed a "mid-life crisis" and was now questioning the wisdom of his commitment to our humble clinic. Somehow his present ambivalence over continued employment with us seemed less bizarre than his original acceptance of the job.

Before I had time to reflect adequately on Dr. Martinez's diplomatically worded ultimatum, I was confronted by another petitioner. Dave Goldman was standing patiently at the threshold, like a mendicant. His plea today was quite different from the typical staff request for a free prescription; Dave, I soon learned, wanted furniture.

Once I had beckoned him in, Dave stood awkwardly before me, nervously tugging at the black beard he had apparently shaped as best he could to match the chin whiskers on the bust of Freud that dominated his studio apartment. "You know my patient Joanne Norman, don't you, Vince?" he ventured.

I nodded thoughtfully. "The tall blonde woman, thirtyish, usually wears very fetching skirt-and-blouse ensembles?" We *all* have our favorites, don't we Dave?

He nodded self-consciously. "I've been seeing her twice a week for several months now. I feel she needs the couch."

"Needs . . . the . . . *couch?*" I echoed, stroking my beardless chin as I raised my inflection to encourage Dave to elucidate.

"Er . . . uh . . . yes," he stammered. "She's getting very uncomfortable in sessions with some of the repressed material that's been emerging. I really feel that the psychoanalytic approach, where she wouldn't be looking directly at me, would help her relax and free associate better."

I failed to see how the poor woman could relax with that dirty-minded satyr hovering over her recumbent body, asking the type of questions that would better lie repressed. Besides, Dave knew my views on psychoanalysis—and that the only patient I would consider treating supine would have to be one on total bed rest. If a patient had bathroom privileges, that ruled out the need for psychoanalysis. "I suppose the analytic method might be a viable alternative," I said charitably. "Unfortunately, none of the therapists' offices have couches."

"Yours does," he said timidly. "Could I please borrow it?"

"The couch?" I squeaked. "I don't think it would fit in your office. Besides, wouldn't it look a little silly to have staff members toting a sofa around the corridors? The patients might think we were now adding psychoanalysis to our outreach services on home visits, or, worse, that we were being dispossessed."

"I want to borrow your office," Dave whined.

I couldn't believe my ears. It was like asking the President whether you could use the Oval Office as a crash pad. I looked dubiously at the brown leatherette sofa with its rounded, puffy arms. "Gee, Dave, that's not really the sort of piece that *real* couch-jockeys use in therapy. And Joanne's a rather tall gal, too—are you sure she'd fit?"

"Oh, it will be fine!" he said eagerly. Dave was so hot to put down the lady that I'm sure he would have let her crawl into a sleeping bag if we had one. "Just for two hours a week, Vince?"

"And what am I supposed to use as a base for medically directing this madhouse?"

"I'll use it during your lunch hours," he volunteered. "You always go out to lunch."

I looked pointedly at my watch, which indicated that most of my lunch period had elapsed. "Not always," I growled, my stomach joining in chorus. Dave looked imploringly at me with the sad, soulful eyes of a puppy in a store window. I thought of all the less-than-stimulating cases that Dave and the others handled daily: the "crocks," with their hypochondriacal complaints, dumped on us by the medical clinic; the guys who only wanted disability letters that would enable them to get paid for staying out of work to spend their time drinking and broad-hunting; the junkies looking for a free minor "high"; the throng of impoverished, uneducated unfortunates incapable of more than mere survival. For doing their best with these depressed and depressing clingers, rejected by every other sort of doctor or agency as unworthy of effort, Dave and the rest of my crew deserved at least one Joanne Norman to validate their worth as therapists, on whom to expend that extra bit of clinical effort, even to try promising techniques heretofore only read about in the journals or heard about in postgraduate classes. If Dave, the aspiring psychoanalyst, was no Freud yet, neither had our budding behaviorist, Carl Brock, become a Joseph Wolpe, nor had Dennis Boyle's family therapy attempts yet measured up to Nathan Ackerman's heights, nor had Pat published anything to displace Karen Horney's works from the booksellers' shelves. But they were still young enough to learn and dream and grow, and about the only advantage I could give them as director of a crumbling ghetto clinic was an atmosphere where they could dream and share with their peers amid the frustrations and limitations and squalor.

"Okay," I said sternly. "You may have the office on Tuesdays and Thursdays from twelve-oh-five to twelve-fifty-five. I expect you and your patient to be out of here precisely on schedule."

He grinned like a seventeen-year-old boy being handed the keys to his father's new sports car. "Absolutely. Thanks a million, Vince!" He clutched my hand, which I had wadded defensively into a fist, and nevertheless shook it heartily before turning to go.

"And make sure," I called after him, "that your patient takes off those goddamn sexy French heels she wears before she lies on *my* couch!"

I braced myself for Dave's reappearance as the door swung open again, but this time it was his sister-social worker, Pat. "What's this I overhear about people taking off sexy garments in your office?" she asked eagerly.

"In an acute attack of softening of my cardiac musculature, which spread quickly to my brain," I confessed, "I agreed to lend Dave my couch twice a week so one of his patients won't have to look at his face."

"Well thanks, friend," she snapped. "After all I've done for you, do you offer *me* a chance to move out of my closet into this presidential suite even for an hour, so I could take a deep breath without bruising my bosom on the opposite wall? I also have a patient or two who might profit from the application of my psychoanalytic knowledge—or isn't a woman's head permitted to be higher than a man's in this clinic?"

"I might *consider* letting you use my couch during lunch hour," I said, "but only if you can correctly identify the source of the following quote, uttered just a few days ago by one of our staff. Quote: 'I can do whatever I want during my lunch hour, even if it's a quick screw with my lover . . .' I trust you appreciate my reservations about who uses my couch."

"I hope," she said malevolently, "that Dave's patient ego-regresses to the bed-wetting stage. Meanwhile, the illustrious director is wasting good adrenaline fretting over a mangy sofa when he should be occupying his overpaid hours with much weightier problems."

"Such as?"

"Such as, should he consider abandoning his position of isolationism long enough to intervene in a case of piracy," she intimated.

"Only if he gets to keep ten pieces-of-eight," I swaggered. "Or, allowing for inflation, eight pieces-of-ten. What's being pirated?"

"Patients!" she charged. "Carmen Ortiz sent one of her patients to Dimitri Niarhos for medication, and he asked the patient to come and see him in his private office. He even accepts Medicaid!"

"Dimitri has a private office? Since when—and where?"

"I don't know how long, but I do know where," Pat reported. "He gave the patient, Gladys Grier, a business card, and he's located only about eight blocks from here— 'Hours: evenings and Saturdays, by appointment.'"

"Shiver me timbers, the swab's raised his sail in *our* catchment area!" I exclaimed. "Didn't even have the decency to respect the twelve-mile limit. Are you sure, lass?"

"Captain, kid you not!" she assured me. "What are you going to do about it?"

"Scuttle his butt, if it's true!" I promised, sailing out the door.

I gave Dimitri's office door a perfunctory rap and entered without awaiting clearance from inside. I knew the odds of interrupting the aging Aegean in the midst of some work were about as remote as catching the Partridge family in an incestuous activity. Sure enough, he was as alone as a lighthouse keeper with halitosis.

"Dimitri," I began, pulling up a chair close to his desk, "I hear that you asked a clinic patient to come and see you at your private office."

"Me?" he protested. "Where would you ever get such a notion?"

"From Gladys Grier, the patient you asked to come and see you at your private office," I answered.

Dimitri frowned and pursed his lips. "Ah!" he said, followed by a disdainful snort. "Ah yes, *that* one. A very difficult woman. Always complaining. You see, she does not like to fill her prescriptions at the main hospital pharmacy because it is too far away; but the drugstores will not fill her prescriptions and charge them to Medicaid because they are written on clinic prescription blanks. The only way the drugstore is authorized to fill a clinic prescription is if the hospital pharmacy stamps it to indicate it may be filled outside."

"Yes, that is the law," I agreed.

"Well the problem is, to get the prescription approved to be filled outside the hospital, she must walk the ten or twelve blocks to the hospital pharmacy—which she is trying to avoid doing."

"She could take a bus," I mentioned.

"That costs fifty cents. Each way. The woman says she cannot afford that," Dimitri elaborated. Then, passionately, "'Madam, you *need* your medication,' I emphasize. But she is stubborn. 'No, no,' she protests, 'I cannot come all the way to this clinic and then all the way to the hospital. I am sick and weak.' What am I to do with her? Can I abandon her, let her decompensate? Finally, I throw up my hands and say, 'All I can offer you is to come to my office, which is several blocks closer to your home and where I accept Medicaid and will give you prescriptions you can fill at a pharmacy right down the block from my office.'"

"That was really considerate of you, Dimitri," I said un-enthusiastically. He responded with a simpering smile. "Only thing I don't understand," I went on, "is why the woman complained to Carmen Ortiz, as though she were being barred from coming back here."

The question didn't faze him. "I told you she is a very difficult woman," he sighed. "Very crazy. That's why she comes here, you know."

"Perhaps she will keep coming, then," I said. "It would seem to me that there are more than enough indigent people in this neighborhood to stock your Medicaid practice without your having to waste your time on our ambivalent ones."

He shook his head sadly. "I was only trying to do her a favor. Well, this is what comes of being too good-hearted."

"Yes," I agreed. "You really must be more careful in the future."

Having taken the wind temporarily out of our would-be brigand's sails, I brought an end to another chapter in the ongoing saga, only to begin a new episode of "The Princess and the Pirate" the following morning. Connie Rodriguez called to me as I walked past the reception desk at ten thirty: "Vince, this patient of Pat's has been waiting to see Dr. Schaeffer for medication for more than half an hour. Do you want to see her?"

"Who, Dr. Schaeffer? It sounds like I've got a long wait ahead of me," I said.

"I meant the patient," Connie clarified. "Though maybe you could get Dr. Schaeffer to move her *trasera*."

"Who's she with now?"

"No one," Connie said placidly. "Same as all morning."

"Is she on the phone?"

Connie merely pointed at the phone sitting near her elbow. It was one of those rare moments when every button was unlit, every line free.

"Then what the hell has she been doing in there for the past hour and a half?" I demanded.

"Past hour," Connie corrected. "You know she never gets in before nine thirty. And all I can tell you about what she's doing is that she's doing it alone."

Exasperated, I burst into the Princess's chamber. Sharon quickly rolled her swivel-chair backward a few inches as I entered, and dropped her hands into her lap before sliding her lap back under the desk. This puzzled me; it's not uncommon for kids to jerk their hands *out* of their lap when somebody walks in unexpectedly on their idle activities, but not vice versa. I was reasonably sure she hadn't yanked a paper or other secret object off the desk. The Princess opened her wide blue eyes and, giving her platinum waves a saucy little toss, piped in her breathless, childish voice, "Oh hi, Vince!"

"Good morning, Sharon," I intoned with deliberate paternal sternness. "You seem to be having a little trouble getting started this morning." She responded only with an inquisitive little humming sound. "There's a patient in the waiting room who's been waiting to see you for quite a while," I explained. "Are you busy with something?"

"Ah, no," she said with a guilty smile. She started to lift one of her hands off her lap, then thought better of it, and merely nodded her head in the direction of her uncluttered desk. "I'll see her in a minute."

"You were waiting for something?" I pressed. "An incoming phone call, perhaps?" As if on cue, the intercom buzzed as one of the button-lights came to life. The Princess started to reach for the phone, jerked her hand back again, then looked at me indecisively.

"It's probably for you, Vince," she said, smiling graciously. With a quizzical look, I stretched my hand across her desk to pick up the receiver. The call *was* for me. One of my patients had missed an appointment and was calling for a new one. As I settled into one of the patients' chairs opposite Sharon, I lifted the body of the phone to bring it closer to me, uncovering a small object that had been hidden by the phone—an open bottle of Pink Frost nail enamel. I glared at Sharon as I quickly rescheduled the patient who had called. She looked back apprehensively.

"No hard feelings, Sharon," I boomed good-naturedly as I hung up the receiver and extended my hand. "Shake!"

She did not accept the proffered hand, but did slowly bring her rosy-tipped fingers to rest in full view on the desk.

"And how long does the entire clinic have to wait for that fingerpaint to dry before you're willing to risk your artwork on manual labor, such as writing a prescription?" I inquired.

"I wasn't just waiting for my nails to dry," she protested in a thin, reedy voice. She looked around her desk for a prop on which to support an alibi, but only the pink bottle with its white plastic mitre stood sentinel on that barren plane.

"Sharon," I said gently, "you are an uncommonly attractive woman."

Taken aback by this unexpected mildly flirtatious and thoroughly masculine comment, she smiled shyly and whispered an embarrassed, "Thank you."

"Uncommonly attractive for a psychiatrist," I continued, in a colder tone. "On the other hand, we have several secretaries and mental health workers on the staff who can make you look like a duck among the swans. Though I appreciate beauty, I don't hire the women on this staff just to look attractive; but if I ever do get into human decor, I'm not going to waste the hospital's money beautifying this place with psychiatrists when I could get three stunning secretaries for the same price. Now, if your hands are operable again, can you lend us one out front?"

The Princess looked at me accusingly, pouting her scarlet lips like a scolded child. I avoided her eyes, not wanting to deal with the tears that I was sure were forming there. Pat always saw her as just about the most difficult staff member to deal with, yet here I was reducing this rock-hard star to tears, whereas Pat probably hadn't cried since she learned how to ask for a diaper change. Yet, I had to admit, I'd rather look into Pat's angry eyes, which were like two pieces of dry ice that smoked but never watered. If Robert Frost had a hard time choosing between fire and ice, he should have come up against fire versus water—where women are concerned, I frankly prefer fire.

As if the fates were inviting me to second-guess myself, Pat was waiting by my office door as soon as I got back. "Vince, I have to talk to you," she said, entering behind me. "It's very important."

"If it's about your patient who's been waiting for medication, I just took care of it," I said with annoyance, not even looking up at Pat. "I just laid out the Princess and she just may shape up for two or three days."

"This has nothing to do with Sharon," Pat said quietly. "May I sit down for a minute?"

I glanced, then stared at her. There was a firm, composed look about her that boded more ill than her fiercest snarl. "Don't stand on ceremony or on anything else, particularly on my account," I said.

She eased herself uneasily into one of the chairs, took a deep breath, tried a smile and failed, then said, "This isn't going to be easy, but I can't put it off any longer. Vince, I'm resigning."

I gave her a placating smile. "Okay, okay, Pat, let's talk it over. Whatever is bugging you, I'm sure we can work it out, so let's skip the theatrics and get down to issues."

"I'm serious, Vince," she said. "This has nothing to do with any grievances."

"Nothing to do with my hiring Scovetti, or your annoyance at all the psychologists?" I said skeptically. "Or with Dimitri's and Sharon's shenanigans? McGonigle's snooping or Diego's griping? Your squirrel-powered air conditioner, or your office's dollhouse dimensions?"

"No," she said quickly. "Even if you could somehow change all that, I'd still be going. Here, this will explain it." She reached across the desk to hand me an envelope.

I took it from her and flipped it away from me, sailing it to the side edge of my desk. "I don't want to read your damn letter of resignation!" I snapped. "If you have something to say to me after all these months together, you can say it to me face to face."

Pat stood up to retrieve the letter. "This isn't my letter of resignation," she said softly. "It's my letter of acceptance. To Columbia University."

I pulled out the letter, skimming past Pat's unfamiliar address under the familiar university seal to the body of the letter. "Doctoral program in clinical psychology," I read aloud. "Fall semester." My eyes returned to the top of the letter and the date.

The letter had been sent last spring. Pat had obviously been incubating this time bomb for months. "Well, you certainly know how to keep a secret," I finally said.

"I'm giving more than four weeks' notice," she said. "I'm sorry I didn't say anything sooner, Vince, only . . . well, if I changed my mind, why upset everybody for no reason."

"Upset everybody?" I said, rather bitterly. "Isn't that a little grandiose, Pat? Did you really think we'd all go into a panic, build a funeral pyre in the clinic, and immolate ourselves rather than go on without you?"

"Okay, then," she said harshly. "Six weeks should be more than adequate for notice."

"It will be . . . if your mind's really made up," I said.

She nodded. "Of course it's made up. It's about time I finalized things, with classes starting in six weeks. God knows, I've had long enough to decide for sure."

"If you don't mind my asking," I said, still scrutinizing the letter as though looking for some secret message, "just how long has this been going on? I mean, one doesn't apply to and get accepted into a graduate school overnight."

"No," she said, "I put the applications in about the end of last November. Back in the clinic's stormy adolescence."

"Yeah," I reminisced. "I can understand your wanting to bail out back then. But why now? Now that things are so much better."

"So much better?" she echoed. "You just reeled off a partial list of problems with this place that would make, by comparison, the Declaration of Independence sound like an endorsement of George the Third."

"We're having our growing pains . . ." I started to say.

"I could stand the pain if I saw some growth," she replied, "but it looks more like regression to me. Doctors getting rich and fat, the little people being overworked and persecuted, McGonigle bugging conversations and people, inadequate office space, faulty equipment, empty promises. We were going to make it so different, Vince."

"Give me a break, Pat!" I groaned. "They gave me the ball with a first-and-twenty-five on my own one-yard line, and you're looking to kick the extra point already. Well, maybe I haven't scored yet, but I'm not giving up the ball. Are you going to punt?"

"No, I'm going to Columbia," she said. "Remember? That glorious palace of marble and ivy you speak about in hushed tones? That place where you acquired your vast knowledge while I was building sand castles and growing marijuana in that hippie colony we called a university? I mean, wouldn't turning down a chance to go there be like telling St. Peter you'd rather go elsewhere?"

"Go to Columbia—or elsewhere!" I said. "If that's what you want, to start all over again at your age!"

"Oh, it won't be so bad, Vince," she simpered. "They've got ramps for wheelchairs and plugs for hearing aids for us old folk, and if I can't make it in for graduation, they'll mail my diploma to me along with my Social Security check."

The intercom buzzed. "Can you see some patients for medication?" Connie whined. "We've got a lot of people out here."

"And I'm busy losing people in here," I said. "I'll let you know when I'm free." I turned again to Pat. "Well, good luck, though frankly I don't know what you've got to gain."

"How about a doctorate in psychology?" she suggested.

"Oh, one of those credentials that you're always putting down?" I said. "For the past year, I've heard you complain about the inequities based on meaningless pieces of paper, the *papelitos,* as you call them. How dare Dimitri act superior to Sandy because he has an M.D., why should Maria kowtow to Ramon because he has an M.A.? Now, suddenly, Dr. Patterson has joined the paper chase."

She closed her eyes and nodded. "A late starter perhaps, but I'm tired of running last in the rat race."

"Last?" I questioned. "Seems you were number two the last time I looked back. Did I ever let anyone give you orders or push you around?"

"No, Vince, *you* didn't let anyone. You made me number two. Tomorrow you could make me number ten or twenty-six, couldn't you?" she said.

"And I'd do that only when I came to believe that your abilities were less than those of eight or twenty-four others in the pack," I said. "I never put anyone over you because he had a fancier piece of paper. You preach about a world where people are judged on their own merits, not on educational and social advantages, and yet when you have a chance to be one of the new breed, a woman who can take on responsibility far beyond the traditional norms of her profession, you go running back to school like a kid."

"Funny, but at this moment," she observed, "I don't feel very responsible. I feel like a little girl being lectured by her daddy on the joys of keeping house for someone instead of pursuing higher education."

The intercom buzzed again. "Call for you on six," Connie said.

"Oh, take a message, for God's sake, Connie. I'll call them back," I barked.

"Sor-ry," she said huffily. "Are you with someone?"

"No, against, I think," I explained before hanging up.

"You could have taken the call," Pat said airily. "I came in to resign, not hold a debate."

I looked at her impassive face, trying to recapture my fervor of a moment ago. It was gone, and I realized I had been unfair, trying to impose my wishes, my philosophies, *my* clinic on her. The captain goes down with his ship, the books says; I don't think that includes the first mate. "Pat," I asked suddenly, "how come you never asked me for a letter of recommendation when you were applying to Columbia?"

"Like the letter Hamlet gave Rosencrantz and Guildenstern?" she asked sardonically. "If you wouldn't recommend a graduate school to me, why should you recommend me to it?"

"I wouldn't have double-crossed you, Pat," I said. "If you're good enough for me, you're too good for those bookworms who wouldn't know a split personality from a split infinitive. If you can handle real patients, I'm not worried about your ability to deal with paper ones."

"Thanks, Chief," she said. "I got a recommendation from the head of social service at the main hospital, plus a few letters from former teachers. I imagine the admissions committee is more interested in past classroom performance, anyway; not many of the incoming kids would have any real job experience like this old lady. Apparently, things worked out."

"Yeah," I said, handing back the precious acceptance letter. "Congratulations. It is a far, far better thing you do than you have ever done."

"Don't forget the rest—a far, far better rest that I go to than I have ever known . . ." she quoted. "At least during the past year."

She clutched her letter of safe passage to her chest and disembarked, leaving me alone in the captain's chair, with a sinking feeling.

There followed immediately one of the most unproductive days of my entire life, until Connie interrupted my aimless pushing of papers from one side of my desk to the other with a buzz on the intercom. "Vince, can you see a patient for medication? She's been waiting to see Dr. Krumpel for two hours."

"Christ, Krumpel's not here today!" I barked. "She called in sick. Didn't anyone out there bother to tell that to the patient?"

"Listen, my dear, how were we supposed to know that Stacy was waiting to see her? You know that Stacy sits in the waiting room all day."

"Oh. If it's Stacy, okay. I'll see her," I volunteered.

Stacy had lost some of her beautiful bronze tan spending so many hours in our sunless waiting room, but far from the sickly pallor that afflicted most of us shut-ins, her skin had merely lightened to a becoming rosy hue, accentuated by her shining golden hair. It was with a tinge of satyric regret that I noticed Stacy had abandoned her scandalous shorts and halters for a more proper blouse-and-skirt ensemble, summery enough to complement what was still revealed of her long, trim legs and sandal-shod feet. It wasn't just her dress that was more appropriate; there was something definitely improved about the entire Stacy.

"How are you, Stacy?" I asked, knowing she was better.

"Not too bad, Doctor," she said with a little smile. She looked you in the eye now, no longer letting her own eyes drift in a mysterious reverie. "Spacey Stacy" Carl Brock had called her once in conference, and the epithet caught on, even at the front desk, though my malevolent glares usually prohibited its use within my earshot. I didn't think they would be saying it anymore now.

"How do you feel on the medication?" I asked.

"Much better," she reported. "More clear-headed, not as frightened, less nervous. The only thing it doesn't help much is the depression."

"Are you depressed? Can you tell me about it?"

She looked at her watch, apparently aware that I usually left at five, and trying to be considerate. "Oh, it's not so bad usually," she said. "I don't feel it at all right now. But, then, I'm here with people. It's only when I'm alone that it comes back. But when it does, it's terrible. I feel strange and frightened, as if I'm going to die. Then, sometimes the fright gets so bad I actually want to die."

"Are you alone much?" I asked with concern.

"Oh, practically never," she replied. "I live with my father, you know. And his second wife. But even at night, when I'm in my room, the depression comes on, even though I know there are other people in the house. I try to go to bed while they're still up and hope I don't wake up in the middle of the night."

"What happens if you do wake up?"

She sighed. "That's when my thoughts go out of control. It's like when I took that acid. If I don't do something about it, I start hearing weird voices, seeing strange shapes. It's like the devil's in the room with me."

"What can you do about it when it happens?"

"I've learned that I can't stay in bed," she explained. "I put on the lights real quick. I get up and sit in the living room awhile. Sometimes I turn on the radio, just to hear a human voice. But knowing my father's there in the house is enough to keep me from flipping out. Funny, isn't it? It's like being a little kid again. If there really were devils or evil spirits in my room, what could he do against them? If I really am going crazy, how could he help? It's just a fear of being alone, I suppose. A very crazy fear. When I'm in my room, in the dark there, I get this incredible feeling, as though there's no one else in the whole world. If I pick up the telephone, there won't be anyone in the world to answer. If I go out into the street, there won't be cars or people. All the houses around me will be empty. When that feeling comes on, I know I'm still crazy, regardless of how good I feel during the day. I think alone is the most depressing feeling there can be. Do you know what I mean, Doctor?"

"Yeah, Stacy," I said glumly. "I think I'm beginning to."

# 6

**F**OUR WEEKS' NOTICE. THAT'S WHAT ST. DYMPHNA'S OFFICIAL personnel manual says I have to give when I resign. That's what my union says I have to give. *Six* weeks' notice—that's essentially what I wound up giving. Fifty percent more than mandated by clinic law or common sense.

If Bellino anticipated undergoing a difficult mourning period after my departure, he gave no indication of beginning the grief work early, unless denial was a phase of the process. He insisted we continue to meet for our weekly supervisory sessions, even though I strongly suggested we both put the time to better independent use. But, no, he said that termination of patients was one of the most vital parts of therapy and he would be remiss as my supervisor if he let our own personal feelings about termination interfere with patient care.

So, I picked up the case we had left off discussing at our last session, clearing my throat with deliberate noisiness and folding my hands primly in my lap before beginning my dutiful recitation. "Betty is feeling much better; in our last therapy session, she said she thought it was about time to start looking for a job again."

"Tell me," he interrupted before I could really get started, "is Betty still coming to that women's therapy group that you run?"

"She came to a few meetings a while back," I affirmed, "but she dropped out."

"Rather too bad," he muttered under his breath. Then, in a more audible voice, he said, "Running a group like that is quite a challenging . . . and rewarding assignment, I would imagine, from our discussions of it here."

"Yes, you might say so," I replied cautiously. I wondered why he was suddenly bringing up my group.

"Would you mind if I observed your group this week?" he blurted.

"Huh?" I exclaimed. "You mean, actually sit there in the group?"

"Well," he said hesitantly, "someone else will have to take it over when you leave, and since it is a very sensitive group, I'd like to be able to give the new therapist a little guidance."

"And have you selected the group's new therapist?" I wheedled.

"It depends to some extent on what I observe," he explained. "But I'm leaning very heavily toward the new nurse, Julia Scovetti."

"If you're set on this Scarpetti woman taking charge," I suggested, "why don't we simply let *her* observe the meeting?"

"Her name's *Scovetti*. You mean, have two observers? Me and her?"

"No! Why do *you* have to observe, too? Hasn't this girl . . . *woman* had any experience with groups?"

"Plenty!" he asserted. "In the day hospital she headed, she conducted group as well as individual therapy."

"Then there's no need for you to sit with her and hold her hand!" I snapped. "I'll be glad to talk to her about the group and offer my suggestions."

"May I make one thing perfectly clear?" he said, nearly shouting. "*I* want to observe. I, your supervisor, your director, want to observe a therapy group being conducted in *my* clinic, where, according to the regulations of New York State, all therapy is to be carried out under the supervision of a duly licensed . . ."

"We meet the day after tomorrow at one P.M.—sharp," I said in exasperation. Damn, I'd been sandbagged! But rank has its privileges, and when it came to throwing his considerable weight around, Bellino was among the rankest.

I felt terrible the morning of the group's weekly meeting as I slipped into my office a few minutes late, under the surveillance of

Rosie McGonigle, the threat of Bellino's imminent sit-in, and the influence of a rapidly proliferating virus.

And today was Observation Day, a day on which I myself was in no shape to be observed, much less any group I dared to conduct. Let Bellino observe something else—National Censorship Week or Male Supremacy Day—anything but my group!

I had originally invited eight of my patients to participate, but only four came regularly, two drifted in and out depending on how wet the weather was or how dry they were, and the last two had thus far resisted being seen in the company of "mental cases," especially since there were no men to meet in the group. So as starting time approached, I stood out by the reception desk to assess the size, strength, and sanity level of today's challenge.

The first to come in was Pam, a legend among the men who habituated the seedy bars on the avenue. Pam had been first sent into a bar by her mother, who took her tea clandestinely laced with whiskey in an attempt to deaden the pain of trying to raise five kids on no money. The purpose of Pam's bar visits was, at that time, to persuade her father to give the family some of the money he had earned from erratic day jobs before his wages were consumed. As a child, Pam had long blonde hair and big blue eyes, the sort of appeal that even the hardened clientele of the saloons found irresistible. As Pam continued to grow, so did her attractiveness to her father's drinking buddies, and she soon learned that by flirting with them, she would be rewarded. At first, she accepted their quarters for candy bars, then a five or a ten to help her mother meet the rent. At the height of her popularity, one of her barroom sponsors had even financed a weekend trip to the Bahamas. More recently, she had been going home with anyone who would buy her a sandwich and a beer.

At forty-five, Pam was tired and sick. Her blonde hair was now gray and sparse, though she tried to conceal the change by trips to the beauty parlor whenever she could put something aside from her meager welfare allotment and dwindling gift fund. Her body was scarred, and she wore bangs to hide the gash on her hairline where an irate "lover" had slashed her after she stole twenty dollars from his coat pocket. Internally she was scarred, too. Her "insides were all messed up," as she put it, and a gynecologist had told her on a recent visit that she needed that delicate procedure called "a good cleaning out," after the ravages of three abortions (two before they were legal) and recurrent bouts of the clap. Pam would occasionally find a waitress or barmaid job, only to leave it abruptly and follow the first man who gave her a smile and a beckoning nod. Pam had lost her youth, her looks, and her health, but never her neurotic belief in the inevitable coming of the one man who would make everything right for her.

Mildred, on the other hand, was a very different sort of person. She had always been the good girl, doing exactly as her rigid, dominating parents directed. After marrying at eighteen, chiefly in an attempt to escape the subjugation of her parents, she discovered that her husband was a worse tyrant than the ones she left behind. By the time she was twenty-five, she had four children. Her husband could not hold a steady job, and she had to work full-time as a waitress in order to pay the bills. At night, she had difficulty falling asleep. She had cause to be overtired, after waking up at 6 A.M. to feed and clothe the oldest kids and get them off to school before going to her job, then returning home at 6 P.M. to care for the children and clean the house before finally collapsing exhausted into bed at midnight. When she eventually consulted her family doctor about her insomnia, he prescribed some barbiturates. When one capsule failed to work, she tried two and then three each night. When her doctor warned her against taking too many, she sought out additional doctors, getting a respectable amount from each. Soon she was taking over a dozen capsules a day and was a genuine addict.

Chris had no vices to speak of—not that she had many opportunities to speak to anyone. Taking care of an invalid mother by night and working in a clerical job all day, she had few chances to develop friends of either sex. Chris didn't mind that much, especially the lack of men. Her mother had always warned her about how evil men were, citing her no-good father, who had run off with another woman when Chris was only two, leaving Chris and her mother to struggle alone. Well, if a girl had a good job and a loving mother, what more did she need? Chris had never been aware of wanting more out of life. Then, one day, while her mother was chiding her for arriving home fifteen minutes later than usual, Chris had a convulsion. The doctors at the emergency room could find nothing wrong with her, nor could three different neurologists with their electroencephalograms, X rays, and brain scans. The convulsions continued, despite trials with various medications, until one of the specialists had the courage to tell Chris she was suffering from an emotional problem and the "convulsions" were merely a symbolic protest against a conflict that she couldn't otherwise express.

Barbara, the fourth member, once had everything. She had been the wife of a rising young executive, with a beautiful, new suburban home and three healthy, happy children. Then, Barbara began to experience mild feelings of depression, loss of appetite, difficulty sleeping. She received little sympathy from her family or friends— how could she not be happy, possessing as she did every woman's dream in the best of all possible worlds? She came to dread the many social functions she was expected to attend with her husband to promote his career. Barbara's inability to radiate the mandatory degree of enthusiasm was considered by her husband at first to be a drawback, then a positive hazard to his goals. When psychotherapy and medication failed, she was hospitalized and given electroshock treatment. When the more drastic courses of treatment did nothing to improve Barbara's mood and only seemed to impair her ability to remember the names of important men to whom she was introduced, her husband forcefully convinced her that if she could not be happy with the lifestyle she shared with him, divorce was the only sensible course. As a documented psychiatric case, Barbara didn't dare contest his custody of the children and she lacked the emotional stamina for a lengthy legal hassle, so she accepted a very meager alimony settlement. Barbara had felt at the time that a quick, "civilized" agreement would spare her and the children she no longer saw the humiliation of having a formal charge of insanity launched against her.

Today's last group member was Didi, whom, despite lagging attendance, I had felt considerable misgivings about admitting to the group. Didi was the only member who was frankly psychotic.

In addition to her chronic anxiety attacks and paranoid ideas, Didi was, most of the time, delusional and subject to auditory and visual hallucinations. Didi fervently believed that her mother, who had died when Didi was six, was looking for her to punish her for failing to go directly to the store as asked. On that fateful day, Didi got diverted in the course of an errand by a playmate, who enticed her into a game of jacks. When Didi finally approached her house, an hour behind schedule, the ambulance was just taking her mother away. Her mother had tripped on the landing and taken a fatal fall down a flight of stairs on her way out to look for her missing child. So overwhelmed with guilt was Didi that her internalized mother became an externalized demon that haunted her daily. From time to time, her mother would visually materialize, call Didi a bad girl, and advise her to kill herself. Didi had been hospitalized for psychiatric treatment seven times, three after suicide attempts. Even today, she was out on a pass from the state hospital for the purpose of maintaining continuity with the group during her brief in-patient confinement. Didi's hold on reality seemed so tenuous that I debated her admission to the group, but she was so isolated from others that I decided to include her as long as the rest of the group could tolerate her.

And close behind Didi followed our leader, Dr. Bellino, craning his neck as he surveyed the waiting room like a tourist from Des Moines on a sightseeing tour of the Bowery. "Hi, Pat," he called chipperly. "Isn't it just about curtain time?"

"Just counting the house," I informed him.

"Oh? And how does it look?"

"I'd say one too many," I answered pointedly.

He shrugged obliviously, deflecting my barb. "Well, just bring another chair in. Which room?" I pointed the way to the stranger, and Vince and I took adjacent chairs in the circle already occupied by four of the women, all of whom except the distracted Didi scrutinized Bellino and exchanged wondering, mischievous little smiles with their cohorts.

"I didn't know that bitch was going to be in the group!" Pam whispered to me very audibly, pointing a derogatory finger at Barbara, who had just entered after a preliminary trip to the ladies' room. Pam then loudly addressed Barbara, who had nervously retreated toward the empty chair opposite her adversary asking, "How's your love life? Bob giving it to you good?"

"I didn't know he was your boyfriend when I met him at McDonnell's," Barbara pleaded in self-defense. "I don't even remember that night . . . very well."

What was this all about, I wondered? I was aware that Pam had been involved off and on over the years with Bobby Borgia, a shady character who frequented OTB, the racetracks, and local bars, took numbers, and was rumored to have connections in the upper realms of the underworld. Extremely jealous, probably to the point of paranoia, he had once pushed Pam out of a moving car when he suspected her of having "doings," as he called it, with one of his friends. Despite black eyes and blue bruises, Pam always went back for more.

From the skirmish in progress, I surmised that Bobby had made a play for Barbara, who had attempted to enrich her lonely life with a visit to McDonnell's, a local refreshment establishment where if they do it all for you, it's because you're in no shape to do it yourself. Bob and Barbara may even have had a one-night stand, but after having received a total of over fifty electroshock treatments, Barbara probably couldn't even remember as memorable a swain as Bobby.

"I saw you flirting with him, your tits hanging out, rubbing your ass against him!" Pam ranted.

Barbara blushed, staring across the circle at Bellino, then with a quick little head jerk in Vince's direction gave Pam a glare of reprimand. Since I was sitting between Pam and Vince, the noisy plaintiff had literally lost sight of the director's presence. Barbara's warning look caused Pam to clap her hand over her offensive mouth, masking the apologetic smile that followed.

"I want a fish sandwich," Didi announced suddenly. Good old Didi, always there with the appropriate comment!

"Please excuse me, Doctor," Pam apologized with a little bow, as decorously as if she had spilled a bit of tea while pouring.

"Oh, please don't let my presence here inhibit you in any way," Bellino replied graciously. "Just carry on as you usually do."

"Are you going to be our new therapist when Pat leaves?"
Mildred asked, rather hopefully.

"Ah, no, I don't think so," Vince said hastily. "I'm just observing,
if you have no objections."

All quickly tittered their compliance, except for Didi, who was
off in a fishy reverie. "Let's all go around the room, introduce
ourselves, and tell the doctor why we're coming to this group!"
Pam enthusiastically suggested. Great! We hadn't even officially
kicked off and already they were playing directly to an audience of
one, the supposedly unobtrusive observer. Pam shouted gleefully,
"You first, Chris!"

"My name is Chris," she began shakily, apparently addressing
Vince, though looking at her sensible, dark, low-heeled pumps. "I
have bad nervous attacks. I lose consciousness when it happens and
it really frightens me. The doctors tell me it's an emotional
problem, and I hope that by sharing my feelings with others, I
might get some help with this."

"Are you a nun?" Didi blurted, grasping the collar on her own
dress to illustrate. Leave it to Didi to give voice to the thoughts
that flickered ever so briefly before being snuffed out by the censor
in the minds of others. Always conservatively garbed, alternating
between gray and navy blue dresses, Chris had outdrabbed her
finest efforts today with a dark blue gaberdine dress featuring a
high white collar and did, indeed, look like Supernun.

"No," Chris answered, and shook her head sadly as though
regretting that she wasn't currently sitting in some pleasantly dank
abbey instead of her present hot-seat.

"My name is Didi," her interrogator piped. "When *I* get upset, I
feel the world is closing in on me, and then I start to see things and
try to hurt myself. See what I did last time!" She stood up and
crossed the circle to stand in front of Vince, then hiked up her skirt
to thigh level and proudly displayed several thin red lacerations. "I
wanted to cut my leg off because it always took me to bad places."

I glanced around the room, like a good group leader, to monitor
the reactions of the other members, from Chris's cringe of horror to
Pam's smirk of bemusement. I realized that Pam often laughed at
everything defensively to avoid dealing with painful issues. I knew

from my individual sessions with Pam that she had lost a maiden aunt, one of the kindest people in her life, to suicide, and aware of Pam's childhood experience with the consequences of self-destructive impulses in mentally ill people, I could understand why she now had to pass off Didi's tale of madness with amusement. Perhaps on a less turbulent day I would have questioned her directly about her reaction to Didi's exhibitionistic confession, but Vince's unnatural presence had already thrown proceedings way off their customary course and, deep in troubled waters already, I was determined to attempt nothing more heroic than drifting with the collective tide and preventing Bellino from rocking the boat as best I could.

Besides, Chris looked as though she were about to faint already, being the extremely sensitive sort who would break into tears during the eleven o'clock news if she heard a report of an earthquake causing deaths in some remote land. In the course of her sheltered life, I'm sure she had never heard firsthand about any act of violence, even one as relatively harmless and bizarre as Didi's attempted autoamputation.

As Didi dropped her hemline and pattered back to her seat, I compared her outfit with Chris's Mother Seton original and could not help wishing that, as far as dressing were concerned, Didi would get into some of Chris's habits. Didi's outfit today looked as if it had been selected by programming a random-number generator with a Salvation Army inventory of rejected contributions. How else could you possibly match a red plaid maxiskirt with an orange-striped blouse, coordinated with a red-and-green Christmas bow in your hair?

Didi nodded to Barbara with a smug can-you-top-this expression, but Barbara was not in a competitive mood and kept her introduction as brief and direct as possible: "I'm Barbara. I lost everything when I got sick. Now I'm trying to put my life back together."

"I'm Mildred," said the oldest and tiredest member of the group. "I have to stop taking pills. Can't function anymore. Some days I can't even get out of bed. And my kids are running wild; I guess they don't respect me anymore." Poor Mildred, always self-deprecating! Overworked and overwhelmed, she now had to give up her one pleasure in life, the shiny red, yellow, and "rainbow" capsules that paved the road to blessed oblivion.

"I'm Pam!" bubbled the ringleader, launching into the grand finale. "Most of you know me by now." (Come off it, Pam! What are you doing, describing your problem or announcing your candidacy?) "I didn't want to join this group, but Pat talked me into it. I don't have any problems now. Since I last got out of the hospital, I'm feeling fine, better than I have in years, thanks to the doctors there." She paused to give Bellino a long, appreciative look. "But I told Pat I would give group a whirl."

The preliminaries over, the group fell into silence. The women, without exception, stared raptly at Bellino, as though waiting for him to commence the healing service. He merely looked expectantly at me, as if to imply, "You're the group leader. So, lead!" Vince's intrusion had the effect of pouring a gallon of maple syrup into a gas tank; I feared I would never get the group to run again. Bellino's face may have featured a blank expression and sealed lips, but so had Medusa's when Perseus sprang her on his group, with much the same result as Bellino was having here. Unobtrusive observer? This deus in machina had gummed up the therapeutic works.

I perceived that the prolonged silence was inducing the group members to kill time and bronchial tissue by reaching for fresh cigarettes. Clearing my throat which, under the progressive assault of the smoke screen and my cold germs, now felt less like an emery board and more as if I had been grazing on cactus, I turned to Millie, who looked as though she had last slept three days ago and said, "Millie, you seem exhausted today."

"Well, I really didn't sleep much last night," she confirmed. "My son Tom called about two A.M. that he had just run away from a residential drug program upstate. He said he had a fight with one of the attendants and couldn't stay there any longer. He wants to come home, and said he would be there later today. I don't know what to do."

"Why is that?" I encouraged Millie to continue.

"I had so many problems with him when he lived with me before," she moaned. "He was always getting arrested, and I had to go to court with him. Once the police even got a warrant to search my house, since he was messed up in a big drug deal and they thought I had helped him hide the drugs in the house. Another time, he took my TV set and sold it to buy some heroin. I just don't know if I want to go through all that again." She paused, then added firmly, "But he's my son! It kills me to think of him sleeping on the subway. He has no other place to go."

"*I* wouldn't let the bum back in. He'll only rip you off again," Pam warned. "Right, Doc?"

Vince started up in his chair, surprised by this sudden remark directed at him. "Uh, there certainly is a strong possibility that her son will behave as he's done in the past," he said blandly.

"He *is* her son, though," Chris joined in. "I guess it's really hard to think about your own flesh and blood sleeping on a park bench, no matter what he's done. Don't you think, Doctor?"

"Uh, that certainly is another valid viewpoint," Vince said, indecisively.

Who the hell designated him umpire-in-chief? Why not ask *me*, Chris? Your old beloved therapist, remember? I know how very sensitive you are to this whole area of family responsibility and guilt. Once a man from the accounting department had invited Chris out to lunch, but her lunch—as well as his interest—cooled when she had to spend a half hour on the phone, first with her mother and then with her mother's doctor, because her mother, upon learning that Chris was out to lunch with a man, immediately had a "bad breathing spell," requiring an emergency house call.

"You're right, Chris," Millie responded, more emphatically than the doctor had. "It tears me up to think of him without a place to go. Why, someone could rob him, even kill him, riding the subways all night long."

That would be a switch! Usually people had to watch out for Tom, who had a history of train robberies to support his drug habit that would rival the exploits of Jesse James.

"Maybe he could stay in the hospital where I live," Didi suggested, seeming to come out of her trance. "Could you get him in there, Doctor?"

"Um, I don't think they would take someone simply because he has no place to stay," Vince answered, though obviously confused about the precise spot from which Didi had been launched into our midst this afternoon.

Vince was correct about the state hospital's limiting its clientele to psychotics and excluding sociopaths and addicts. It was tough enough to get in even if you were psychotic; because if you had enough insight to request admission, you were deemed not sick enough, and if you were too crazy to know you needed help, they wouldn't interfere with your civil rights by locking you up. At least Didi was relating more appropriately to the proceedings than when she was preoccupied with fish sandwiches.

"At least your son tries to keep in touch with you," Barbara commented sadly. "He doesn't forget you're his mother." Barbara was especially upset by the failure of her children to contact her after her husband divorced her and secured their custody. Barbara accepted, after a time and after a fashion, that her two younger children had broken off contact with her. But the silence of her oldest son, Wayne, was genuinely distressing, for she had always been very close to him. He had always been the supportive and encouraging one, far more so than her husband. It was Wayne who had visited her most often in the hospital and who had once tried to protect her when his father slapped her during one of his characteristic lectures about the need for her to "shape up and stop wallowing in self-pity." Wayne had accompanied her to "Recovery" meetings in an attempt to learn more about his mother's illness and how he could best help her. Barbara knew he was very busy in his freshman year of college, and she had heard through her limited connections on the family grapevine that he had become engaged— but not a word from him. It was as if she had never existed, as if they had not been so close during all those difficult years.

"I wish *my* son would call me," Barbara lamented.

"You're better off without him," Pam retorted with her all-purpose pearl of advice. "Children—or, I should say, people in general—just bring you grief." She punctuated her philosophical pronouncement with a hard, cynical wink at Vince. "Right, Doc?"

Vince fortunately did not have time to come up with a response to this provocative question, nor did I, unfortunately, have time to impress my supervisor by guiding Mildred, Barbara, and Chris into a highly insightful and therapeutic sharing of their conflicts involving close relatives. Just as the group seemed to be getting underway toward some sort of sensible destination, a newcomer lurched aboard, one of the veteran group members, though in her present state I hesitated to call her a steady member.

It was Peggy O'Laughlin, whose fading red hair, freckles, and pale blue eyes gave testimony to her County Cork heritage, while the flabby rolls around her upper arms and midriff, and her ruddy complexion, testified to her fondness for opening bottle corks.

"Hi, Peggy! You look like you've had a few," Pam greeted the newcomer with her usual tact.

"I haven't been drinking," Peggy slurred.

Not since you came into the clinic today, I thought, getting a whiff as she passed, smelling like a Bud and not that of a rose.

"I'm a little late because I had to run back to check on a leak in a tenant's apartment," Peggy offered as explanation for her tardiness. Peggy, when she could be lured out of the bars, was the second-string super for her building. The leak must have been in a wine cellar, I speculated.

Pam never suppressed a snide comment the way the rest of us ladies tended to do. "Oh," she needled, "are you handling the repairs for McDonnell's bar now? I saw you going in about ten, right after they opened." Pam held a grudge against Peggy ever since Bobby Borgia had favored her with his attentions one ill-fated night at that notorious hangout, just as he had later approached Barbara and every other woman spry enough to mount a bar stool without the aid of her cane.

"What's it to you?" Peggy sneered. "I had some business to take care of with the bartender."

"Yeah, I'll bet," Pam scoffed. "Boosting his sales, no doubt."

"Are we going to have men in our group now?" Peggy asked suddenly as she spotted Vince.

"He's only a psychiatrist," Didi hastened to explain helpfully. "I don't think he's supposed to say anything."

"Well, I *haven't* been drinking, Doctor," Peggy said, with a little bob something like a curtsy, as though Vince were a monsignor paying a visit to Holy Inebriation Grammar School. I was debating whether to confront her with having knocked over three ashtrays and a cup of coffee when she walked in—one ashtray with her breath alone.

"I'm just a little nervous today," Peggy added, to explain her unsteady locomotion.

"Why is that?" I asked gently, as Peggy managed to sit down without knocking over the chair.

"Well, John, my ex, came over yesterday," Peggy began. "He just got his pay check, so he brought a case of beer." (Ah, that's where Peggy's present "slip" began, which means she's been sliding now for nearly twenty-four hours, I calculated.) "We were talking, getting along pretty well." (That boded ill. Peggy would soon be going back with him for round fifteen.) "Then my son, Barry, came knocking on the door, real spaced out. He'd been doing speed for the last three days and hadn't slept. My husband and he hate each other. They got into a big, noisy fight and someone called the cops."

I looked around the room, waiting for someone to prod Peggy on to the punch line.

"What happened?" Didi obliged, surfacing once more from her daze. Ah, improvement already! See how she's relating to others, Dr. Bellino? Who said autism was a chronic symptom?

"Nothing happened," Peggy said, anticlimactically. "My son ran out and then a few minutes later my husband left." Leaving Peggy alone with the beer. And shortly thereafter, alone.

"How did you feel?" I queried in proper social work fashion, going after the feeling as I was taught to do.

"I don't know. I guess a little down. Empty." (As empty as you can feel, that is, after several quarts of beer.) "Now I don't know when I'll see my son again and my husband may never come back."

"Peggy, would you really like to get back together with your husband?" I asked, trying to give her and the group some semblance of direction.

"I know he's no prize," she sighed, "but we really had some good times together and I'm awfully lonely since he left."

"Aaah, don't let the bum in again!" Pam advised, predictably.

"Once you even ended up in the hospital," Barbara recalled.

"Well, John says that's all in the past," Peggy shrugged. "That only happened because he felt so insecure about me because I was drinking."

So, what's all in the past, if you drink every morning in McDonnell's and every pay day with him?

"My main problem," Peggy continued, "is if I go back with John, my son can't stay. I don't know what to do. I feel torn apart."

"Did your husband always hate his own son?" Chris asked with astonishment.

"Well, that's part of the problem," Peggy confessed, her skin flushing to nearly the shade of her hair. "I don't like to talk about it, but this is group therapy and you're supposed to be able to share *everything*." I nodded encouragingly, with a knowing smirk toward Vince underscoring how much confidence I had inspired in my patients.

"You see," she explained, "John isn't Barry's real father. I was drinking pretty heavy in those days and the truth of it is that I don't really know who my son's father is. When I met John, I was four months' pregnant, and going to lose my job as a barmaid because I was beginning to show. Welfare wasn't what it is now, and I was really in a jam. John helped me out and then we started living together. Of course, John knows he's not Barry's father, even though we never talked about it. I guess John never could stand the kid. When he was just a little boy, John would just stand there and look at him; I mean, never hugged or kissed him or anything. And then when Barry got to be a teen-ager and started to experiment with drugs, the shit really hit the fan. Frankly, I don't know what to do now. John was in such a mood after the police came that he might never come back." (I wasn't about to make book on that.) "That would solve all my problems, I suppose. Or would it?"

"Of course it wouldn't!" Pam countered. "You'd still be stuck with your son—and you know what a pain in the ass he is. Pardon my language, Doc."

"Yes, but you don't understand," Peggy said, as she began to cry silently. "It's my fault he's the way he is. If I hadn't been drinking so much when he was growing up . . . if I hadn't pushed him away with the excuse of being sick every time he asked for help with his homework . . . if he didn't have to look for me at McDonnell's to get into the apartment . . . if he hadn't seen so many of my drunken fights with John . . ." All this was true, I feared, but I hoped nobody in the group felt obligated to confirm it. Peggy had enough guilt as things stood now.

"Sounds just like me and my son Tom," Mildred said sadly. "Only with me, it was pills instead of booze."

"You both did what you could," Chris said kindly.

"What's with *you*, anyway, sister?" Pam said skeptically to Chris. "I never could figure out what the hell you're doing here. All the rest of us have taken some pretty hard knocks, known really rough times, but what have *you* seen of life? Nice job, comfortable home, no old man to beat on you or kids to run you ragged. I frankly don't think you know what problems are!" Pam looked around the room for a little of the applause and recognition she craved, though nothing was forthcoming except a stifled sob from Chris. Didi folded her arms and walled herself off from the group, as though she had just received firm instructions from her dead mother to have nothing further to do with these madwomen. Mildred was slouched in her chair, looking very forlorn. Barbara seemed lost in thought. Bellino looked like he'd rather be writing prescriptions. The group had ground to another halt; time to wind it up again!

"Chris, maybe you can share with the others . . ." (standard therapist's openings like that always sound so condescending), I essayed, "just what happened that led you to come to the clinic and join this group." Though Chris had attended a few sessions, she had never really opened up. In fact, she had said more during this meeting than ever previously, limited though her interaction was.

Chris stopped crying abruptly and courageously directed her gaze at Pam, who had folded one wrist over the other in her lap, like a lioness crossing her paws. "You don't have to grow up in a slum or get hooked on drugs or alcohol to have emotional problems," Chris said. "After my father left, when I was only two, Mommy and I were unhappy nearly all the time. I wasn't even conscious of how much the early hard times and Mommy's illness later were affecting my nerves until I began having spells."

Chris paused for a breath, and Pam pounced. "What's this 'Mommy' crap? I haven't used that word since I was five years old."

Pam would be a good candidate for one of those California encounter groups, a psychological demolition derby where you get points for traumatizing your comembers: two for making them cry, four for making them hit you, seven for driving them into a hospital, nine for a suicide attempt, and two free sessions for driving someone to actual suicide.

However, Chris seemed to be able to take care of herself very well. Though trembling slightly, she explained, "She's always been Mommy to me, I guess because we're so close. After my father left, there were just the two of us all those years."

"How can you be so close to your mother?" Pam said, perhaps with a trace of envy. "I couldn't stand *my* old lady. She never did nothin' for me. Always drunk and crying."

"My mother, may she rest in peace, is always with me," Didi said, now that the group had stumbled onto a topic of supreme interest to her. "I can hear and see her now." I found myself involuntarily scanning the room for an eerie figure under the coffee urn or behind the potted plants.

Barbara, possibly noting my own impractical search, also surveyed the room and said apprehensively, "I don't see anything."

Vince gave me a disapproving look, as though I had let the session degenerate into a seance, silently urging me to inject a little reality into the proceedings before he injected a little Prolixin into the group. "After a mother has died," I said, addressing my comments to Didi, "she is no longer with us, she doesn't exist as a physical presence. Still, mothers can continue to affect us emotionally and influence the way we behave."

While I was mentally reviewing the diversity of mother-daughter relationships, wondering whether and how I could get the group to explore this vast and crucial topic in the limited time we had left, Vince impulsively abandoned his neutral-observer role and challenged Pam just like a group leader. "Do you see any ways at all in which you and your mother were similar, Pam?"

Pam seemed flattered that the new leader had favored her with his professional attention. "Gee, Doc," she said, almost shyly, "I don't see how we had anything at all in common. She never got any fun out of life. Not even the drinking cheered her up. She would always just sit around and cry. Not me! No matter how bad things get, I always like to party and have a good time. That's for sure!" Her voice seemed to carry a touch of sadness despite her carefree philosophizing. As if aware of this herself, she added boisterously, "What else in life is there but having a good time? Live, laugh, and be merry, for tomorrow you die!"

As if to verify Pam's statement, there was a loud crash as Peggy slid off her chair onto the floor. I knew Peggy had come in drunk, despite my short-lived desire to believe her story about being merely nervous, but I never figured she was drunk enough to pass out, especially with the clinic director there to disapprove.

"She's dead. I know she's dead!" Didi panicked.

"You mean dead drunk, sister," Pam drawled lazily. "All she needs is some place to sleep it off and a few aspirin when she wakes up."

Pam, you're absolutely right, for once, and I nominate you to be next directress of the clinic. You could certify her diagnosis as APA number eighty-six proof: drunkenness, dead type.

"Somebody help her!" Chris sobbed. "You can't just leave her lying there. Call a doctor!" At that suggestion, every eye in the room turned toward Vince, who reluctantly rose from his seat of judgment and strode authoritatively over to the supine redhead. Carefully giving a slight tug to one meticulously creased trouser leg, he knelt beside Peggy and slid his arm behind her head, elevating it slightly. With the other hand, he grasped her wrist, feeling for a pulse. "I'm sure she'll be all right, ladies," he said confidently. "Pat, see if they've got a stretcher here and get hold of a blood pressure cuff." Peggy's eyelids fluttered. Almost tenderly, Vince leaned closer toward her and said, "How are you feeling, Peggy?"

His patient grunted sleepily, then parted her tremulous lips. "I'm . . ." she said. The next thing out of her mouth was her beer-and-pretzel breakfast, which splattered Vince's Bonwit Teller shirt, Pierre Cardin tie, and Brooks Brothers suit. As far as his wardrobe was concerned, it was Schaefer all around.

"Okay, women," I announced, choking back a most unprofes-

sional giggle, "I guess we'll stop for today. See you all next week."
And I sauntered off to find a stretcher, leaving Vince in a state of
consternation, with Peggy snoring peacefully in his arms.

The group had ended a little early, but by the time we found a
set of wheels for Peggy and enough able-bodied personnel to hoist
her hefty frame from the floor, there was no longer enough time
left over for an extra coffee break, so I headed back to my office.

"You have a patient waiting for you," Dolores said, as I passed
her. "Gee, you look happy. Was it a good group?"

"Oh, it was terrible! Wait till you see Dr. Bellino!" I tried to
convert the chuckle that escaped into a fit of coughing as I
retreated to my office.

Laura Morales had come in that afternoon weighted down by more
human misery than I had alleviated in the past two days. Not only
had her husband run off with her sister and her welfare allotment,
her oldest son been arrested for stealing, her youngest daughter
been bitten by a household rat, and her oldest daughter impreg-
nated by a human one, but this morning's mail had brought a letter
stating that she had flunked her welfare recertification because she
had not complied with regulation 476.3. With the help of a phone
call to the welfare center, I learned that Laura had been bounced
off the rolls because she had failed to prove to the department's
satisfaction that her husband (the rat who just ran off with her
sister) was not living in the house. I quickly promised Laura that I
would enlist the powers of the highest authorities in her behalf,
and redepositing her in the waiting room, I went straight to the
top, the office of the mighty medical director.

It's a good thing that I didn't bring Laura in with me, because
Vince did not look very impressive. Following an attempt to make
himself presentable after Peggy had doused him with semidigested
beer at our group session, he now sat sans jacket or tie, scowling in
his sopping shirt sleeves.

"Oh, I see you're striving for a more casual look," I said
encouragingly. "You know, I think it rather becomes you, and is
very appropriate for a clinic geared to the needs of the common
man."

"Pat, state your business or get the hell out of my hair and my office," he warned. "I have taken more than my share of aggravation from women today."

"Well, we take more than our share of abuse from the system," I retorted. "Look at this ridiculous letter Mrs. Morales got from the welfare department. They won't give her any more money until she can supply them with positive proof that her husband isn't living with her. Look what they consider acceptable as proof! A letter from her landlord—I'm sure that he won't help, especially because he's pissed at her for turning down the pass he made at her when her old man split. The school—I'm afraid her six-month-old daughter isn't enrolled yet, though how the hell the school is supposed to know anything is beyond me. Are they supposed to interrogate little children about their fathers' whereabouts, like police agents for the welfare center? The police, of course, are acceptable. Sure, just dial nine-one-one and ask them to send the cops to write a letter saying there's no man in the house; you can't even get them to do something when there *is* a man in the house and he's in the process of murdering you. And how's this one—her parish priest? She's an agnostic and doesn't have a priest. Anyway, even such a dumb suggestion should be unconstitutional—why should someone have to show their religious affiliation in order to be eligible for welfare? The whole thing is so inane."

"So is the whole welfare system that you crazy liberals have saddled this country with!" he griped. "Not only does our society give everything free, it pays people like you to make sure the parasites get it."

"How is someone with a second-grade education in Las Crobas, R.P.R., supposed to fill out an application that reads: 'List all available resources not listed in Column A but reported in Column B on page 9. If there are additional sources of revenue, turn to page 33, paragraph 6, line 5'? You'd need at least a college degree, even a Ph.D., to fill out something like that."

"Only, when you get *your* Ph.D.," he complained, "you won't want to bother wrestling with the monster you nursed along before you got bored with social work!"

"Look, I did not come here to debate my career plans," I stated.

"I came to ask you to help Mrs. Morales prove her husband isn't living at home."

"What do I look like, a priest?" he objected.

"It just so happens that Mrs. Morales's last hope is a letter from a hospital or clinic, an established institution in the community," I explained. "So, can you write the letter?"

"Absolutely not!" he decreed. "How the hell am *I* supposed to know that her husband isn't living with her?"

"You can take my word for it. I'm her therapist," I said.

"And how do *you* know?"

"Because she was all upset about his having run off with her sister and the money from her last welfare check," I confided.

"Then he *was* living there!" he said vindictively. "Even though she was collecting checks, he was *there*."

"Rarely," I insisted. "He was usually shacked up with somebody else. Besides, he was never regularly employed anyway. Are you going to penalize her for an occasional night in the sack with the guy?"

"I don't feel the government should be in the business of subsidizing adultery," he proclaimed. "Not with *my* tax dollars, at least."

"Adultery? But he's her legal husband," I pointed out.

"Oh, nuts!" he grumbled. "Sex within an immoral context is immoral, hence adultery, regardless of irrelevant technicalities. If the welfare department is so damn interested in who's living with her, let them send investigators up there some night and . . ."

"No, no, no!" I screamed. "They *used* to do that, but they were made to stop. That's a terrible violation of the rights of privacy."

Vince looked as though he were about to cry. "Then how could *anyone* say who's living anywhere if you're not allowed to check?"

"Just write the letter, please?" I insisted. "Think about her child, a poor, tiny baby about to starve to death. You have children of your own. How can you make a poor baby suffer . . ."

"Okay, I give up!" he interrupted. "I've put up with enough sickening drivel for one day. I'll give Mrs. Morales the letter. I'll give her a certificate of virginity if she wants. The whole system's so dishonest, it's a wonder the checks don't bounce."

The intercom buzzed. Vince picked it up and said, "Not really all." Noting my questioning look, he explained, "Connie wants to know if Pat's there." With a smug grin, he handed me the phone.

"Call for you on four, Pat."

I picked up the call and said, in my most professionally modulated voice, "Hello, this is Ms. Patterson. May I help you?"

"Hello, hello," came the frantic response. "Is this Mrs. Patterson? This is Mr. Silber, your psychiatric patient, remember me?"

I'd only been seeing him every week for the past year, but that was the way Archie Silber always began his telephone calls to me; so insecure was he that he didn't expect anyone to remember him.

"Yes, this is Ms. Patterson. Hello, Mr. Silber."

"Can I see you today?" he shrieked. "I feel very anxious! Can I come in?"

"Well," I said reluctantly, "I could see you for a few minutes around a quarter to five. And I've got a few minutes right now."

"I'll be there in a minute," he jabbered.

"Where are you now?"

"Right across the street. With my laundry."

I paused, trying to decide whether to try to squeeze in his crisis before my next scheduled appointment.

"Are you still there, Mrs. Patterson? Do you remember me?" he persisted.

"Okay, come on over now," I sighed into the receiver.

"And who was *that* maniac?" Vince asked irritably.

"Archie Silber. Do you remember him?"

"That weirdo!" Vince snorted. "Is he really coming up here at this hour, in the middle of the week? I thought he owned you exclusively first thing Monday mornings."

"He's in a crisis," I said simply.

"You should have let one of the assistants handle it," Vince remonstrated. "I heard you: 'I can see you for a few minutes around a quarter to five.' He would have kept you here half the night. You pander to his craziness too much. How is he going to deal with the realities of the world when you give in to all his obsessions and compulsions? Don't expect his next therapist to cater to his every whim!"

Mr. Silber, disciplined by many years spent in the regimented atmosphere of the state hospitals, obediently trooped over, or should I say crawled, weighted down as he was by his tent-sized winter coat plus two enormous shopping bags filled to the brim with old newspapers. Someday he might be enshrined in the Patients' Hall of Fame as the original shopping-bag man.

"Hello, again," I said, ushering him into my office. "How are you feeling?"

"Not so good, not so good," he mumbled, as he took a seat farthest from the door.

"What's the matter?" I asked sympathetically.

"You know that man who's been staring at me in the laundry? When I went back to my hotel, who was sitting in the lobby but him! I quickly bought a paper and walked out. I didn't want him to see my laundry, so I came straight over here. I can't go back. He might see what I washed."

So what, I was tempted to say. What difference does it make, Mr. Silber? No skin off your ass! But one look at his anxious face made me realize this was not the appropriate therapeutic comment to make—not even a laundered version. "It seems very important to you that he not see what you wash. I wonder why." (This is the polite way for a trained therapist to say, "Tell me." And we encourage our patients to be open!)

"Because he might know that I wash dirty underwear at the laundry."

"And you have every right to!" I said vehemently, feeling like the Susan B. Anthony of the B.V.D. movement. "That's why people go to the laundry—to wash dirty clothes." I had decided to opt for an ego-strengthening approach as opposed to a more psychoanalytic exploration of Mr. Silber's paranoid attitude toward this man.

"Yeah," he said, without enthusiasm. "I guess I have a right to do my laundry there. But I wish he wasn't so nosy. I'm just going to look the other way when he starts staring at me and my laundry."

"That sounds like a good idea, Mr. Silber." (Positive reinforcement.) "Don't give him the satisfaction of knowing that you noticed his staring." (Getting into the patient's pathology and helping him to use it to his advantage.)

"Okay," he resolved. "When I go back to the hotel, if he's still there, I'm going to look the other way. I can't stand to even see him.

"Well, I guess I'd better be going," he said nervously. "I want to unpack my underwear before the cleaning woman comes by." Still far from cured, but with the crisis of the day apparently satisfactorily resolved, Mr. Silber stumbled out of my office carrying his two shopping bags, one containing his troublesome underwear.

What next, I thought, taking a deep breath and attempting a ten-second TM relaxation exercise for the busy working woman which I had just read about in the latest issue of *Ms*.

I was no further than the thought when I heard a loud commotion out in the waiting room. This sounds very serious, I judged from the decibel level of the voices. Maybe I'd better check it out, especially since my mood for the relaxation exercise had dissipated.

Within ten seconds, I was out in the corridor beyond the waiting room, witnessing our security guard, Brian, in the act of trying to wrest Mr. Silber's shopping bags from his grasp.

"What's this all about?" I demanded in my most authoritative voice. I knew in a flash. The security guard, a recent recruit from a discount store, had suspected Mr. Silber of hiding stolen goods under his size fifty coat and in the two bulging shopping bags. Maybe not clothing or costume jewelry like at the discount store, but possibly a couple of packages of Bic pens, since Rosie McGonigle had alerted the guard recently about a few that had mysteriously disappeared from her office.

"This man looks very suspicious to me," said Brian, who hadn't been with us long enough to realize that most of our clients did. "Who knows what he might be hiding under that coat?" Good point, but at least it wasn't one of the electric typewriters periodically confiscated in night raids by the aspiring authors and secretarial students of our community; no coat is *that* big. I couldn't wait until Brian met up with our resident exhibitionist.

"It's an old trick these crooks use," Brian confided with a knowing wink. "They used to come into Danny's Discount wearing a coat five sizes too big and then walk out with all kinds of merchandise underneath. But you can't fool me. What kind of a nut would wear an overcoat in August?"

I just love the kind of screening and training they give the
security guards they send to work in Mental Health. Maybe we've
found a new way to cut down on the number of psychiatric hospital
admissions in this great era of community mental health. Any
schizophrenic who wore baggy clothes (as many did, whether
because of some sartorial form of claustrophobia or merely because
tailors don't take Medicaid) could be sent to jail as a potential
shoplifter.

"I'm sure Mr. Silber didn't take anything from here except his
very own clinic card," I testified. Properly indoctrinated and
thoroughly experienced in the bureaucracy of hospital systems, I
was sure he had carried the card to every therapy session as
religiously as an insurance salesman carries business cards to a
convention.

"I don't know. You can't trust these guys," the guard said, staring
my patient in the eye while fingering his nightstick, a maneuver
that increased Mr. Silber's paranoia tenfold.

"Well, Mr. Silber doesn't have anything with him except for
dirty . . . excuse me, clean laundry," I interceded, "as he'll be glad
to show you."

Mr. Silber recoiled in horror and, rather than obliging with the
proposed demonstration, hugged the shopping bags closer to his
chest, not even granting his supposedly trusted therapist a
glimpse.

Apparently equally uneager to peruse Mr. Silber's laundry,
whatever its state of cleanliness, the security guard growled, "If
you can vouch for him, I guess I won't have to search him . . . this
time, anyway." Turning to Mr. Silber, he barked, in true depart-
ment-store security fashion, "Okay, you can go down, but don't
come back again!"

"What are you saying?" I howled, then said sweetly to my
patient, "See you on Monday, Mr. Silber." Despite his burdens,
he sprinted down the stairs and out of the clinic, since by now even
the man at the hotel seemed benign compared to the nosy macho
man with the big stick.

"I don't know what you've managed to accomplish in over a year
of therapy with that creep," Vince's voice cracked behind me. "But
you always were a sucker for the worst of the dregs. Maybe you can

take him with you to graduate school and let him carry your books around in those shopping bags of his. Not that anything will change there for either of you—once a social worker, always a social worker!"

Before I could come up with a reply, he had ducked back into his office, probably as self-conscious about his tieless shirt as Mr. Silber was about his laundered underwear.

Brian, the security guard, was not the only man in our midst who carried a big stick. We also had to contend periodically with Gerald Groueff, an overgrown psychotic and convicted murderer who stood well over six feet tall and carried a staff that was heavier than most of our staff members, probably the trunk of a small tree whose top Gerald had eaten for lunch. His name was pronounced *Gruff*, as in *rough* and *tough*—or so he said. Not that we would have argued with him if he said it was pronounced *La Rochefoucauld*. That's one of my little Gerald Groueff jokes. There are a lot of them going around the clinic, a sort of defense mechanism we use to relieve the anxiety he provokes. For example, if you ask a clinician how much Groueff weighs, you're likely to get a reply like, "I don't know what he weighs now, but the last time he stepped on a penny-scale, the card said, 'Your weight is two hundred eighty pounds—sir!'"

"I'm God!" he bellowed as he approached the reception desk. "And I need more pills!"

Oh God, are you here again, I thought. I really hoped that Brian, the security guard, who was automatically summoned whenever Groueff was on the premises, had no hard feelings about yesterday's encounter with Mr. Silber, because today I was self-appointed to deal with this character who would give King Kong inferiority feelings.

"I'm God," he repeated as I advanced toward him, just in case I had been more than two blocks away at the time of his original announcement ten seconds previously.

"And I'm the clinic coordinator," I said, pulling rank. "Sit down, and I'll see you in a few minutes."

I hadn't psyched myself up to deal with him today. He had been in less than a week ago and had walked out with a two-week supply of Valium. As intimidated as we might have been at times, the drug laws stated that controlled drugs were not to be renewed prematurely and Groueff, for all his alleged insanity, was not about to confront the United States Department of Justice, Drug Enforcement Administration, head-on over a piddling high like Valium. Not that Groueff wasn't greedy for any substance that held the promise of better living through chemistry. In fact, it was his overzealous pursuit of psychopharmaceutical bliss that had led up to this morning's confrontation, for which I was in no shape. But then, four weeks at Esalen and another six in Stillman's Gym wouldn't have been enough to contend with this bruiser on equal terms.

I had become aware of his last visit when the opaque window on my office door rattled with the blood-curdling cry, "Give it to me," which was followed by a thunderous crash. Ever the impetuous fool, I bounded from my office in the direction of the sound. I quickly identified the site of the battle, apparently already over, as I saw Groueff emerging triumphantly from the Princess's office clutching a prescription. But what shape was our shapeliest shrink in? Should I try to detain Mr. Groueff until I examined the doctor he had just seen? That was an absurd notion, lacking as I did the sort of high-powered rifle employed in detaining charging elephants and other Groueffian fauna.

Seconds later, I was reassured that the Princess was safe, despite a few bleached blonde hairs out of place and a pallor that matched that of the porcelain figures on her window ledge.

"What happened, Sharon?" I asked, noting the newly formed crater almost a foot in diameter in the wall plaster, just about the size of a behemoth's fist.

"I'm not sure," she said, frantically rearranging her stray hairs. "As I was writing out his prescription, I asked him how he felt Valium helped him. And the next thing I knew, there was a loud crash, then he grabbed the prescription out of my hand and ran out of the office."

Joke: What sort of medication do you prescribe for Gerald Groueff when he's feeling agitated and paranoid and homicidal? Anything he wants!

That's the most popular of the Groueff jokes, more so than its infinite variations, such as: "What appointment time do you give Gerald Groueff?" and "How long do you spend with Gerald Groueff?" The punch line always makes it clear that what Groueff wants, he gets. Of course, the jokes do serve a purpose in addition to tension relief; they remind us not to let things get too much out of hand. Once, the front desk made the mistake of routing Groueff into Dr. Feliciano's office. Now, Iderlina usually flatly refuses to see adult patients, but when we're really busy, our child psychiatrist consents to handling routine medication renewals and by "routine" I mean she just goes through the motions of writing prescriptions for the same medication the patient has been taking for months. Well, Dr. Feliciano would just about be a mouthful for the jolly-seeking black giant, and having quickly sized up his pea-sized opponent, Groueff began dictating a list of his pharmaceutical needs such as a junkie would present to the genie of the lamp. It was like Christmas in April as Groueff hastened with seven-league strides to the hospital pharmacy with visions of Tuinal, Dexedrine, Quaalude, and Miltown dancing through his head. Fortunately, the pharmacist couldn't believe that anyone other than Groueff himself would have written up such a combination of mind-benders and called the clinic to verify our therapeutic intentions. Vince took the call, vetoed the prescriptions, and made Groueff return for a more modest dole.

Firmness had some effect in controlling him, which is why the headstrong Princess fared as well, if not better, than the more muscular male medics. I couldn't understand how it worked, but then I never could understand how a cageful of lions allow themselves to be controlled by one man, less than half the weight of any of them, wielding a whip and a chair. Groueff was *dangerous,* not one of those biteless barkers, and he was even stronger than he looked. He had picked up the front desk, complete with several office machines, one day when a secretary had dared to question him about his lost Medicaid card.

Groueff had come to St. Dymphna's following a six-year hitch in an upstate hospital for the criminally insane. He didn't land there on some flimsy premise of "potential danger to others," either—Groueff gained admittance through the ax murder of his wife. He must have had a Legal Aid lawyer as sharp as the murder weapon to have gotten off so easily.

Even a traditionalist like Dr. Bellino, staunch proponent of home life and family, had to agree that the Groueff code of law didn't give honest weight to the late Mrs. Groueff in the scales of justice, but it was too late to declare a mistrial. It hadn't even been clearly established that the infidelity of the deceased was anything more than one of Gerald's paranoid delusions. Knowing how macho and mad he was now, it's reasonable to suspect that his wife might have lost her head over an innocent hello to the counterman at the local deli. Even before the murder, Groueff had been admitted to psychiatric hospitals. He had been at a county hospital for a ten-day observation period following a barroom altercation in which he broke every bottle he hadn't already emptied, as well as assorted bones belonging to three patrons, who were hospitalized for nonpsychiatric reasons. He also had spent a restful summer at Coven Glen State Hospital following a questionable suicide attempt. The admission summary reported that Groueff had climbed to the top of a nearby bridge and threatened to jump. After being coaxed down by the police, he had been hustled off to Coven Glen. One of our regular pillheads, who breaks ampules with Groueff on occasion, once told his therapist how Groueff had boasted that the bridge night had been staged exclusively for the purpose of obtaining a nice vacation. With its sloping green hills, indoor-outdoor swimming pools, private and semiprivate clean, modern accommodations, and very liberal pass privileges, Coven Glen offered a resort experience otherwise beyond the reach of an indigent crazy. I believed the story, since there was no other adequate explanation of why Groueff would have traveled miles outside the city to spend his final minutes on a bridge that happened to be within the catchment area of the country club of the state hospital system.

That was the extent of his early psychiatric treatment: ten days in a county hospital and three months in a state spa. His criminal record was much lengthier—over thirty arrests in all, starting at the age of thirteen, for crimes ranging from purse snatching to armed robbery. Killing his wife had been his first murder charge, though, and his Legal Aid lawyer, fresh out of law school and probably eager to start a career as a successful criminal attorney, had gotten maximum mileage out of Groueff's brief contact with the mental health system and diverted his client to the hospital for the criminally insane.

A requisite for his early release had been regular attendance, upon discharge, at a mental health clinic. Thus, he had come to the clinic without prior warning late one Friday, a tattered referral slip from his parole officer in hand. Groueff said he had to bring the officer proof by Monday at nine that he had been registered at a legitimate out-patient clinic. We usually closed intake at 3 P.M., especially on Fridays, but for Gerald Groueff we made a notable exception. When he slammed his fist down on the reception desk, breaking Dolores's flower vase and spewing water and daisies all over the appointment book, we decided that there was need for an emergency intake. And the lucky Princess, who was just on the way out to her beautician, got to do the initial evaluation. What was her diagnosis of Gerald Groueff? As I recall, "(?) Chronic undifferentiated schizophrenic, rule out antisocial personality, rule out alcoholism," and so on down the page. What's his diagnosis now? All together—"whatever Groueff wants!"

We had tried to keep Groueff on the nonaddictive, nonhabituating antipsychotic drugs, even though he wasn't showing evidence of any delusions, but predictably, he rejected one after another with progressive vehemence, damning their ineffectiveness and claiming his imminent death from their side effects. Finally, he brought his two "sisters" to plead his case. Even with their low-cut tops and skin-tight pants suggestive of a nocturnal occupation, they might have been more convincing if better color-coordinated to Gerald, whose skin was as black as a headline. One bronze-skinned sister spoke more Spanish than English and the other, though a tad swarthy, was a more convincing blonde than the Princess; but they swore they had devoted their entire lives to caring for little Gerald and had made the astute clinical observation that the only pill that helped soothe his poor, frayed nerves was that little blue one marked ROCHE 10. Touched by this loving demonstration of family solidarity, Vince rationalized that any medication that made

Groueff a little calmer or even less discontented was better than nothing, and Groueff got his wish, leaving with the two women who had shared so much of his life and were about to share his good fortune.

The Valium Compromise marked the start of a brief era of détente with Groueff, an uneasy armistice under whose unwritten terms he came to the clinic once every two weeks, was ushered into a doctor's office as quickly as possible, and spent as much time as it took to write and sign a three-line prescription. Perhaps Sharon had unwittingly committed a breach of the truce when she asked a question that subtly cast doubt on his need for the drug, but we were wrong to let Groueff get away with his display of force.

"Enough of Groueff," I had proclaimed, marching into Bellino's office. "He just knocked a hole in the plaster in the Princess's office and scared the wits out of her, a commodity not that easy to scare up in her case. I'm sure she'll recover quickly enough, with the assistance of her analyst and her hairdresser, but the way administration maintains this place, that hole will still be there when this building is torn down, which may be during Groueff's next clinic visit as things are going. I wish there was some way we could get rid of him for good."

"Strychnine isn't on formulary," Vince said disconsolately.

"I am merely suggesting a referral to a facility with services more specialized to meet his unique psychosocial needs."

"Columbia is going to have a hell of a time reprogramming you as a psychologist," Vince warned. "You can take the girl out of social work, but can you? . . ."

"Wait, I think I have it," I cried, pointing at an entry in the chart. "Groueff's address is Forty-seven Oh-nine East Ninety-eighth Street."

"What are you going to do, send a hit man to make a home visit?"

"Don't you even know our catchment area by now?" I scolded. "We only extend to East Ninety-sixth Street. You know we're not supposed to accept anyone who lives on the wrong side of the street, much less two blocks away. What will the Department of Mental Health say if they audit us and find this chart?"

"Oh, Pat," he said, "do you honestly think they care? They use those catchment areas to coerce us into accepting patients, not to prohibit us from picking up additional problems. It's our damn commitment to a catchment area that forces us to pick up a loser like Groueff, who frightens away three Medicaid dollars for every one he brings in."

"It would serve you right if the supreme director of the Medicaid program, who I understand is a bright young computer in Albany, rejects your claims for Groueff because of catchment-area violations and tacks on financial penalties just to be spiteful, which they are now programming computers to be. You know how important Medicaid is in meeting the financial needs of this clinic." Not to mention your fat pay check, which I would not mention for the sake of keeping my wave-making within the limits of tidal. "Yes, that's the answer. I'll have a little chat with Mr. Groueff the next time he happens to visit the clinic."

"*You?*" Vince said in disbelief. "The peaceful pacifist of the Pacific Coast Conference, the purge of the Pentagon, protestor of police action and policies short of total appeasement? *You* are going to take on Groueff and essentially throw him out of the clinic? You might as well try to throw a bull elephant out of Nairobi National Park."

"Leave it to me," I said with more bravado than bravery, not willing to admit to Vince that Gerald did make me the tiniest bit anxious.

"Gladly," he agreed.

I had anticipated having two full weeks to screw my courage to the sticking place, but Groueff fouled things up by showing up a week early, in his state of God-like wrath. I think my unemotional command that he wait for me to speak with him—an act I performed more in a state of numb shock than cool courage— momentarily confused him into placid compliance, although there were more arduous ways to have to pass the time than by ogling Dolores's tits, all the more prominent today in her clingy T-shirt. He seemed almost reluctant to leave his vantage point when I returned to the waiting room after having taken the precaution of removing from the top of my desk and hiding as many fragile objects as possible, lamenting that there was not much I could do about the windows or my jaw.

Striding boldly to where he was sitting, I pronounced, "I would like to see you first today, Mr. Groueff."

Meekly, he followed me into my office. See, Pat, I guess the trick to intimidating someone is to act authoritatively and unexpectedly. I wonder what his fantasy is. Maybe he's being so agreeable because he thinks he's been selected for a special study to test a new drug guaranteed to provide more satisfaction than Valium. Well, I was sure his calmness was not going to last for long. About ten seconds, to be exact, I estimated.

"You're a little early for your appointment," I noted as he wedged his hulking frame into a chair.

"Yeah, I got mugged and they took my medicine," he growled. "See?" He raised the short sleeve of his shirt to display a scratch on his upper arm to prove his story. "Took everything," he pouted. "My identification, my parole card—even my Medicaid card." He had probably sold the latter to some sucker, passing it off as a ticket to an ongoing supply of free drugs—which perhaps it was.

"Mr. Groueff, where do you live?" I asked pleasantly.

"I told you, they stole my identification," he answered, suspecting a trap.

"You don't have to prove your address, just tell me it," I explained.

"Forty-seven Oh-nine East Ninety-eighth," he obliged reluctantly. "What's it to you?"

I wasn't very happy to hear him fall into his customary tone and form of personal address, but I had realized his civility could not possibly last, and now that he was acting like his old self, I knew better what to expect.

"Unfortunately, our catchment area does not cover that address. You should be going to Overland Hospital, and I can arrange to have all your records transferred there," I enunciated quickly.

"What?" he said, bolting upright in his chair with a stunned expression. "What? Ketchup area?"

It seemed that I had lost Groueff, limited as he was in verbal skills, back at the third word.

"Catchment area refers to the area which we are mandated by the city and state to serve," I rattled. "We are not allowed to take patients from outside that area."

Gerald's fist worked more quickly than his brain and, though I had vaguely anticipated it, I barely saw the blur as he swung his fist at the wall. Wow, I wonder if the Office for Vocational Rehabilitation handled prizefighters. Maybe Muhammad Ali could float like a butterfly and sting like a bee, but could a bee go fifteen rounds with a rhinoceros? I looked to the side of me and saw a big hole right through my Fritz Perls poster, which formerly read, "I do my thing, you do yours . . ." I hadn't intended that sentiment to include doing it in *my* office, of course. Groueff pulled back his fist again and looked at my jaw the way he had been looking at Dolores's chest. I had to admit that this guy was beginning to make me nervous.

"You better not," I said, looking Groueff straight in the eye with an air of authority I did not feel. To this day, I don't know what made him waver. Was it the thought of spending the rest of the summer in jail or, more likely, that his Valium supply might be cut off for all time? Whatever, Groueff reconsidered and lowered his fist.

"We'll try to make the transition as easy as possible," I resumed as though I had edited from existence the last half minute of action the way you can with a film. "In fact, I'll call Overland Hospital now and see if I can set up an appointment for you. Let me look up the number in the Red Book." I pulled out the *Directory of Social Agencies*, unfortunately ten years old, as more recent vintages had been ripped off. I dialed 871-7678.

"The number you have dialed is out of service. Please check your number and redial," the telephone operator recited. I checked and redialed. "The number you have dialed is out of service. Please check your number and redial," the operator repeated.

Okay, I give up. I was not about to spend eternity this way. I called Information and got the new number, 873-0879.

"Overland Mental Health Clinic is open from nine A.M. to nine P.M., Monday through Friday. We are located on Fifty-six Oak Street. No appointment is necessary. If further information is desired, call eight-seven-one one-nine-eight-seven. This is a recorded announcement."

I had surmised as much. Only catatonic schizophrenics and

people talking into recording machines ever speak that way. I dialed 871-1987, since I wanted to find out when Groueff could be seen and also to give the intake worker some information about their new patient. "The number you have dialed has been changed, but at the request of the customer, it is unlisted. There will be no charge for this call."

My, that's a good way to keep your patient census under control in a mental health clinic—get an unlisted phone number. Keep the address a secret as well and you'll have no trouble at all in managing your case load. But how was I going to manage Gerald, who sat glowering at me across the desk?

"Well," I said briskly, "I can give you the name and address of your new clinic, and also a letter of introduction." *(This is to introduce Gerald Groueff, whose presence speaks for himself and who, therefore, needs no introduction.)*

Groueff looked ready for round two.

In a frantic attempt to placate him, I said, "Since I don't know how long it will be before you'll be seen at the new clinic, I'll have one of the doctors give you a substantial supply of Valium to tide you over."

Who will be the lucky one to give Groueff his farewell present? Maybe I should give this honor to our esteemed director himself. I decided I definitely had to refer him to Dr. Bellino, if only to show him how easy it is for a competent therapist to handle the most difficult, belligerent patients. What a nice surprise for Vince!

What a surprise for me when I opened my office door and saw a phalanx consisting of Vince and two security guards, poised and ready to spring into action. The presence of Brian, the security guard, was no real surprise; Connie routinely summoned him whenever Groueff came in. The extra guard was no surprise either, since Brian's limited experience at Danny's Discount had left him ill prepared to cope with ax murderers and quick to request reinforcements. But what had led Vince to join the ranks of these uniformed club wielders, armed with only a Bic pen or two?

"Dr. Bellino, here's Mr. Groueff's chart," I said at the threshold. "Can you see him today on his last visit to our clinic before he transfers to Overland Hospital?"

Instead of taking the chart and heading toward his office, Vince brushed past me and took one of the patients' chairs. He beckoned Groueff to sit beside him, then reached for the chart and pulled a prescription blank from his pocket. "A month's supply okay?" he asked, without hesitating in his writing. Groueff made an indistinct grunt of assent. Taking the prescription, he rose toward the door.

"Mr. Groueff," Vince said, his voice halting the patient's departure, "I want to wish you luck." Vince stared directly at my battered poster and then pointedly at Groueff. "Since you won't ever be coming back here again." Groueff raised his staff like Moses about to part the waters, then left without making further waves.

"Leave everything to you, huh?" Vince sneered, jerking his thumb at my poster and the underlying wall. "If you'd wanted to get rid of that swingers' credo, I would have taken it down with less wear and tear on the plaster."

"What were *you* doing outside the door?" I asked. "Trying to pick up pointers?"

"Hardly. The only thing I expected to be able to pick up were a few of your teeth."

"Don't you think the services of two security guards would have sufficed?" I said with a pleasant smile.

"As clinic director, I'm concerned enough in a case like this to get directly involved," he stated.

"Concerned about what, Vince?" I asked. "Even foolhardy social workers who think they're competent enough to handle aggressive psychotics? I'm surprised you three didn't come bursting in like gangbusters when Groueff punched the wall."

"The guards almost did," he said. "I held them back."

"So as not to spoil Groueff's fun?"

"So as not to spoil yours," he replied. "If you had let out a sound, even a gasp of amazement or a squeal of protest, I would have been in there with them. But you had something to prove and I was out there with the guards to give you every chance to prove it. You got away with it this time, Pat. You proved what you set out to, didn't you?"

"What was that?"

"That you can handle anything this clinic can throw at you. I wish I could come up with one more dragon, but I'm tapped out," he said sadly. "Now it will be much easier for you to move on, won't it?"

By the next week, everything was back to normal, except for the wall plaster, of course. That Wednesday, nearly everyone made it in to our weekly conference, a small miracle, considering how our staff seems to have as many crises as the patients—ranging from broken legs to broken hearts.

Dr. Sharon Schaeffer hadn't made her grand appearance yet; she was probably in the ladies' room putting the final touches on her hair or her nails or her lips before coming in to vie for the Miss Mental Health crown against Frau Krumpel, her lips red with apple-raspberry jam; Chris Pappas in her black patent army boots; and me—though I was too liberated for beauty contests. Nurse Spaghetti, or whatever the hell her name is, was there—probably sitting there since 8:45, right after she signed in. Looking bright and shiny in a new blue suit, she kept glancing expectantly at Bellino, waiting for him to open the meeting. She apparently had not been with us long enough to realize that we begin 9 A.M. meetings at 9:20 and 2 P.M. meetings at 2:15. When Dimitri Niarhos is due to present a case, we usually don't begin them at all.

Nobody seemed to have come bearing a chart, burning to seek peer input on a challenging case, so I decided to bring up Monica and her four teen-age daughters, who were faced with crisis number 546.

"Monica," I explained, "lives with her four daughters, ages eighteen, seventeen, sixteen, and fifteen, and her three grandchildren, ages two, one, and two months. You've heard me speak about this family before. It seems that each time one of the daughters reaches the magical age of sixteen, she becomes pregnant. This precipitates a family crisis. Monica becomes hysterical and assaultive, threatens to kill both daughter and boyfriend, and two out of three previous times has ended up in the hospital for a short vacation. Then, after discharge, she returns home, her daughter has the child, and she takes over the raising of the baby. Well, now her fifteen-year-old daughter, Maureen, is pregnant.

She's younger than the others were—I guess kids are more precocious now than they were even a few years ago. Maureen seems to be brighter than the others; does well in school and, in fact, was even planning to go to college, which really makes her a rarity in this community. Monica is so proud of her, but she doesn't know Maureen's pregnant yet.

"Maureen called me only yesterday and said one of her friends knows about an abortion clinic where they will accept adolescents without telling their parents, and she's planning to go there without her mother's knowledge."

"Then why did she tell *you?*" asked Dave, our psychoanalyst. "She knows you're her mother's therapist. She must have an unconscious need to have her mother find out, and she wants to involve you as a buffer against her mother's anger. I think Maureen is fixated at the separation-individuation state of development and can't really effect a separation from her mother."

"That's probably somewhat true," I said politely, not really wanting to offend Dave this morning by rejecting his undeciphera- ble Freudian jargon, "but I don't think Maureen's all that dis- turbed. I'm sure she's going through the normal adolescent ambivalence about how truly independent she wants to be of her mother. The real reason I think she called me was to find out about the credentials of this abortion clinic. She's too sensible a kid to go to some back-room abortionist."

"What did you tell her?" piped up a voice from an unexpected corner. It was the new nurse, Miss Barbetti, who up until now had never spoken at a conference unless spoken to, preferably by a doctor.

"I told her that I had heard of that particular clinic and that it was supposed to be the best in the city." What I didn't add, either to Maureen or my coworkers, was that one of my best friends had gone there very scared and upset, finding herself three months' pregnant right after her steady live-in lover ran off with another woman. She had found the clinic personnel very supportive as well as very competent. And what impressed me about them wasn't just the service they provided for the working woman who could afford the cost of the abortion, but that they also had a special fund to provide abortions for the poor woman who wasn't Medicaid-eligible or for the fundless adolescent who was too frightened to confide in her mother and use her Medicaid coverage.

"Miss Patterson," Nurse Korvetti asked me very formally, "did you discuss other alternatives with her?"

"No, I didn't," I replied in similarly formal fashion, though not addressing her by name, having forgotten it again. "The patient seemed pretty determined that she wanted an abortion and that she did not want to drop out of school, even for a short time, to have and raise a baby. Besides, Maureen's very aware of how her mother became every time one of the daughters got pregnant. Maureen has too much of a sense of responsibility to throw the family into turmoil and saddle Monica with another child."

"If the child was all *that* responsible, she wouldn't have gotten pregnant," the nurse said caustically.

"I suppose you feel *she* should have borne the responsibility for contraception?" I asked.

"No, I feel a fifteen-year-old shouldn't be having sex at all," she replied coolly.

"Come on!" I retorted impatiently. "We're in the seventies and I'm sure you've heard of the sexual revolution. Teen-agers today have sex. Unwanted pregnancies are often the outcome, usually because of sexual ignorance, repression, and the primitive state of our birth control methods. These are the unfortunate realities of modern life. Given Maureen's situation, since she knows what she wants, she should go ahead and have the abortion without involving her mother. Don't you believe in the importance of self-determination for our clients?"

"Not if they're fifteen-year-old kids who, by your own admission, are sexually ignorant," my adversary said adamantly. "I'm sure you wouldn't advocate giving the vote to ten-year-olds or serving alcohol to toddlers just because they wanted it. Besides, it sounds to me as if your patient has simply accepted the first solution offered to her by one of her little friends; you should at least present her with other options. Why don't you at least let her know that we could make arrangements for her to stay in a home for unwed mothers if things are too tense at home, a residence where the staff will find a sound couple to adopt the child and give it a good home?"

"And what advantage would that offer over a simple termination of pregnancy?" I asked.

Miss Bombetti bit her lip, and for the first time, that even, modulated voice of hers rose and quavered. "You'd avoid killing a baby, that's one small advantage! Since you're into defending the rights of fifteen-year-olds, why not extend your concern for human life to the youngest members of our race?"

The staff sat rigidly in their chairs, in awed silence, fearing—who knows, perhaps even hoping—that the next interchange would catapult us into a clawing, hair-pulling brawl, like a couple of Wild West saloon girls. Bellino, however, listened impassively, showing as much emotion as if he were hearing a debate over the relative merits of butyrophenone medication versus the phenothiazine type.

"Are you equating abortion with murder?" I challenged.

"No, certainly not," she said, with deceptive softness. "Murder is a crime. Abortion is legal, thanks to the ceaseless efforts of a segment of our population who'll defend their pleasure and comfort to the death—of unborn children."

"When you've been in community mental health as long as I have," I responded, "and seen the bad effects of unwanted children, you might change your attitude—women who each year become physically and emotionally sicker, children who are not properly cared for and who grow up to become criminals, psychotics, or a nasty mixture of both."

"And we should solve those unwanted children's problems by destroying them?" the newcomer questioned. "It sounds like the curious rationale of destroying Vietnamese villages to save them from the communists."

"Peace, ladies!" Vince said, smiling like an amused daddy separating a pair of squalling three-year-old girls. "Pat, I agree with Julie that we should explore several options with Maureen before she plunges into one that seems the easiest yet really runs counter to her culture and her family's traditional values."

"I can give you the Right to Life phone number right after the meeting," Nurse Sculletti said helpfully.

Sorry, that would not be a working number. I looked around the room for support, not that my arguments needed any; but trying to take on both Dr. Bellino and his newfound helpmate, yes-woman Nurse Confetti, called for allies. Nurse Jackie seemed lost in some X-rated fantasy. Ramon was underlining some promising stocks. Finally, David cited an article he had read in a recent psychoanalytic journal that contended the depressive consequences of abortion were far less severe than the cumulative cases of postpartum depression. He couldn't resist admonishing, however, "You really must explore your client's unconscious motivation for becoming pregnant."

Try a ruptured rubber on for size, David! I wondered if Maureen's "unconscious motivation" had led her boyfriend to pick the very packet of condoms containing a defective example of man's highest technological achievements in the science of contraception.

In the midst of an awkward silence, as I was trying unsuccessfully to formulate a civil reply to David's suggestion, the Princess made her entrance, waiting on the threshold just long enough to be sure that every eye was on her before taking a vacant seat to my right.

"Sorry I'm late," she gasped breathlessly. She surveyed the group around the table and surmised that her tardiness might have caused her to miss something more exciting than her own grand entrance. "Any new problems?"

I cast a long, rueful look at Bellino and said, "No, Sharon, just the old ones. Same as always."

Someone tactfully started discussing another case, and I made sure I was the first one out the door at ten. I managed to avoid crossing paths with Nurse Barbelli until 12:10 P.M., when she hailed me as I walked past the reception desk where she was filling out a form. "Oh, Pat," she called. "I was just on my way out to lunch, but if you want that Right to Life phone number, I can get it for you. It will only take a minute."

I broke stride just long enough to reply, "It can wait. I have a patient to see now." I nodded my head toward Oley Anderson, one of the three patients sitting in the near-deserted waiting room, most of the staff being out on a twelve-to-one lunch break.

"Pat," she said, halting me once more in my tracks, "I'm sorry about this morning." I turned toward her, and she walked over so that we would not be overheard by Connie and the patients. "I guess things got a little heated. I didn't mean to come off as critical. We all have our own values, but we still have to get along with one another."

"I don't," I said. "I'm leaving here."

"Yes, I've heard. I'm sure a lot of people will be sorry to see you go. I know you've done a lot of work for this clinic."

"Much good has it done me and the clinic!" I exclaimed sardonically. "We've hardly reached an era of harmony and enlightenment. Well, maybe you'll do better with it. You certainly share more of Bellino's ideas and values than I do."

"My ideas and values, I like to think, are my own," she said sharply. "I respect Dr. Bellino and I'll follow his direction, but that's as far as it goes."

"Then it goes too far, in my opinion," I smiled. "What good is it to have your own ideas if you're compelled to follow someone else's? Especially those of a man who surrounds himself with subservient women!"

"We can't *all* be in charge, Pat," she remonstrated.

"No," I conceded, "but I'd like to be one who can. Even if it's just being in charge of my own life. Now, if you'll excuse me, my patient's waiting."

Still preoccupied by my tense encounter with Nurse Scarfoni, I barely looked at Oley as he shambled along behind me. Oley was a big, ruddy, silver-haired man, a fifty-two-year-old lonely drifter who had once worked in the shipyards until industrial lay-offs and, later, his own growing apathy conscripted him into the army of the chronically unemployed. I should have been aware of his heavy breathing and his uneven footsteps during the few steps we took together in the waiting room, but I didn't notice anything was amiss until I turned to face him in my tiny office. Oley's brow and cheeks were glistening with perspiration, his breathing was labored, and he clutched his upper abdomen as he eased himself into a chair.

"Oley, what's wrong?" I asked, alarmed. "Don't you feel well?"

"Just some indigestion, I think," he gasped, choking out the words. "Feel kind of nauseous. Got some heartburn."

I shook my head with concern. "How long have you been feeling this way?"

He stared blankly at me, as if having difficulty comprehending my words. "I . . ." he grunted. Then his head rolled backward, and he slid forward in the chair until his knees struck my desk, preventing his sliding farther.

Immediately, I dialed Vince's extension on the intercom, but got no answer. He was probably out to lunch—and, I feared, so were most of the other doctors. I rushed out into the waiting room and screamed, "Get a doctor, Connie! Anyone!"

Nurse Sofelli was still out at the reception desk talking to Connie. She sprinted across the waiting room and was in my office practically ahead of me. She took one look at poor unconscious Oley, pressed her fingers alongside his Adam's apple, and said, "Pat, this man's got no pulse. He's not breathing."

"You mean he's . . . dead?" I said numbly.

"Come on," she ordered, shoving his chair backward away from the desk and grasping him by the shoulders. "Help me get him on the floor!"

"There's not much room in here," I said, grasping his arm on one side and easing his body down to the floor with a thud.

"I know," she said grimly. "Pull him out into the waiting room."

I swung the office door open, and before I could reposition myself to help, Julie had both her arms under Oley's armpits and was dragging him out. We pulled him just far enough so that his feet cleared the threshold of my office. Julie dropped to her knees alongside his body, shouting, "Open his shirt," then slid one hand under his neck and tilted his head back by pressing on his forehead with her free hand. As I unbuttoned Oley's lightweight summer shirt, exposing his white cotton undershirt beneath, his chest heaved upward. I jumped back in surprise, then became aware that Julie had her mouth pressed tightly around his and, pinching his nostrils shut as she did so, was blowing air into his lungs. After four quick breaths, she slid her right hand against his neck to check for a pulse.

"Call nine-one-one—ask for a coronary unit," she commanded, then shifted her hands to his chest, placing one hand over the other, and began pressing rhythmically on the base of his breastbone.

I placed the call at the reception desk, watching Julie, in her kneeling position, stop her pumping movements just long enough to blow two quick breaths into Oley's lungs. Then, she returned to her pumping, throwing the full weight of her tiny body against her outstretched arms with each thrust, counting aloud as she bobbed up and down, ". . . nine and ten and 'leven and . . ." I was still giving information on the phone when Bellino charged into the waiting room, Connie at his heels. He knelt down on the other side of Oley as Connie herded the two stunned patients remaining in the waiting room out into the corridor.

When I got back to my patient, Vince had taken over the chest pumping, while his nurse had assumed a permanent station at Oley's mouth for delivering respiration. I noted how jerky and hesitant Vince's thrusts were compared to the young woman's rhythmical technique. "I'll breathe every five thrusts," she said, interrupting herself to blow once more into Oley's mouth. "Pump once per second." Another breath. "Count aloud, 'One one-thousand, two one-thousand . . .'" Another breath. "It will help me keep track."

I realized she was subtly coaching Vince, wording her directions as if asking him to help her. Using her counting technique, he slowed his movements into a more regular, even pattern.

Dr. Niarhos and Nurse Jackie appeared over Vince's shoulder. I could see Nunzio Scaglione, Chris Pappas, and a few of the other nonmedical therapists huddled anxiously near the reception desk, and I felt I ought to join them, being totally superfluous and possibly obtrusive where I was. "Dimitri, get on the other side and see if you can detect a pulse coming through," Vince said, interrupting his counting, but not the thrusts. "Jackie, find the emergency box."

Nurse Jackie, dressed today in a pair of fringed buckskin-colored jeans, a beaded vest, and a white headband, loped away like Princess Running Deer. Dimitri fumbled with Oley's wrist, then said excitedly, "You're getting through, Vince! I can feel a pulse when you thrust."

"Good airway, too," Vince noted as Oley's chest heaved under Julie's efforts.

"One one-thousand!" Julie reminded Vince sternly as his chest compression became haphazard.

Obediently, Vince resumed his counting: "One one-thousand, two one-thousand . . ." while his kneeling partner hovered over the patient like the White Rock girl bending over her pool.

"Tired? Want to switch, Doctor?" she called between breaths.

"I'm . . . fine . . . you . . . breathe . . . him," Vince replied, uttering one syllable per thrust.

Nurse Jackie returned with the metal emergency box, which she dropped beside Vince with a loud clang. "Draw some epinephrine," Julie ordered before dropping her head again. Then, she lifted it to add, "Five cc's one-to-ten thousand." Breath. "Long needle." Breath. "Just in case."

"Where's the ambulance?" Vince grumbled. His efforts were becoming less spirited. Julie blew a strong breath into Oley's lungs, dropped the patient's head, and crossed behind Vince to kneel beside him. Nudging his hands off the patient's chest, she said softly, "Switch, Doctor . . . three one-thousand, four one-thousand . . . five—*breathe*."

Vince hesitantly blew into Oley's mouth. "Pinch the nostrils!" Julie reminded him. Vince blew again as she compressed the chest. "Hyperextend the neck a bit more," she coached.

When Vince seemed to be reasonably synchronized with Julie, I said timidly, "I asked for a coronary unit."

"Good, we'll need it," Vince said rapidly, to be ready to give the next breath. After breathing, he called down to Julie, "Switch again?"

"Change . . . on . . . three . . . next . . . time . . ." she said, her voice flat and cadenced like that of a robot. "One one-thousand . . ."

Vince exhaled, moved to kneel beside her, and picked up the compression maneuver on the fourth count, giving Julie time to get back to Oley's head by the count of five, in position for a breath. They did it with the precision of a pair of circus aerialists switching trapezes in mid-air.

"Here, let me do some, Julie" Dimitri volunteered.

"Leave her alone!" Vince snapped, still pumping. "Here, take the chest if you think you can, but let Julie go as long as she can."

"I'm fine, Doctor," Julie affirmed.

As Vince stood up, two policemen rushed in. "Thank God!" Vince exclaimed. "Is the ambulance here with you?"

"Yeah, they'll be right up, Doc," one cop said.

"Coronary unit?" Vince attempted to confirm.

The cop stared blankly. "No. They didn't have one available. It's a regular bus. They got oxygen, though."

"Oh, shit!" Vince exclaimed as two attendants came in armed with a leather bag but no oxygen tank. "We can't transport this man like this. He'll die en route . . . if he's not already dead."

"Hold it, Doctor!" Julie called to Dimitri. She felt Oley's neck. "No pulse. Resume compressions."

"You guys don't have a defibrillator aboard, I suppose?" Vince asked the attendants.

They shook their heads sheepishly. "We can call for the coronary unit," one suggested. "May take some time, though."

"Switch, Doctor," Julie was saying to Dimitri.

"I'm fine," he gasped, pumping away.

"Change on three next time!" she commanded. The switch was made, though far less smoothly than she had effected it with Vince. Now, Julie was back on the chest, counting as she pumped till her body fell into the rhythm as smoothly and effortlessly as her own heart was beating. She broke off her counting to say over her shoulder to Vince, "We've got epinephrine drawn up."

"Uh . . . how are we going to inject it?" he asked timidly.

"Intracardiac. It's the only way," she said calmly.

"Keep breathing, Doctor!" she reminded Dimitri, who had gotten so absorbed in the conversation that he lost track of what he was doing. "Dr. Bellino, this man still has no spontaneous pulse or respiration. It may already be too late."

Vince took a deep breath. "Jackie, stand by with that syringe and a swab—iodine if you've got it." He knelt beside Julie, who removed her hands from Oley's chest long enough for Vince to lift his undershirt up under his neck, then continued her rhythmic compressions. Vince swabbed the area over Oley's left nipple without interrupting Julie's maneuvers, then took the syringe. "Keep breathing, Doctor!" Julie shouted at Dimitri. "Hyperextend!"

I watched with incredulous fascination as Vince plunged the needle right into Oley's chest, driving it in as far as it would go. He expelled the contents of the syringe, then abruptly withdrew the needle. The little nurse did not change her rhythm but appeared to be thrusting with new energy, driving Oley's heart down toward his spine. After about fifteen compressions, she suddenly stopped and placed her hand up on Oley's throat. Her grimly set lips parted in an exuberant smile. "He's got a pulse! Feel it, Doctor!"

Vince reached over to confirm it. "Yes. Rapid and weak, but it's there."

"Want me to continue ventilating?" Dimitri asked.

"Wait a second," Vince advised. Oley's chest heaved on its own. "Spontaneous respirations! Leave him alone."

"Should we continue with the heart compressions, to strengthen the beat?" Dimitri asked Vince.

"No," Julie answered. "You'd interfere with the existing rhythm." She had Oley's wrist in her hand. "Peripheral pulse is palpable. If he can maintain his present rate, he can be transported."

"Can we take him now, Doc?" the ambulance attendant asked Vince. Vince nodded. "Want to come with us, Doc?" the man asked hopefully.

"Of course," Vince agreed. The attendants, assisted by Vince and Dimitri, lifted Oley onto a wheeled stretcher and headed out the waiting room door.

"Doctor, should I . . ." Julie started to say, then checked herself. "Good luck!"

"Nice job, Julie," Vince said with a wave.

She had been about to ask to go with them, then realized her place. She was just a nurse, of no special value, especially when they had a doctor in their midst.

"You saved his life," I said to her, very matter-of-factly.

"He's not out of the woods yet, Pat," she said, staring at the door they had exited. "But if he survives, it was a team effort that saved him."

"Bullshit!" I snapped.

This unexpected outburst caused her to turn her face toward me for the first time, her eyes widened in alarm. She looked at me quizzically but did not speak.

"I witnessed the whole thing, start to finish," I reminded her. "You were the only one who knew what you were doing. You were *telling* Bellino what to do, and most of the time, he probably wasn't even aware of it. Without you, Oley would have been dead."

She smiled understandingly but shook her head. "I took special training in cardiopulmonary resuscitation at my last job. As a head nurse, I felt I owed it to my patients there. The psychiatrists here have all been out of touch with these techniques for years—new ones have even been added since they finished their medical training. I just was fortunate enough to have had something to contribute this afternoon. Listen, do you want to notify your patient's family?"

"Oley's got no family," I explained. "I guess there's nothing at all a social worker can contribute today."

"You did your bit, too," she said. "I'm going to get a cup of coffee. Want one?"

"No thanks," I declined. "My nervous system's had enough stimulation for today."

I went into my office and looked at the chair where Oley had "died" that afternoon. It dawned on me that if Oley managed to survive, he would never realize who it was that saved him. I promised myself that I would tell him and give full credit where it was due—to Julie . . . oh hell, maybe by then I'll be able to get her name straight.

# 7

P AT WAS WAITING AT THE ENTRANCE TO THE WAITING ROOM, obviously determined to be the first to reach me at this start of a new week. "Vince, we had a suicide this weekend," she said in almost a whisper.

I came to a halt, my brain automatically flipping through my own case files for a likely victim even as I was asking, "One of my patients?"

"No," she said. She didn't look at all relieved to be able to give me even that much consolation, though, rather selfishly, my spirits rallied with a tremendous bound. When a clinic saw more than seven hundred individuals a month, many of them inadequately treated psychotics released prematurely by the state hospitals, suicides were an unpleasant but inevitable part of the business.

"Okay, Pat, get your coffee and come into my office and fill me in," I said briskly. She followed timidly, without coffee, and stood like a graveside mourner before my desk. "Well?" I asked.

"Vince, it was Stacy Cunningham," she said hoarsely.

I felt as though I had just taken a sucker punch in the belly. If she had told me it was one of the patients I had personally seen in hourly sessions once a week for months, I don't think I would have felt as stunned. "How?" I asked. "When did you find out?"

"Just a minute ago," she reported. "Nunzio Scaglione got a call from her father after midnight. I . . . . thought I should be the one to tell you."

"Thanks," I said, brushing past her to get out of there, practically trotting through the waiting room and down the corridor to Dr. Scaglione's office. I flung open his door, slammed it behind me, and looked at him angrily. He looked up at me sadly, as though he was expecting me and had composed himself with precisely the right expression. "Hello, Vincenzo," he murmured.

"What happened?" I said, forcing my words through clenched teeth.

He sighed and let his hands flutter aimlessly in the air for a few seconds before plopping them on the desk in disgust. "Her father found her dead when he got home late last night."

"Where had he been? How long was he away?" I shot, barking questions like a movie detective grilling a suspect.

"He and his wife had gone away for the weekend. To a resort. New England, or maybe the Poconos . . ."

"For a *weekend*?" I screamed. "They left Stacy all alone for a weekend? How could they? Didn't you warn them . . ."

"Vince," he said, raising his own voice, "I had no idea they were planning such a thing. How was I to know? Her poor father is beside himself with guilt. He told me she had bee so much better at home, cheerful, apparently normal. He and his wife had even discussed their trip with her, asked her if it was okay . . ."

"But didn't *you* know?" I interrupted. "Didn't you know how terrified she was of being alone, how she still had psychotic symptoms even though she was improving? You were her *therapist*, for God's sake!"

"Will you please be rational!" he protested. "What I didn't know was that the family had any thought of leaving her alone."

"There should have been enough contact with the family for them to have felt obliged to discuss *all* their plans with you," I said.

"Her father could have called me," Nunzio agreed. "But he was caught between two women. His wife had been bitching all summer about how Stacy had ruined all their vacation plans by getting sick. He probably had tried to soothe her by promising to go away with her for a weekend as soon as Stacy's condition permitted. Sure, I would have vetoed the weekend, so naturally he wouldn't call me."

"Do you know what pills Stacy was on?" I queried uselessly.

"Did she take an overdose? Did Krumpel give her more than a week's supply?"

"No, not pills," he said glumly. "Ant buttons."

"What?" I said incredulously.

"Insect poison. That's how she killed herself."

"Oh, God!" I moaned. "Did she have your telephone number?"

He looked anxious for the first time. "*My* telephone number? I don't know. I'm sure she could have reached me if she wanted to."

"Did she know what borough you live in? Is your telephone number even listed?" I pressed.

"Oh shit, Vince," he exploded, "she could have called the emergency room! They would have gotten to me. That's how her father reached me last night."

"She could have, but she obviously didn't!" I pointed out. "If you had given her your home number, made her feel welcome to reach out to you, even if you weren't drawing pay for those ten minutes, maybe it would have been different!"

"Look, I'm upset about it, too," he said angrily. "I was her therapist, after all. But you're overreacting. These things are bound to happen sometimes in our field. Look at Irene Blaydow . . ."

"Don't try to compare Stacy with Irene Blaydow," I countered. "Irene wouldn't accept treatment, wouldn't take medication. Stacy Cunningham cooperated with us all the way. She took whatever we prescribed. She came for all her appointments. Hell, she spent every minute she possibly could up here, because she placed all her hope and confidence in us. Christ, if we can't help a patient like that, who *can* we help?"

"It's not fair for you to blame her death on me," he grumbled. "I wasn't the only one treating her."

"I know," I said bitterly. "Stacy was a patient of the St. Dymphna Mental Health Clinic. A patient of Nunzio Scaglione and Ilse Krumpel and Evelyn Larsen and Patricia Patterson and Connie Rodriguez and Vincent Bellino, medical director. She had the entire resources of this clinic behind her—and in the final analysis, that wasn't enough."

I returned to my office through the waiting room with my head down, not wanting to see those rows of chairs without that blossoming golden-haired kid somewhere among them. How can anyone realistically expect the world to limit its crises to the hours of 9 A.M. through 5 P.M., weekdays only? I sat behind my cluttered desk, not really feeling like doing anything yet looking for something to do, when Connie buzzed me on the intercom and said ominously, "Vince, you'd better go to Rosie's office right away. There's big trouble there." As everywhere today.

I approached Rosie's office, just off the waiting room, where she collected fees and, in between making change for the paying customers, wrote statistical reports and kept tabs on everyone's attendance, punctuality, and personal business. From several yards away, I could hear an angry voice raving, "If you don't eject her immediately, I'll have you fired. You're as incompetent as everyone else in this clinic, from this ugly busybody to that flea-brained director." If we hadn't just been audited, I would have sworn we were being reviewed by the state Department of Mental Health.

The source of the critique was Diego Martinez. The object of his immediate ire was Brian, the security guard. Diego stood between the guard and Rosie's desk, which was shielding not only our senior secretary, but her mother, the popular and genial Ethel McGonigle. Harry Chong and Pat were standing just outside the open door, looking very indecisive. I strode past Chong and Pat and didn't even have to ask what was going on, since everyone seemed determined to inform me at the same time.

"Dr. Bellino, it's against clinic policy what this man's asking . . ." Rosie protested between sobs.

"Listen, I don't care who this man is, he can't abuse my daughter that way . . ." Mrs. McGonigle said indignantly.

"I have given this man a direct order to eject this woman, who has no authority to be in this office, and he has refused, and therefore, I want him fired for insubordination . . ." Diego orated, pointing a finger at Brian.

"I ain't going to throw no old ladies bodily out of the clinic just on his say-so! I got a union, you know . . ." Brian was rebutting.

"One at a time!" I said sharply. The group fell into silence, even

Diego with his three-day beard growth, mustard-spotted necktie, and unmatched shoes. "Rosie, what's going on here?"

Dabbing at her eyes with a tissue, Rosie bravely thrust out her chin and whimpered, "Dr. Martinez came to me this morning with this stack of charts." She indicated a neat pile of about ten charts on her desk. "He ordered me to Xerox up each one in its entirety so he could keep it on file at home. Now, first of all, I'm far too busy to take up all that time doing such a thing. But most of all, he's not supposed to take patients' records, even copies, out of this clinic. That's a violation of confidentiality."

"I am a very busy man!" Diego interrupted haughtily. "I have too much to do during the hours I spend here. Some of my patients need more time than I can give them here. I will see them at my home, if need be. Then, I must write up their cases for presentation at the International Congress for Psychoanalysis. Experts from throughout the world are coming there to hear me speak."

"You should have heard what he said to Rosie!" Ethel gasped. "My goodness, he called her an imbecile and a pig, and then a lot of other names *I* would never repeat. And when I told him to stop, he turned on *me* and called this policeman here! But if anyone lays a hand on me, I'll go to court. I *will*."

"Dr. Bellino," Diego said sternly, "this old woman is neither a staff member nor a patient and has no authority to be in a clinic area designated specifically for the implementation of patient care. She is a criminal trespasser and you, as director, are obliged to have her physically removed from the premises. If you are incapable of or unwilling to perform your duty, I, as seniormost staff psychiatrist, must, in this emergency situation, relieve you of command and take on myself the duties and obligations of medical director until such time as the medical board of St. Dymphna's Hospital . . ."

What the hell was this, a summer-stock production of *The Caine Mutiny?* Impatiently, I snapped, "Diego, go to your office and stay there. I'll be there in a few minutes to talk to you."

Chong leaned over my shoulder and whispered in my ear, "You want me to get a syringe of Prolixin?"

"I'm not going to work under these conditions," Diego said huffily. "You may expect my resignation shortly. I will meet my obligations to my patients at home." With that, he opened the large leather briefcase he was carrying and began to stuff the patients' charts into it.

Rosie let out a howl such as she had been able to restrain under more minor stresses, such as being called obscene names and having her mother threatened with physical force. "Oh God, stop him! He's taking clinic charts! Those are the patients' records!"

Pat, whom I had lost track of, was suddenly at my elbow holding out a scrap of paper. "I took the liberty of calling Diego's home, Vince," she said by word of explanation. I looked at the paper, on which Pat had scrawled, "Wife says Dr. M. has history of manic-depressive illness. Was on lithium. Stopped taking it."

I nodded and beckoned the security guard. "Diego, I'm asking the security guard to take your bag. I can't permit you to take any charts out of the clinic. We'll return the bag and any of your own property in it to you later. If you'll leave the clinic quietly, I want you to go home until we give you clearance to come back. You'll be paid just the same."

"I'm not leaving," he said defiantly. "I've been doing my work competently, seeing patients regularly, writing reports. You yourself recently promised me a raise and a promotion. I'll stand on my record."

Pat sidled up to me and whispered, "*Neuf cent onze?*"

"*Oui, ma'amselle,*" I sighed. "*Tout de suite.*"

Pat went off to call 911, for the police and an ambulance. Diego, just like our patients, submitted meekly to the silent authority of Brian's uniform and handed over his briefcase without a struggle.

"Thank you, Diego," I said with genuine gratitude. "Would you please wait for a few minutes in my office with me? Under the circumstances, I'm having you taken to the emergency room for possible transfer to County Hospital. I'm sorry it has to be this way, but since you won't go home voluntarily, I have no choice."

He nodded agreeably. "Of course, I will have my attorney meet me there and have him institute proceedings to sue you and the administration for this outrage."

"Of course," I concurred. "Shall I have someone bring us some coffee while we're waiting?"

Once Diego had left the clinic, exiting with the dignity of a visiting potentate escorted by honor guards, I called administration with the latest disaster bulletin, warned the chief of emergency services what was on the way, and briefed the hospital's attorney. After squeezing in a few medication patients, I remembered poor Mrs. Martinez and called Diego's wife to introduce myself and invite her to join us in the emergency room. Now it was well past noon, so I figured I might as well have lunch at the main hospital and look in on Diego in the E.R. I asked Connie to cancel my afternoon appointments, fearing I might not get back in time, a fear proved justified. Diego never got shipped out to County Hospital until 3:30 P.M., by which time we almost risked committing his lawyer as well—a noisy, agitated fellow who spoke more rapidly and incoherently than Diego and who kept quoting irrelevant laws, such as our failure to have two psychiatrists sign a commitment form, a step that had to be taken at County Hospital, not in the emergency room, since St. Dymphna's had no psychiatric ward of its own in which to commit Diego.

I resolved that Tuesday would be not only a new day, but the start of a whole new week. Monday never happened, I told myself. Go into the clinic in your old, benevolent, optimistic frame of mind, and things will all work themselves out. Then I entered the waiting room and saw that the opaque windows on two of the office doors, one of them *mine*, had been smashed away. Slowly, I began to survey the rest of the area for damage. Within seconds, I saw that the glass on the big wall clock above the reception desk was cracked, the desk itself had a large dent, as though it had been rammed by a Buick, and the IBM Selectric used to type file cards bore a small sign reading, OUT OF ORDER. DO NOT USE.

"What happened?" I asked Connie, my eyes burning into hers as if she had personally rearranged things with a sledgehammer.

"Carla went berserk yesterday afternoon," she reported.

"A *woman* did all this?" I said skeptically.

Connie shrugged. "Carla Malatesta. Pat's transsexual patient?"

I headed straight for Pat's office without even bothering to make sure my own office had been swept clean so I could see patients. She was sitting at her desk framed by two stacks of charts, on either side of her desk blotter.

"What happened with your patient yesterday?" I asked, not very specifically.

"If you mean Carla," she replied nonchalantly, "she had a paranoid decompensation, and we had her sent to the hospital."

"Not before he wrecked half the clinic," I noted.

"*She*," Pat corrected. "Carla is a complete woman. Not only has she had her surgery, but she's even had her birth certificate changed."

"*She* is a six-foot-two-inch, bearded, baritone-voiced, hairy freak," I objected. "In Freud's time, men who thought they were women were locked up until their delusions cleared. Now, we have doctors joining them in the delusions."

"Vince, I had nothing to do with Carla's sex change," Pat protested. "I started seeing her when she was still Carl and only beginning hormone treatment. Then she dropped out of therapy and didn't come back until after she had found some surgeon to do the procedure."

"What's done is done," I conceded. "Let's talk about yesterday."

"Carla's mother brought her in because she was hearing voices," Pat explained. "You know how crazily symbiotic the two of them are. I think part of Carla's motivation for sex change was the mother's constant harping on how she'd always wished for a little girl."

I grunted in agreement. "Yeah, I remember the time the old lady was running up and down the corridors screaming, 'I've lost my little girl.' And then Carla lumbered out of the ladies' room, where she'd gone without mama's permission."

"Well, I don't know if what's been going on between them caused Carla to start hallucinating again," Pat went on, "but you could tell there was a lot of tension there. After I spoke with Carla, I asked her to wait for Dr. Chong to give her an injection. She and her mother started arguing in the waiting room, so furiously that I asked them to please sit apart. Then, the mother made some crack about Carla being crazy and that she was going to have her locked up. Carla let out a scream. Instead of going for her mother as I feared she would, she picked up the trash can and hurled it through your office window, smashed another window with her fist, then picked up a chair and started battering everything in sight."

"Did anyone try to stop her?" I asked.

"I kept calling to her to calm down, not that it did much good," Pat said. "Connie rang the security guard's extension, but he was apparently off in another part of the building. Dolores was out sick yesterday, so it was just me and Connie. Finally, I ran to find the security guard."

"Just you and Connie?" I said, perplexed. "Where was everyone else? The doctors? The other staff members? Didn't they know what was going on?"

"Are you kidding?" Pat grinned. "With Carla tearing the place apart, it sounded like Genghis Khan was sacking the waiting room. Everybody took cover, hiding in their offices."

"They hid in their offices?" I repeated, thoroughly revolted. I sat in gloomy silence for about thirty seconds, then jumped to my feet. "Okay, that's it! I want an emergency staff meeting at four P.M. Get the word to *everyone*, and I want Rosie, the receptionists, and the security guard there too. If *you* don't have the time, get the assistants to spread the word, but make it clear it's *my* order. For the few, if any, clinicians diligent enough to have scheduled four o'clock patients, have them call the patients to reschedule them, and if the patients don't have phones, get the assistants to make home visits to cancel them. There won't be that many appointments, if I know my staff."

Pat looked at me dubiously. "Vince, we have our regular group supervision meeting at nine tomorrow morning. Can't it wait till then?"

"No, damn it!" I insisted. "This is a special meeting and it needs a special time."

"I still don't see what's so urgent about yesterday's incident that you can't postpone this meeting for seventeen hours, sixteen of which are during nonworking time anyway," she said, shaking her head.

"It's not just the incident," I explained. "It *is* urgent that I do something to stop this clinic from its downhill course into apathy, stagnation, and final deterioration, and if I try to do it at one of our regularly scheduled, ill-attended meetings, the staff will pay no more attention to me than . . . I've been paying to them, I suppose."

"Do I detect some sort of guilt reaction?" Pat asked. "Not that I want to swell your ego, given the inadequate dimensions of my office here, but it seems the staff, with its crises and foibles, takes up more of your time than the patients do."

"Maybe I spend too much time on repairs and not enough on preventive maintenance," I said sadly. "I didn't want this place to be chained down by regulations and tormented by spies and surveillance reports, as Rosie would have it. I wanted, as I think you did, a place where therapists could be treated as mature, responsible human beings."

"Oh, don't be so hard on them—or yourself," Pat cajoled. "They really are damn fine therapists, for the most part."

"They're thirty individuals collecting pay checks here and doing their own thing," I said. "They've got no concept of being part of one unit. The doctors hate the receptionists for bugging them to get down to business, the receptionists hate the mental health assistants for avoiding clerical work, the assistants hate the social workers for sitting on their cans in warm offices while they freeze theirs out in the field, the social workers hate the doctors for their air of superiority. Maybe people do care about patients here, but nobody cares about *the clinic*! I'm not surprised that you and Connie were the only two to stand your ground when Carla started tearing the place apart; you two are just about the only ones who think of this place as a whole. Connie never gets to witness the treatment of a patient, but sitting out front all day, she knows that it's *all* the patients and *all* the staff that count, not just one person's case load for the day. And you, as coordinator, reviewing every case that comes in, in touch with every therapist, you know what this clinic's about. Everybody else has lost sight of it. Carla broke a few windows and dented some equipment, all easy enough to fix. It wasn't in Carla's power to destroy this place completely, but if it were, nobody would have stopped it. Everybody was just defending himself and his own little office."

"Can you really change that, Vince?" she asked.

"I've got to try, Pat," I said. "if I've got to shout and threaten and rub their noses in their stinking complacency, I've got to try."

I secluded myself in my office for the rest of the day, not even leaving for lunch. Dave Goldman stuck his head in my office around noon and said, "It's twelve-oh-five."

"Thank you, David," I replied, "but I have a watch."

"Uh, it's Tuesday," he added.

"Thank you, David, but I also have a calendar."

"Vince, it's time for me to see my *analytic* patient," he said more directly. "I have to use your couch."

"Not today, David. I'm sorry."

"But what's my patient going to do?" he cried desperately.

"Tell her to stand on her own two feet for a change," I advised. "Don't slam the door on your way out." David slammed the door.

A few patients came and went. I took a few phone calls, drafted a few letters, and at 3:58 headed for the conference room.

Pat was already there, along with about six others. She was sitting at the corner of one side of the long rectangular table, and I took the chair beside her. "Aren't you going to sit at the head of the table?" she whispered.

"Seating position doesn't insure leadership," I said. "If I've really got the ability to take charge and turn this clinic around, it wouldn't matter if I sat under the table. Today, hopefully, Ms. Patterson, this seat will be the head of the table."

Two or three more came, among them Julia Scovetti. Julie exchanged the most fleeting of glances with Pat, then sat on the other side of me, Pat being on the left, of course. It was now 4:04, and the seats around the conference table filled up, then the row of chairs against the wall behind them. Still the staff kept coming, looking around in momentary confusion, then setting off to retrieve additional chairs from waiting areas and offices. It had been so long since we had a one hundred percent turnout for anything that I had forgotten how large the staff was.

"Thank you all for coming," I began. "It's been a long while since we've had the opportunity to meet all together like this—which is a little strange, considering how often we schedule staff meetings. I've got some things I'd like to say. Maybe some of you also have things you'd like to say, and I'll give you a chance to say them later.

"What's bothering me most is what happened in the waiting room yesterday. I'll deal with the particulars in a moment, but first, let me make it clear that I didn't call this meeting just because of that single incident. The staff's indifference to what was happening out at the front desk wasn't an isolated response to a particularly threatening episode—it's a chronic symptom that plagues this clinic every day. It's an every-man-for-himself philosophy that may work fine in the world of private enterprise but is fatal to a team operation like ours. Do you know what I'm talking about? It's scribbling a renewal prescription without asking, 'How are you?' because you've never seen this patient before and may not again. It's failing to write up a psychological test report for a special school placement because the kid is not your regular patient and you'd rather spend your time with your own cases. It's putting off a home visit to a patient because you think his therapist didn't ask you to do it in a nice way.

"And we can't afford to go on this way. We just lost our most hard-working psychiatrist, and I don't know how long we'll have to try to take on his work load. And we're going to lose our clinic coordinator . . . that will be the toughest loss of all to make up for, but we have to try.

"Let's talk about Carla. She lost control and did some damage to the waiting room yesterday. It was fortunate that she didn't harm herself or anyone else. Until the security guard was able to get up there—and there was a delay in finding him—you left Connie and Pat alone to cope with that patient. Carl, Dennis, all of you knew what was happening, but you chose not to get involved."

Dave Goldman cleared his throat. "Vince, I may be out of line in speaking for the others, but frankly, I don't feel physically subduing assaultive psychotic patients is my job."

"Then maybe you should be working in a different type of setting," I said. "Here, your job is taking care of patients. If a patient passes out, your job is to do whatever you can to insure the patient is breathing and comfortable until you can get medical help. If a patient needs help filling out a form and there's no one else around, your job is to fill out that form. And if a patient needs restraint, your job is to restrain him . . . or her, as in Carla's case."

"You've got to draw the line at risking your own neck," Dennis protested. "I don't want to be killed in the line of duty."

I shook my head in frustration. "Dennis, I'm not asking you to disarm someone with a gun or crawl out on a window ledge after a jumper. Carla's big, but she's human. She didn't have any weapons, except maybe a chair. Now, suppose you and Nunzio and Dave and Carl Brock, the old linebacker, surrounded her and converged on her. She'd crumble like a rag doll. How could any human stand up to six hundred or eight hundred pounds coming from several sides at once? Hell, Carl, how often did you play one on one against someone bigger than Carla? Brian, the security guard, was able to hold and handcuff her by himself and he's nowhere near your size."

"I don't suppose any of us thought of it that way, Vince," Carl said. "I mean, I figured if I went out into that waiting room, it would be just me."

"I'm sure that's what everyone thought. As things turned out, Carl, you would have been right, because we're not a team here anymore."

"In our field," Dave said, "we're oriented against violence. All our training, our conditioning, stresses control and logic."

"If by your field you mean psychology or social work, maybe so," I said. "In medicine, it's different. In a hospital, if there's an outburst on the ward, a crash in the emergency room, everyone instinctively runs *toward* it, not away from it. Let someone or something threaten to go out of control and you've got two dozen people converging on that spot."

"The old medical model supremacy!" Sandy said scornfully.

"Maybe so, Sandy," I retorted. "I don't pretend that I know more about psychoanalysis than anybody in this room, and I don't even profess to be the best therapist, but I know that as a physician I had to face up to it all—blood, violence, the limits of insanity, death. There's nobody for the doctor to pass on the responsibility

to. And if turning your back on a patient because she's too violent
or too crazy is the opposite of 'medical model,' I call it gutless. I call
it chickenshit."

"I was out sick yesterday," tiny Julie said, "so I didn't witness the
incident. But I've worked several years in psychiatric hospitals, and
as Dr. Bellino says, there's not much you can't handle if you're all
in it together. As you can see, I'm no physical threat to anyone, but
I've been in my share of situations with agitated patients and I've
never been hurt—nor, fortunately, have any of the patients."

"Hey, Vince," Dennis Boyle exclaimed. "I just got a terrific
insight about why everyone punked out when that big transsexual
went ape. See, if it had been a regular guy, even that Groueff
monster, we probably would have handled him. But what do you
think of when you see a six-foot guy with curly hair in a dress
screaming like a maniac? *Psycho*, right? That picture scared the
hell out of me as a kid, and probably everyone else in this room saw
it!"

"An interesting case for the theory of conditioned responses,"
Nunzio said thoughtfully.

"Don't overlook the Oedipal implications of Tony Perkins's
assuming the role of the murderous mother," Dave said. "He
introjects the bad mother as a result of unresolved oral conflicts . . ."

"Would you stop this theoretical crap!" I shouted. "I want less
talk and more action around here. I want you where it's happening,
so that we don't have two women trying to save what's left of this
ruin we're in."

"Chauvinist," Sandy muttered.

"Not at all," I demurred. "I wasn't exempting the women from
my criticism. If Julie here is willing to throw her petite frame into
the fray, I expect you to contribute your more ample poundage as
well. No sense limiting your physical altercations with psychotics to
your personal love life."

"I suppose we should have handled Pat's patient differently,"
Ilse said remorsefully.

"Not 'Pat's patient'!" I contradicted. "Carla is this clinic's patient.
Pat might be her prime therapist, but that doesn't exempt any one

of you from assisting in the treatment, whatever she might need. We lost a patient this weekend—a young, intelligent, sensitive girl. Not Nunzio's patient or Ilse's patient, but *our* patient, *our* loss. We'll lose others someday, I'm sure, but we'll cut those losses if we stop thinking of patients as belonging to the other guy. Any questions, about anything at all?"

"How is Dr. Martinez?" Rosie asked. "Is he in the hospital?"

I pursed my lips in dismay and shook my head. "I learned from administration today that the county hospital released him right after he got there."

"Oh, Vince," Rosie moaned, "couldn't the psychiatrists there tell he was sick?"

"Of course they could," I assured her. "But he's still got a lawsuit hanging against them from the last time his wife slapped him in there, and when he showed up with that wacky lawyer, the administration said the hell with him, it wasn't worth the hassle. So, he's out and suing everyone in sight."

"Don't you worry, Vince," Harry Chong beamed. "He no can sue *you*. We got Good Samaritan law now. You Good Samaritan!"

I smiled condescendingly. "Harry, I don't think carting someone off to a mental hospital against his will is quite the same as giving emergency aid at the scene of an accident or trying to pull someone through a life-threatening medical emergency. But I'm not worried, even if he does try to contend he was sane all along."

"He did make one or two valid points in his criticism of the clinic yesterday," Pat said smugly.

"They were duly noted, I assure you," I bowed in her direction. "Now, since we're trying to tidy up our house, is Lynn Rossman still under the rug where you swept her, or have you tried to find her a decent placement, away from her lewd and immoral mother?"

"Don't you remember?" Pat begged off. "We weren't going to do anything drastic until we'd seen about Gregg's crisis."

"Ah yes, the little match-boy," I recalled. "Dr. Feliciano had referred him for in-patient hospitalization. Is he safely tucked into a bed on a county ward, Iderlina, preferably one with a fireproof, waterproof mattress?"

"Ah, hospital say they not think he need to be in-patient," she reported. "They gonna see whole family there in intensive, short-term, crisis-oriented family therapy."

"They're going to what?" I exploded. "What the hell have we been doing here all this time? Crap, we may not have in-patient beds, but we can do everything else."

"What makes them think they're so special?" Sandy joined in. "Just because they've got a bigger budget than us?"

"We can do family therapy here as well as anybody!" Nurse Jackie said indignantly.

"Better!" Carl Brock said. "Because we can really work as a team."

"We have good, open communication," Chris said.

"Yeah," said Nunzio. "Dennis, get Pearl Rossman on the phone and tell her to get her ass back over here, and those two little bastards of hers as well. She'll get all the treatment she needs right here."

"Right!" Dennis agreed. "She's got the best damn mental health clinic in the city here and doesn't even appreciate it."

"She will pretty soon, I think now," Harry Chong chuckled, puffing his pipe contentedly. "Lotta people gonna appreciate lotta more now."

"Meeting adjourned," I decreed.

# 8

**P**AT, CAN YOU SEE SOMEBODY?" CONNIE INTERRUPTED through the intercom. "He says it's an emergency."

Mr. Silber, my nine o'clock patient who would have arrived at eight thirty even if he had been my four o'clock patient, increased his fidgeting in annoyance over this interruption of his firmly established personal hour.

"Who is it, Connie?" I asked, eager to pass this interloper on to one of my highly skilled, personally trained mental health assistants whom, by now, I expected to act in sessions like virtual clones of their mistress. "Is it one of *my* patients?" I was having enough trouble with the regulars without taking on new cases—especially since, as I had carefully noted by my desk calendar at the start of the day, I had only fifteen days left as a St. Dymphna employee.

"He *says* he's Nilda Perez's husband," Connie reported, unwilling to take responsibility for the accuracy of that statement. "He looks very upset."

"I have a ten o'clock patient," I sighed (not mentioning the 11, 12, 1, 1:30, 2:10 and others I had crowded into every cranny on the desk calendar's appointment sheet). "But I'll see him for a few minutes."

Mr. Silber gripped the arms of his chair, determined that the interloper was not going to usurp any portion of *his* hour. The rest of the session was particularly unproductive, as my patient kept checking his watch every thirty seconds to determine how many minutes he had left to defend. I didn't dare attempt to dismiss him before 10:01; this was certainly not the day to sell him on the merits of the Park Avenue fifty-minute incredible shrinking hour. Murmuring a brief apology to my ten o'clock patient, I summoned in the designated emergency, a muscular, craggy-faced Hispanic in a white T-shirt and well-worn jeans. Subtracting five years for the erosion effects of alcohol on his features, I estimated his age at thirty-six. He was the type of guy you saw by the dozen on the streets of our neighborhood and never saw in the clinic—this *had* to be an emergency.

"Miss Patterson?" he asked. "I'm Ernesto, Nilda's husband. Can you call her for me, please? She's gone crazy this morning, and I'm afraid she's going to hurt somebody."

Nilda had a diagnosis of paranoid schizophrenia and had been in state hospitals on at least three occasions in the past, so the danger was likely to be real. "Well, can you tell me what happened?" I asked.

"Aw," he said, looking very embarrassed, "she started getting funny ideas in her head. Suspicious, like. She even thought I was . . . interested in Blanca. I mean, I look at Blanca like my very own daughter."

Well, I'll bet he looks at Blanca, that much is sure. Blanca was fifteen, looked nineteen, and acted like twenty-five. Nilda was forty-two, looked fifty, and acted like the world was out to screw her, which made her paranoid about twenty percent of the time and very perceptive the other eighty. Blanca was the only one of her five children currently with her, the rest having been forcibly or voluntarily placed in formal or informal foster care, some through courts and some with relatives. Blanca had gone over the wall from an institution about eight months ago, and since the home was more geared to younger, more tractable kids, the authorities were eager to give Nilda another shot at managing her daughter, in spite of her abominable track record. Ernesto had been with Nilda almost as long as Blanca. I had never met him before, but from Nilda's reports, he was the perfect choice for a professional victim like herself—fond of rum, women, and nights on the prowl in search of both.

"You had a fight with Nilda this morning?" I prodded.

"The kid was going out with friends for the day," he shrugged. "She came over to give me a good-bye kiss, like you'd give your father, you know? Nilda saw us and just went crazy. Started raving, said she was going to kill us." Ernesto was now perspiring in spite of his light attire and my air conditioner, roaring away as if about to take off. "She pointed the gun at us . . ."

Freeze, Mister! Hold it right there! "Gun?" I interrupted. "Where did Nilda get a gun?"

Ernesto's eyes pleaded with me not to ask too many questions. "I was holding it for a friend."

Everybody in our neighborhood holds guns for friends. Undoubtedly, a pal somewhere at that moment was holding Ernesto's gun. People can pack a dozen relatives into three rooms, but nobody can find space for his gun.

"See," he explained further, "this guy has to carry a lot of money from time to time in his line of work, so he has a gun." Ernesto didn't attempt to explain how a gun in Ernesto's possession was going to protect the money the guy was carrying.

"Where's the gun now?" I asked.

"With Nilda."

"Where's Blanca?"

"With Nilda."

I was getting to like this guy even less than when Nilda had described him. "You mean you just ran out in the middle of all this?"

He looked at me with his big brown eyes wide in amazement. "Did you expect me to stay there and let Nilda shoot me?"

I conceded to myself that was really a bit much to expect from Ernesto. "I think we should call the police," I said firmly.

"No, please, Miss Patterson, call Nilda first," he implored. "Maybe she's done something terrible already, but if she hasn't and police come, she may panic. She's so upset, she doesn't know what she's doing. She was threatening to kill Blanca, kill herself, shoot up the neighborhood. Blanca told her she belonged in a hospital, and she said she'd die before she went back. Police will only upset her more."

Maybe he was right. If she was really hell-bent on homicide or suicide, she would have done the deed already, and it would be too late. If she was just in emotional turmoil, a screaming squad car and a troop of armed men beating on the door with clubs was no substitute for Thorazine. "What's your number?" I acquiesced. As the phone rang, my mind flashed a gruesome scene of the two women's bodies sprawled on the floor, Blanca's chest splattered with gore, Nilda's right temple gaping, the gun still clenched in her hand as the phone tolled its monotonous dirge. I let the phone ring six, ten, fifteen times, unwilling to give in to that scene. Mercifully, someone picked up the receiver and gave a mournful, inquisitive grunt.

"Nilda, is that you?" I said urgently. "It's Ms. Patterson. How are you, are you all right?"

She broke into sobs, which further thickened her heavy accent so that I could barely understand her. "Miss Patterson, I want to die. I don't know what to do. Help me, help me, please." She ended her plea with a wail plainly audible to the trembling Ernesto and possibly half the waiting room.

"Is Blanca there with you?" I asked. She moaned an assent, and I realized I had asked the wrong question, being interested not so much in Blanca's bodily presence but the state of that body. "Is she okay?" I persisted.

"Miss Patterson, I got nothing to live for," Nilda whined, ignoring my question. "My husband's a bum, my daughter's a tramp, my kids were all taken from me. I'm old and I'm poor and sick. I want to shoot myself—and Blanca, too." At this point, the sound of a scream reassured me that Blanca was alive and alert to the situation. "You stay right there and don't move again!" Nilda barked to her daughter.

"Nilda," I urged desperately, "I want to help you. Will you come here to the clinic, right now?"

"No, I won't leave here," she declined. "Not till I decide what to do. I won't let Blanca leave either. That rat Ernesto got away—I should have shot him in the back like he deserved. Please, you come here?"

Oh, lady, have a heart! I've got a full schedule of patients and only fifteen days left here, don't do this to me. I mean, isn't it better for you to come here, where we can get everything properly charted? You can check your gun with Connie . . . "Nilda, things are very busy here. If I send someone over to get you, will you come to the clinic with them?" Hah, fat chance of my getting a volunteer for *this* assignment—I can just see explaining to Andy or Evelyn about the paranoid schizophrenic lady with the gun. They'd probably rather spend the day down at the welfare center instead.

"No," she insisted. "You're the only one I trust. You were always my therapist, my friend. I won't do anything till you come, I promise."

"Please, please come," a second voice screamed suddenly into the phone. "She's crazy, she'll kill me. She's got a . . ." The plea ended in a groan, as Nilda had apparently wrested the phone from Blanca's grasp and intimidated her into cowering silence.

"You come and talk to me," Nilda said, with sudden calmness. "I'll wait half an hour." She hung up. Ernesto looked at me inquisitively. "What're you gonna do?"

"I guess I'll have to go over there," I replied numbly, trying in vain to think of other options.

Ernesto was on his feet and halfway out the door. "You won't call the cops?" he begged. "That could cause all sorts of problems."

Sure, fellow, like your having either to explain where you got that gun or take it on the lam for a while and lose access to Nilda's disability checks. I shook my head, though it was not for his sake that I was forfeiting the services of the denizens of the local bullpen, whose psychological expertise was about as sharp as their nightsticks. Ernesto disappeared to lose himself in the sweltering neighborhood mobs until the heat was off.

Oh God, what was I in for now? A girl could get killed this way. Sorry, Ms. Steinem, I mean woman. Oh hell, I *am* just a girl—I'm far too young to die, here with my life full of promise, about to enter a Ph.D. program and all. And what about my ten o'clock appointment who's been waiting more than fifteen minutes already? Will she understand if I tell her it's a matter of life and death? Maybe *my* life and death? Boy, will that look great on the letters Connie might have to send out this week: "Dear Mrs. ———
————: Ms. Patterson will not be able to keep her appointment

with you on Tuesday, August 18, at 11 A.M. because she is dead. Please call the clinic coordinator for a new appointment."

No, that won't do, *I'm* the clinic coordinator. They'll have to call Bellino, or whomever he designates to replace me. I suppose he's got somebody in mind already, knowing I'm leaving at the end of the month—probably that prissy little nurse Scutteri, or whatever the hell her name is. Still, out of respect for the dead, he could at least let me serve out my term posthumously.

Now, pull yourself together, Pat, Nilda's not going to kill *you*. Herself perhaps, Blanca perhaps, but why should she harm her kind, concerned therapist? Get yourself over there, quick. Make your apologies to your ten o'clock patient, get Connie to cancel your next couple of appointments, tell Dr. Bellino . . . tell him what? That you're making a home visit to a suicidal-homicidal paranoid schizophrenic with a gun? He'll not only veto that, he'll call 911 and have a fleet of cop cars, ambulances, and S.W.A.T. teams on the scene—it'll make the raid on Entebbe look like a troop of school crossing-guards. I've got to make it sound just important enough for me to go there, but I can't make him feel it's dangerous. I'll sign out like any routine home visit, walk down the avenue, take the subway home, and never show up here again . . . what am I saying? It's *not* dangerous, Pat—tell Bellino that and, most of all, keep telling yourself.

"Vince," I said sweetly on the telephone, "I don't want to bother you if you're with a patient, but I just wanted to let you know I'm going out on a home visit for a few minutes, and I'll be right back."

"Just a minute," he said, before I could hang up. "Why do *you* have to go? Why can't you send one of the assistants?"

"Uh, it's for Nilda Perez and she's in a mild paranoid decompensation and I'm the only one she trusts," I improvised. "Listen, you're busy, I'll explain it all when I get back."

"I am *not* busy," he informed me. "Let me finish writing this prescription and I'll be right in."

I looked nervously at my watch. What was it Nilda said? "I'll wait half an hour." And then what? Would my not showing up on time be enough to make her give up all hope, pull the trigger on Blanca or herself, or just start shooting randomly? How I wish she had been more specific!

Waiting for Vince only cost me about ninety seconds on the crucial clock. He emerged from his air-conditioned office on this humid morning already looking a bit wilted but stubbornly clinging to his three-button gray jacket and proper necktie. "Okay, now what's the story on this emergency of yours?" he asked, sitting down despite my attempts to hasten his departure by standing and clutching my purse as if on the way out.

"Oh, nothing major," I lied. "Nilda hasn't been taking her Haldol, and her daughter called to say she's become rather delusional, talking to God and such. She threw out her medication because she was convinced it had a spell on it, so I'm going to bring her a fresh supply."

"So why can't one of the assistants bring it?" he asked.

"She wouldn't trust them, the daughter says. You know, I used to see her in Social Service even before this clinic opened. She *trusts* me, I'm like a good-mother figure, you know. The pills I bring would be like an equivalent of the good mother's milk . . ."

"Okay, spare me the Freudian crap," he snapped. "You're starting to sound like Dave Goldman, who can't drink a beer without thinking of his mother's breasts. But why bring it now—can't it wait till your lunch hour?"

His question set me to wondering whether the container of black coffee and buttered roll I had picked up on my way to work had been my very last meal; the thought unnerved me so much, I scarcely resented Bellino's expecting me to give up my lunch hour to work, though I invariably did. "Well, my ten o'clock patient had to cancel, so I might as well get down there," I told him. Of course, she had to cancel, because I told her I had an emergency.

"Where is Nilda's house?"

"Oh, only about six blocks from here," I reassured him.

"Which direction?" he demanded. "Toward the river, isn't it?" I nodded pleasantly. Of course, toward the river—you don't think welfare clients live in the neighborhoods you feel safe to walk in, do you?

Vince scowled and shook his head. "That's a bad section, Pat. You'd better not go alone."

"Look, I'll leave my purse here," I wheedled, stuffing it into my already crammed desk drawer. "No jewelry, no golden bands to encumber my fingers. What are they going to rob, my ten-dollar Timex that's too cheap to have cleaned and too dirty to run without stopping several times a day?"

He lowered his eyes and looked a little embarrassed. "You're a woman, Pat. You know what I mean. There are other dangers. Take Carmen Ortiz with you."

"Carmen? Gee, Vince, and here I always thought she was a woman, too," I said, trying to stay calm. "What the hell is *she*, anyway . . . a musk-ox? You send *her* alone into these neighborhoods."

"She lives around here," he grumbled. "She chooses to take those risks."

Yeah, I'd choose to live here, too, if I had to manage on Carmen's salary and my only other option was to spend ninety percent of my earnings on rent. It's okay for the Puerto Rican and black girls to get raped, but you white men have got to protect your property, us white girls, right? "What risks?" I finally exploded. "Vince, it's ten thirty in the morning and the temperature's eighty-eight degrees. It's too hot to rape anybody! I didn't even wear my chastity belt to work, it's so hot."

"Pat," he sighed, "there's a difference between being liberated and being foolhardy. If you want my okay to go, take somebody with you—on second thought, take a male. Get Amos to go with you."

Molasses Mosley? He had to be kidding. If a rapist struck, by the time Moe swung into action, I'd be in my second trimester of pregnancy. Well, no need to worry, I happened to know that Moe was already downtown at the Social Security office with a client.

"Do you want me to write out the prescription?" Vince asked.

I shook my head. More lies. "Evelyn got one filled at the pharmacy but never brought the pills down because Nilda refused to see anyone but me."

"Okay, Pat," he said softly. "Be careful. See you later."

This may be the last time he ever sees me, I thought. Alive, I mean. Do you suppose they'd ask *him* to identify me in the morgue? I'm sure they'd cart me off to St. Dymphna's, it being only a few blocks from Nilda's house. Maybe I should paint my toenails before I go. Oh, what's the use, a toe looks ridiculous with a morgue tag on it, no matter what you do to it. "Good-bye, Vince," I said, not wanting him to suspect the danger yet somehow wishing I could share my terrible feelings of fear and isolation with someone.

But three minutes later I was out on the mean streets without either Mosley or the mythological pills. Nobody was sleeping late in this heat, and the streets were already mobbed. A group of young Hispanics, any of whom might have been Ernesto's brothers and half of whom probably were, swilled beer from cans and munched fried pork rinds—the local "breakfast of champions." One sang a snatch from a Puerto Rican ballad in tribute to my femininity while his comrades smacked their lips lasciviously in the prescribed ritual as I passed. The gutters were awash with streams of debris-polluted water that had spouted pristine from every fire hydrant, forcing me to vault the flood with running leaps at every crossing, generally unsuccessfully. With the soles of my panty-hose clammy and my sandals squishing out an ooze of garbage broth at every step, I continued my soggy journey. A couple of Spanish girls, not more than fourteen years old, giggled as they sauntered past me, their long slim legs on display for any man to see—any man who could tear his eyes away from the brightly colored knit tops that clung to their newly acquired bosoms like eager hands. Close behind them trudged another young woman, probably eighteen, pushing an infant in a stroller, her belly swollen with the carriage's next passenger. As I got closer to the river, there were more abandoned buildings, some charred by fire, others merely crumbling away from age. In the scattered buildings still occupied, plump black women in faded housedresses exchanged weary greetings, as they hung out the windows, with their neighbors, a motley assortment of blacks, West Indians, and Hispanics. In the ruins of the abandoned buildings, dungaree-clad teen-agers perched on the sills of paneless windows or sprawled on crumbling staircases, like the lean alley cats that I've seen in photographs who live in the ruins of the Roman forum. Half a dozen windows emitted disco music with ear-shattering force from those damn battery-powered radios as big as attaché cases that the youngsters tote around constantly, dependent on them as a cardiac patient on his pacemaker. This neighborhood was a natural for urban renewal—with a few million dollars, some federal agency could upgrade it into a slum.

On Nilda's block, there were more rubble-strewn vacant lots and abandoned buildings than inhabitable dwellings, but at the end nearest the river three decrepit brownstones, probably leaning against one another for support, were somehow still standing. One had to be hers—and as my failing luck would have it, the numbers revealed hers to be the one with four swarthy black-clad youths, looking like a road company of *West Side Story*, spread out to block the staircase. The only fantasy I would permit myself at that point was the one in which I turned around and went back to my office, but knowing the state Nilda was in, I just couldn't let myself give in to common sense. Look them in the eye and don't let them know you're afraid and they won't attack you, I told myself—or did that just apply to dogs? Then, I got a brainstorm—if they thought I was a policewoman, they wouldn't dare attack me. After all, they obviously knew I didn't live there, so I must be there on some sort of business. I doubt the Avon lady makes many calls around here and I had no sample encyclopedias with me, so they would figure I was on some noncommercial errand. I didn't look like a cop, but that was the whole idea of being a plainclothesperson, wasn't it? Now I wished I had carried my purse, so they'd think I had my gun and shield in it. The thin summer dress I had on unfortunately made it clear there were no menacing bulges on my person, other than the few extra pounds on my hips I had been trying to shed since trying on my bikini in May. Maybe they'd think I had my gun strapped to my thigh—I patted my hip for reassurance like Gary Cooper did prior to the showdown in *High Noon*. I was trying to remember where Angie Dickinson packs her gun on that TV show of hers—hah, no wonder she's so cool, she's always got at least two devoted, brawny guys backing her up ten yards away.

Hey, that's an idea, make them think I've got somebody covering me! I spotted a man sitting behind the wheel of a parked car, about twenty feet off. Probably the neighborhood pusher and those kids on the stoop are his best customers, but what choice have I got? Glancing back over my shoulder at the parked car, waving my left hand at my side in a sort of nebulous signal, and patting my hip repeatedly with my right hand, I stumbled over to Nilda's building, whose facade bore the ironic inscription, ELYSIA. With my left foot propped staunchly on the first step, I posed for an instant with one hand on my hip, glared at the four punks, and snapped, "I'm looking for Perez."

One looked away, one smirked, one shrugged. I fixed my steely gaze on the one who hadn't committed himself yet. "Nilda Perez," I said, my voice coming forth in a squeak that sounded more like Suzanne Sommers than Angie Dickinson. I tried to salvage the situation with another look at my formidable back-up man only to find that he had driven off. Shit, even Cheryl Ladd wouldn't pull this kind of confrontation without two exquisitely coiffed, armed Angels behind her, and here I was auditioning for a remake of *Cry Rape*. The punk looked hard at me, spat over the railing of the staircase, and said, "She moved."

I caught my breath. If he had offered to escort me in, I probably would have turned and run. If he felt I was worth lying to, I must be intimidating him on some level. I couldn't speak for his friends, of course, but what the hell, even turning around at this point was no guarantee they wouldn't turn on me.

"Thanks, I'll check it out myself," I said, trying to pretend they were the third graders I once taught in my distant past. There was just enough space on the third step between the standing liar and the seated smirker for me to place one soggy foot. The gang remained as immobile as the steps themselves—more so; at least the steps crumbled away in spots—forcing me to pivot like a burlesque dancer to advance my leg to the next step. As I made it to the battered door, one of my harassers called out, "Hey, are you a social worker?"

I turned at the threshold, feeling like the Lone Ranger unmasked. Finally, I decided to be a cop pretending to be a social worker. "You might say that," I replied with a cryptic nod. With that brilliant, sardonic remark, I sauntered into the four-by-four vestibule lined on either side by a row of rusted mailboxes, several of which had broken locks and hung ajar. There was no inside door between the vestibule and the two ground-floor apartments beside the staircase to protect the tenants.

I had barely stepped inside when I felt a rough arm around my waist turn my body toward the stairs and push me forward. One of the punks hissed in my ear, "We know where Mrs. Perez lives. Come on upstairs, we'll show you." I heard his buddies crowding in behind him, one already pressing against me on the other side.

I twisted my torso hard enough to break his grip and turn around to face the barricaded door, but my attacker grabbed my arm and pushed his body directly in front of me. There was just enough room in the narrow vestibule for his pal to squeeze beside him, and with the other two directly behind, there was no way I could get out that door. There wasn't enough room in the hallway behind me for a bridge game much less a gang rape, so they were going to force or intimidate me into going up to the roof.

"You come with us and don't give us no trouble, if you want to live," the leader commanded, lowering his brows menacingly and squeezing my arm hard.

"Let go of me and get the hell out of here!" I yelled at the top of my lungs. "Hel . . ."

The punk standing beside my assailant slammed the heel of his hand into my open mouth, attempting to stifle my cry for help while trying, as best he could in the cramped quarters, to maneuver himself behind me. The narrowness of the vestibule was my one advantage, reducing my fighting odds, for the moment, from four to one to a still-unenviable two to one. I bit down hard on the hand that was thrust against my mouth, eliciting a yelp from its owner, who quickly withdrew the hand. At the same time, I kicked the shin of the guy directly in front of me, a stimulus which, coupled with the surprised cry from his buddy, unnerved him long enough for me to be able to free my wrist.

I whirled around and raced for the stairway, taking a deep breath in preparation for the scream of my life. But before I could get the scream out, a deafening female shriek, more one of anger than distress, came from one of the ground-floor apartments. It was followed by the crash of something heavy being thrown inside the apartment, and this unexpected commotion froze my adversaries for two seconds in their pursuit, just enough time for me to reach the first step of the staircase. A big muscular black man bolted from the ground-floor apartment in a panic, just brushing the back of my dress as I sped past him while screaming "Help!" with ear-splitting intensity. He may not have even noticed me, since the lady inside the apartment was screaming as loudly as I was and he had the added distraction of my pursuers plowing right into his chest. As I raced up the stairs, I could hear him cursing at the punks and scuffling with them. Going up the second flight of stairs shrieking like a banshee, I realized that I was heading precisely where the gang had wanted me to go. My only hope was that someone would reply to my screams for help, but it seemed nobody was about to get involved; in fact, I could hear several apartment doors, apparently left open to alleviate some of the stifling summer heat, being hurriedly slammed shut as I approached.

Fortunately, the combination of my screams and the unintentional interference by the first-floor tenant with marital problems had discouraged the gang from further pursuit. Since the attack on me had been an impromptu venture, one which I had probably to some degree provoked by my defiant attitude, they were not very organized and quite unprepared for the complications that developed; even teen gangs could benefit from the skilled services of a coordinator, I later reflected.

By the time I had reached the third floor, I realized from the silence below that I was no longer being followed. I also realized that I didn't know where Nilda lived. With my heart pounding wildly and my body visibly trembling, I was in no emotional shape to confront an agitated, dangerous patient; on the other hand, turning back was out of the question. I wasn't sure which possibility I dreaded more, facing my assailants, who might be lurking on the street outside, or facing Bellino with the admission that I not only had failed in my mission but nearly gotten myself raped as he had warned.

I had to find Nilda. Maybe I could call the police from her apartment. Perhaps my own distress would make her forget her hostility and even provide the key for resolving her crisis. Then again, how could I throw my own problems on her at such a time? I leaned against the wall, heaving deep breaths and listening for sounds on the staircase below. What would the cops do anyway? I'd have a hell of a time proving attempted rape; I had no bruises on me and I hadn't been robbed. Half the kids who had attacked me were probably under sixteen and would be classified as juvenile offenders. They'd throw me and the case out of court.

One of the four apartment doors on the third floor where I was standing was wide open, and a scrawny, bushy-haired child, about five years old—or seven, allowing for malnutrition—sat, clad only in underpants, just inside, clutching two rag bundles that might once have been dolls.

"Mrs. Perez?" I queried. "*Señora* Perez? Do you know where she lives? *Se donde habita?*" I was sure I hadn't gotten that one right. She probably thought I was asking where to get a fix for my habit. Yet the child pointed knowingly to another apartment two doors away, and I was desperate enough to believe her. I knocked timidly, still listening for footsteps on the stairs and suddenly fearing that I would be confronted by a seven-foot hunchback (taller if he could straighten up) who would sink his fangs into my neck . . . horrors, I think I've gotten my monster movies mixed up!

"*Quien es?*" said a hoarse voice I hoped was female.

"Nilda? Is that you?" I answered in a stage whisper. "It's Ms. Patterson."

I waited for what seemed a full minute, wondering if I had the right apartment. Slowly the door creaked open, and I saw Nilda's reddened eyes glowing at me. She tugged at the shoulder of my dress, pulling me quickly inside. I was never so glad to see a woman with a gun before.

"Help me, Blanca's dying!" she croaked. So much for *my* problems! I decided.

I could hear Blanca's gasps not far away. My head suddenly swam as I realized I had come too late after all. The gun barrel was probably still hot after firing the fatal shot. Unthinkingly, I staggered through the shabby living room, following Nilda's shuffling form. She led me to their only bedroom, which mother and daughter had shared prior to Ernesto's arrival judging from the Mick Jagger posters and Elvis Presley glossies enshrined incongruously among Nilda's madonnas and Saint Barbara statues. A garish purple-and-yellow teddy bear sat with protruded tongue on the bed, where Blanca lay on a gray tattered sheet, her head rolling back and forth on a faded violet sofa-pillow as she fought noisily for breath. "Asthmaaaaa," Nilda pronounced fearfully, the word blending into a plaintive bleat. She gazed at her daughter with deep maternal concern, pointing the gun at Blanca's belly as she wept.

"Nilda, for God's sake, watch where you're pointing that gun!" I yelped. My cry caused Blanca to lift her head off the pillow long enough to glimpse the weapon, whereupon her breathing became even more wheezy. I had never seen a full-blown asthma attack before, and I knew little about the disease, except I was aware that one does need to be able to breathe for most of the activities of daily living, and Blanca was doing a very poor job of it.

"You've got to let me call an ambulance," I said firmly. "She's very sick."

"No ambulance!" Nilda said more firmly, punctuating her sentence with a wave of the gun. "They always send police."

"She . . . *wants* me . . . to die . . ." Blanca moaned between labored breaths.

Nilda looked helplessly from her daughter to the gun and back again. "Miss Patterson, call a doctor. Not nine-one-one, just a doctor. You know somebody? You work with doctors."

Actually, I usually seem to be working against them. And I'm not sure I'd want a shrink treating *my* terminal asthma. "Nilda," I suggested, "there is an emergency service where doctors make house calls. Maybe they'll come . . ."

"No good," she frowned. "My friend tried to call them once. They want twenty-five dollars soon they walk in—I don't have. Once they see I don't have, they call nine-one-one, and the place full of cops. All doctors are like that, anyway—'go to emergency room, go to hospital, call ambulance'—if patient got more than lousy cold or nervous attack, they don't want to be bothered."

Blanca had said nothing further. It seemed to be taking every bit of energy she had left just to move the air in and out of her lungs. Her limbs were motionless, her eyes were shut, and she was perspiring heavily.

"Please," Nilda went on, "you call good doctor from your clinic to come here—alone. Okay?"

How do I get into these things? I come down here to help a routine case of homicidal-suicidal paranoid schizophrenia, and wind up with a medical emergency as well. Well, one thing for sure, I was not equipped to handle this latest development alone, so I might as well use the limited consultation facilities available to me. As I started to dial the clinic, Nilda laid down a further prohibition. "You don't mention gun, okay?" I nodded at the gun.

"Vince, hi!" I opened cheerfully. "Listen, hate to bother you, but there's a *medical* crisis here. Nilda's daughter, Blanca, is having a really bad asthma attack. She can barely breathe at all. That can be really serious, can't it?"

"Sure Pat," he said. "Status asthmaticus can occur, where they can't be pulled out of it—it can be fatal. Don't mess around, call nine-one-one."

"No, Nilda doesn't want that," I told him. "Remember our discussion before I left about how she's been feeling about people lately."

"I don't give a crap about her delusions," he barked. "A girl's life is at stake. You've got to take charge, not give in to the judgment of a psychotic!"

"Yes, but there's a major complication here," I persisted. "The kind Dr. Paul Ehrlich would look for?"

"Ehrlich?" he asked, in obvious consternation, trying to remember his medical history. "Somebody there's got syphilis?"

"The *cure* is what's the problem," I wheedled, like a game-show contestant. "Ehrlich's cure?"

"Pat, what the hell are you talking about?" he fumed. "Salvarsan? Six-oh-six? Arsenic?"

"The basic principle of the cure, not the specifics, Vince," I said as Nilda regarded me with a puzzled look. "Ehrlich knew what he had to find?"

"Magic bullets?" he guessed.

"That's *it*, Doctor!" I exclaimed. "That's the problem we have here."

"Somebody there has magic bullets?" he asked, totally confused.

"Just the ordinary kind," I said ominously.

"Bullets? Where?"

"In the usual receptacle," I said as calmly as possible.

"A gun?" he shrieked as I pressed the receiver tight against my ear, despite the pain to my eardrum, to keep Nilda from overhearing. "Are you trying to tell me Nilda's got a gun?"

"Yes, Doctor," I said with clinical authority.

"Did you know that when you went on your home visit?" he demanded.

"Uh, yes, doctor," I affirmed.

"Pat, I'll kill you!" he warned.

"You may have to wait your turn," I replied.

"Listen, I'll get help there right away," he sputtered. "Just try to keep both of them calm . . ."

"Vince," I interrupted loudly, overriding his piercing voice, "*you* stay calm. Do *not* call nine-one-one . . ."

"No nine-one-one!" shrieked Nilda.

"That's what I'm telling him," I answered, still talking directly into the receiver. "Dr. Bellino will *not* call ambulances or send police or do anything that might upset you in your present highly emotional and impulsive state. Vince, we've got the emergency medical kit in the nurse's office. Isn't there enough stuff in there for you or one of the other doctors to pull Blanca out of her crisis?"

"I just don't know," he groaned. "How bad is the kid? Is she blue?"

"Under the circumstances, she's hardly euphoric," I reported.

"Her skin, damn it!" he explained. "Is she cyanotic?"

"I don't think so," I equivocated. "More pale than blue, I'd say."

"Okay, I'll be there in ten minutes."

"Vince, listen," I said. "You don't have to come yourself, you know. If you want to send Chong or somebody else, it's okay."

"I wouldn't send a dog or a social worker into that kind of a mess, let alone a psychiatrist who would have too much intelligence to go anyway," he fumed. There was a brief silence. "Pat, please be very careful, huh? I'll be right there."

I put the receiver down and stared again into Nilda's worried face. "Dr. Bellino is coming, alone," I informed her. "Let's make sure Blanca's all right." We walked back toward the bedroom. The sound of Blanca's noisy breathing throughout the phone conversation had reassured us she was still alive, but I was getting uneasy about leaving her alone for so long.

"The doctor's coming, Blanca," Nilda announced. But the sight of the gun seemed to have more effect than the sound of the announcement; the girl began to tremble, and her breathing, which had been regular though difficult, stopped completely for a very uncomfortable part of a minute, then noisily resumed in a series of completely asynchronous wheezes.

"Nilda," I hissed, "can't you put down that gun for a few minutes? You're making her worse!"

Nilda gave me a haughty look in return, as though I had asked a queen to stop toting her scepter around to state occasions. "Let's go wait in the living room for the doctor," was the most she would concede.

She padded back in her floppy, deteriorated plastic bedroom slippers, drawing her faded, wispy pink housecoat around her as though warding off a nonexistent breeze. She slumped wearily into a drab olive armchair whose innards herniated out from half a dozen holes. I lowered my tense frame onto a thin-cushioned sofa and tried to recall what to do until the doctor arrived, though I was reasonably sure *Reader's Digest* had never dealt with this particular situation. Nilda turned the pistol slightly upward and seemed to be sighting along its nose at a fly on the ceiling.

"Nilda, do you really know how to handle that thing?" I challenged uneasily.

She shrugged. "I think so. If I pull this here trigger, it shoots, no?"

Perhaps yes, perhaps no. Maybe Ernesto hadn't even loaded it. Maybe there was a safety device on the gun—even then, with the shape these cheap Saturday night specials were usually in, I wouldn't be about to trust one. Maybe Ernesto *was* holding it for a friend, and it was only a toy, or replica, or piece of inoperative junk. What difference did it make? I had no choice but to presume it was real, loaded, and would go off if Nilda pulled the trigger. "Yeah, I guess that's all you need to know, isn't it?" I said to Nilda. "Now, suppose you tell me why you're so upset."

She tightened her grip around the handle of the gun as I jolted her memory into a collision with that morning's bitter realities. "I'm a damn fool, that's why. I take Ernesto off the streets, give him a good home, hot meals, sex whenever he wants it. He takes my welfare money and buys booze with it, comes and goes as he pleases. I take Blanca back in after she's so bad none of the institutions or foster homes want her. I buy her nice clothes, feed her whatever hour of the night she comes in. Next thing I know, the two of them, the two bums, are playing around with one another. With my own eyes, I see it this morning. Maybe I seen it before, but I try to look away. It's hard when it's your own daughter, your own boyfriend—the only two people I cared about." Her eyes misted over and one tear rolled down her leathery cheek to be thirstily sucked up by her washed-out garment. "And you think Blanca's going to be happy with him, any more than me? He'll make her life miserable, too, like he made mine. Better we're both dead."

"You don't really mean that, Nilda," I told her. "Look, the fact you've been so concerned about her since she got the asthma attack proves it, doesn't it? If you wanted to see her dead, you wouldn't have asked me to get a doctor, right?"

Nilda wrinkled her brow and her nose, shaking her head in disbelief at my deficiencies in elementary logic. "I said I wanted to kill her. I'm not sure, but I'm thinking about it. Now, if I decide not to and she dies of asthma, that's a terrible thing. And if I decide to and she dies of asthma before I can kill her, I don't get to kill her the way she deserves, and I'm gonna get angrier and more depressed. Maybe I kill her and maybe I don't, but I sure as hell can't let her die of asthma and make me depressed no matter what I finally decide. Right?"

"I agree we can't let her die of asthma, at any rate," I said. "But, Nilda, how could you think of shooting your own daughter? How could you live with such a thing afterward?"

Nilda thought a moment, then sighed, "You're right. No mother could ever do such a thing to her own daughter, no matter how much she deserved it, and live with the memory." I smiled triumphantly. Once Dr. Bellino got here, he could pull Blanca out of her crisis and then we'd all go off merrily on our separate ways, now that I'd eradicated Nilda's homicidal propensities. "That's why," she went on, "I got to shoot myself right afterward." She looked at the pistol. "They got six bullets in these things, right?"

Lady, what do I know? Cowboys always had six, but this isn't a Roy Rogers movie, though I wish it was, because I could at least hope Roy's posse would come riding out of the west, and now the best I can hope for is Dr. Bellino. Even if that rusty hunk of scrap metal you're holding originally came with six shells, Ernesto probably traded a couple in for beer. I majored in social work, not ballistics. "Nilda, you've got to stop this thinking about killing. I'm sure we can come to a better solution."

"It's all I can think of right now," she said glumly, shaking her gray-streaked shaggy black hair. "The more I sit here holding this gun, the less I can think of anything else."

"Then I think you should stop sitting there just holding that gun," I said briskly in crisp Mary Poppinsish tones. "Is there any tea in the house?"

She shrugged. "We never got anything in this house. Tell you, though, if there's something left in this house that Ernesto ain't drunk up, it would be tea."

"Go see if there is any," I urged. "You can make some for Blanca."

She looked at me perplexed. "Tea ain't no good for asthma. Orange-water maybe, or some kind of herb tea, but I only got supermarket stuff, nothing from the *botanica*."

"Dr. Bellino will take care of the asthma," I explained. "I think you should have some tea ready to relax us all afterward." It saw the Londoners through the Battle of Britain didn't it? Actually, the tea was extraneous; I just wanted to get her active in something other than fondling that gun. After all, how homicidal can you feel handling a tea kettle?

Nilda's kitchen was more respectable than many in that neighborhood. Of course, you wouldn't film a coffee commercial in it, but it did have an ancient iron stove and a weird refrigerator with a coiled apparatus on top. The sink had an adjacent porcelain tub for washing clothes by hand and bathing babies. No overhead cabinets, though, so everything from utensils to bags of rice was crammed in drawers or piled on available surfaces, such as the top of the refrigerator, the sink's drainboard, and even on whatever gas jets were not in current use on the stove. Nilda proceeded through a noisy search for the needed tea-making implements encumbered by her gun. She would lay the weapon on the stove, rummage through the oven for the kettle, lift the gun, put the kettle on the burner, put the gun on the kettle, search for the lid, move the gun to make room for the lid, find the box of tea bags, lay the gun in the box while she removed three bags, lift the kettle, put the gun on the sink, and so it went as she filled the kettle with water and inserted the bags. Amid the clatter of kettle, lid, and pistol, I suddenly became aware of banging at the door.

"That's the doctor, Nilda," I said, gratefully.

Nilda jerked the gun up from its resting place on the stove. "Wait," she warned. "I go with you." She inched around the perimeter of the living room toward the apartment door, her back flush against the wall, the way she had seen it done in countless cops-and-robbers films. Give some people a gun and they become instant movie stars! I momentarily considered throwing myself on my belly and crawling across the uncarpeted floor, at the risk of a navel full of splinters and the more horrifying prospect of an eye-to-eye confrontation with one of the resident rodents; then I remembered that, after all, Dr. Bellino didn't have a gun—we did. We? Well, we therapists have to stand by our patients—especially when they're armed.

Nilda and I stood against the door, one on either side of the knob, as I asked, "Who is it?"

"The Daughters of the American Revolution—we're recruiting new members," Vince's peevish voice answered. "Open up, Pat!"

I swung open the door, trying with my cordial smile to offset the inhospitable appearance of Nilda's gun. Vince seemed to be paying more attention to the gun than my smile. He clutched a paper bag about the size of a half-gallon milk container to his chest.

"Did you bring some medicine?" I asked eagerly.

"What do you think I've got in here, a cheeseburger and a side order of fries?" he snarled, raising the bag from his rib cage.

"You don't bring doctor's bag?" Nilda asked, his rapier wit wasted on her.

"In *this* neighborhood?" he asked impatiently. "I wouldn't have gotten past the steps of the clinic. If it was a half hour closer to noon, they would have mugged me for the cheeseburger."

"How did you know we were in this apartment, Vince?" I asked, suddenly remembering I had not given him the number on the phone.

"Logical deduction, intuition, and reading the apartment number on the mailbox," he explained.

"I must try that approach some time," I sighed.

"Blanca's in there," Nilda interrupted, pointing with the gun to the room from which the wheezes wafted.

"So I hear," Vince nodded. He strode behind Nilda, looking more like a junior executive brown-bagging it at lunch hour than a doctor on a life-saving mission.

Blanca lifted her sweaty, matted locks from the pillow and looked apprehensively at the entourage entering her room. "Is that the doctor?" she gasped hoarsely.

Dr. Bellino nodded with a forced little grin that barely progressed beyond the left corner of his mouth. He began emptying the contents of his sack: two small bottles of injectable medication, two ampules of more medication, a half-dozen disposable syringes in two different sizes, a rubber tourniquet, and a dozen sterile alcohol swabs.

Blanca eyed the impressive array of paraphernalia and still looked doubtful. "Ain't you a shrink?"

I winced, expecting Vince to respond with one of his icier barbs, but he merely gave the frightened girl a wistful little smile and said, "Yes, but I used to be a doctor before. Don't worry, miss, I still remember a few tricks." He took one of the tiny syringes out of its paper casing and filled it from one of the ampules.

"Didn't you bring a stethoscope, Vince?" I asked.

He glowered at me in a silence broken only by Blanca's creaky respiration, an eerie sound reminiscent of Lon Chaney at the keyboard in *Phantom of the Opera*. Finally, he snapped, "Why? Do you think that sound needs amplification? If she was having a seizure, you'd expect me to bring over a goddamn EEG machine, wouldn't you?"

Swallowing my irritation, I changed the subject. "What's that injection you're giving her?" I inquired pleasantly.

Swabbing her left upper arm with alcohol, he answered, "Point-three cc's of epinephrine, one to a thousand, sub-Q. Okay with you?"

Nilda suddenly raised her left hand to halt him and gave the gun, pointed at his head, a menacing shake. She looked at me questioningly. "Okay, Miss Patterson?"

Stifling my smirk, I paused thoughtfully for two seconds, then nodded slowly. "Proceed, Doctor," I commanded.

Vince scowled as he slipped the point of the syringe, no thicker than a sewing needle, just under her skin. Blanca let out a perfunctory little moan a second after he had already withdrawn the needle. Vince now liberated one of the larger syringes from its envelope and began filling it from one of the bottles. "With Dr. Patterson's permission," he grunted, "I would like to administer five hundred milligrams of aminophylline intravenously." I responded with a magnanimous wave of my hand, and he applied the tourniquet to Blanca's arm.

"Oh no," she wailed, "not another injection!"

"You *got* to give it by injection, Doctor?" Nilda interceded.

"Well," Vince conceded, "it is occasionally given by suppository . . ." He was obviously bluffing—I surveyed his meager arsenal laid out on the table and there was nothing designed to traverse the road less traveled by. Blanca quickly volunteered to submit to the needle, which Vince promptly administered. Having drawn back just enough thick maroon blood to verify that he had hit his mark, he snapped off the tourniquet and began to ease the plunger of the syringe ever so slowly forward.

Maybe it was just the power of suggestion, the pungent scent of alcohol, the pop of the tourniquet, the bite of the needles, but Blanca seemed to be actually responding. The frightful squeaks and rattles emanating from her lungs gave way to heavy rhythmic sighs, which became progressively quieter. Her clenched eyelids fluttered nervously, blinked, then were raised, revealing her clear brown eyes once more, eyes which regarded her doctor with a grateful reverence. I had heard Vince bitch on occasion about what a fool he was to abandon the world of clinical medicine for the uncertainty and chaos of psychiatry, but now, for the first time, I realized those gripes were more than theatrical rantings. Sure, we get results at times; some patients even give us credit for them. But never do we get such quick, dramatic resolutions, such snatched-from-the-jaws-of-death rescues as that which I had just witnessed.

"I think it's your round, Chief," I murmured.

Vince leaned back in the rickety bedside chair and gave me a wary nod. "If we were in the E.R., she'd have a dextrose I.V. running, maybe even a little oxygen, but it's the best we door-to-door resuscitators can do." He turned to Nilda. "How about it, mama? Can we take her into the hospital and get her some first-class medical attention?"

Nilda, who had looked ready to explode with joy moments before, curled her lips in a sneer and vetoed the suggestion with a shake of her head. "She's lucky I let you come. She didn't even deserve that, the no-good little tramp." At that, Blanca took a deep gasp, and though the wheezing didn't resume, Vince decided to separate the two in the interests of preventive medicine.

"Come on, Nilda," he urged. "Let her rest for a while. Let's go into the living room."

Nilda nodded but beckoned him with her gun hand to go first. As we trooped single file into the shabby room, I felt more like a prisoner than a therapist. While I didn't want to leave just yet, I couldn't help wondering how free I was to go at this point, specifically gunpoint. Vince wrinkled his nose at the moldering sofa cushions, then settled gingerly into the armchair after wiping its seat with a whisk of his hand, which he wiped in turn on his neatly creased fifty-percent silk trousers.

When Nilda and I had, less fastidiously, settled ourselves on the sofa, Vince cleared his throat, straightened his tie and, in his calmest, analytic tones, understated, "You seem to be angry at your daughter. Can you tell me about it?"

"I already told *her*," Nilda snapped uncooperatively, stabbing a finger in my direction. "She knows all about it."

"Ah, yes . . ." Vince said with obvious irritation. "But perhaps I can help, too. What exactly happened?"

Nilda folded her arms stubbornly. "Miss Patterson's my therapist. I don't want to talk to no one else." The folding of her arms served to direct the gun toward Vince, who was seated to her left.

"Pat," he commanded, "would you tell me what the hell is going on!" I looked nervously at Nilda, who sat between us, for her approval. She nodded in assent.

"Doctor," I began, "this goes back quite a bit, of course. Nilda's had problems both with Blanca and Ernesto, her . . . husband, but things sort of came to a head today. Nilda suspects Blanca may have become somewhat . . . uh . . . involved with Ernesto . . ."

"Suspect, shit!" Nilda interrupted heatedly. "I *know* the little bitch has been playing up to him. I know what goes on here when I got to go to the store or the welfare center. Now, they're doing it right under my nose. Well, no more! I'm going to kill her." Nilda waved the gun threateningly in the direction of the bedroom. "I'm going to kill her and me and maybe a few other people." She looked back and forth at the only other people around. The room was silent except for the banging of the tea-kettle lid as the water steamed away unattended in the kitchen. "Hey, you like some tea?" she asked suddenly.

"Uh, yes, I would!" Vince said with unconvincing enthusiasm. "That's *just* what we all need about now." Not exactly, Doctor; one of us needs an antipsychotic agent, one needs oxygen, and some Valium all around wouldn't hurt any.

"Pat," he hissed in a stage whisper, pointing at the door. "Go, get out!"

I looked at him in shock, as though he were making an indecent proposition. "What are you talking about?" I answered softly. "Where do you want me to go?"

He leaped out of his chair and catapulted himself onto the sofa beside me, snarling in my ear. "For God's sake, this is your chance. Make a break for it. I'll handle things. I'm pretty sure I can disarm her when she comes back, but I don't want to risk your getting hit by a stray shot."

Numb with disbelief, I argued, "You can't be serious, Vince! You sound as though she's some sort of criminal. This is a patient we're dealing with, and we're therapists, not policemen."

"Oh, good grief!" he exclaimed. "Sure, she's a patient, but she's got a gun and she just might use it. Even against herself! Didn't you hear her say that? Don't you realize we're in a dangerous situation?"

"Of course," I sighed, with increasing irritation. "Did you think I interrupted my busy morning to come down here for a friendly spot of tea? We've got to talk her out of using the gun."

"If we disarm her, which I'm sure I can when she comes back loaded with teacups, we'll have the problem solved more definitively than by relying on our ability to reach her through words in the state she's in."

"Oh?" I countered, unswayed. "Then what? Get her carted off to the hospital and maybe have her o.d. or jump out a window a month or two from now? Do you think she'd ever trust a therapist again, after her last one attacked her by force and broke a promise by calling the police?"

"I'm not asking *you* to do anything by force or call the police," he insisted. "All I'm asking you to do is save your stubborn neck. I'll handle the rest."

I folded my arms adamantly. "You leave if you want to. I'm seeing Nilda through this crisis, whether you've got the guts to or not."

"You're confusing courage with poor judgment," he lectured. "And I personally think it takes more guts to disarm an agitated psychotic than to cower passively at her mercy!"

"Spare me the macho manifesto, okay, Vince?" I pleaded. "Look, forget what I said about guts. I wouldn't have even dragged you into this if it wasn't for Blanca's asthma. Why don't *you* go back to the clinic, and I'll take it from here. I can handle the rest."

"Oh sure, Wonder Woman!" he scoffed. "I'll bet you've had loads of experience dealing with homicidal psychotics."

"And how much have you had?" I challenged.

"At least I've worked in hospitals during my residency, where I was exposed to an occasional severely disturbed psychotic," he shot back.

"And where do you think I trained?" I angrily responded. "At Miss Abigail's School for Gifted Children? I've worked in hospitals, too."

"Yeah, as a *social worker*," he emphasized.

"Naturally. What did you expect me to work as, a floor lamp?"

"You might as well have for all the responsibility they give social workers—especially student social workers," he chided. "What did they let you do, call Bingo numbers in recreational therapy?"

"It's funny that up until now you never questioned my qualifications to deal with every species of patient that storms through the clinic door," I noted.

"*You're* the one who feels she's in urgent need of more training," he said. "Who decided to go back to school in the fall?"

"Getting a Ph.D. isn't quite in the same class as getting your pencil case and lunch box ready for the next grade. Whether or not I come out of that program any more qualified to handle patients, I might command a little more respect from people who think of social workers as nothing more than form-fillers and hand-holders."

"What's the matter?" Nilda asked with concern as she crossed the kitchen threshold bearing a cluttered chunk of lumber that variously served as a chopping board, trivet, and tea tray.

Vince muttered too softly for her to hear, "There's this crazy lady with a gun who keeps making threats . . ."

"Nothing at all, Nilda," I said loudly to cover his grumblings. "Sit down and join us."

Vince vacated his seat on the sofa beside me to retreat to his armchair. As he stood up, I looked at the gun nestled on the serving board between the tea cups and I prayed Vince wouldn't lunge for it. I momentarily considered grabbing it myself just to prevent his doing so, but I knew Nilda would be bound to misinterpret my motivation. I couldn't very well claim I had mistaken it for a crumpet. Fortunately, Vince seemed to have abandoned his plan to disarm her and was more interested in rushing from my side. "You take sugar and milk?" our hostess asked.

"Plain is fine for me," I said.

"Yes, please," Vince said, sulking in the chair.

Nilda threw about three heaping teaspoons of sugar into one of the cups and added some milk from a guava jelly jar, label still attached, that she had pressed into service as a creamer. "Sorry I got no cookies to give you," she sighed. "I got a few crackers, but it looks like the mice got at some."

"The tea is more than enough," Vince hastened to assure her.

Nilda served a cup of tea with milk and sugar for Vince, a cup of plain tea for me, and picked up the gun for herself. "It's a lousy way to live," she lamented. "Counting pennies and food stamps, counting days until the next check comes, hoping nobody steals the check from your mailbox or that welfare's damn computer don't break down so that nobody gets checks on time. A box of cookies is a luxury, something maybe you spoil yourself with at Christmas— not even then, because you need every cent you can scrounge to buy a few cheap presents for kids and relatives. You know how old those tea bags I used were?"

Vince put his cup down from his lips. "Some things are better left unsaid," he interrupted. "Why don't you have a cup with us, Nilda? It will relax you, make you feel better."

"It's going to take a hell of a lot more than a cup of tea to make me feel better after what I been through," she said. "You know what it's like when your very own daughter, only fifteen years old, is a little whore screwing around with your husband?"

"That's a goddamn lie!" a voice screamed somewhere to my left. "I'm not a whore, I'm not screwing him, and he's not even your husband! That's three goddamn lies!" Blanca was up off her deathbed, standing in the doorway of the bedroom like Lazarus at the mouth of his tomb and looking, I'm sure, a hell of a lot better than he. Her thick dark hair was still in disarray but nevertheless becoming as it framed her flawless beige cheeks. She wore a flowered summer dress that, judging from the stretch of bare leg left exposed, she had outgrown two years ago, her full hips putting added strain on the inadequate material.

"Shut up, you tramp!" Nilda barked, menacing her with the gun. "Sit down, and don't you dare talk to me like that."

"Won't you join us for a cup of tea?" Vince invited, tapping his cup against the saucer.

Blanca strode to a straight-backed chair and pulled it closer to the sofa, to the side opposite Vince. She sat down but did not shut up. "Do you think I'd be interested in that bum, who's old enough to be my father? And young enough to be your son?"

"Now who's a liar?" Nilda yelled. "I'm not that much older than him, honest Miss Patterson. He's older than he looks. And I . . . I ain't near as old as I must look."

"That's for sure," Blanca taunted. "If you were, you'd be collecting Social Security benefits for old age instead of just disability money for being crazy."

"Crazy, am I?" Nilda shrieked, pointing the pistol straight at Blanca. "Well, I'm not so crazy that I don't know what kind of whore you are and how you've been playing up to Ernesto!"

"Hah!" Blanca retorted, seemingly oblivious to the gun. "*Me* coming on to him? It's him that can't keep his hands off me! He's the one that won't leave me alone, always starting in."

Nilda leaped to her feet and took two steps toward Blanca, holding the pistol nearly at arm's length. "You admit it, then?" she screamed. At this, Blanca's smug composure shattered and she, too, left her seat, taking cautious steps backward until the wall behind her ended her ineffective retreat.

"Nilda!" Vince commanded. "Put that gun down!"

Nilda pinned her daughter to the wall with an icy stare, then swung her gaze and the gun barrel in Vince's direction. "You keep outta this!" she warned. "You heard her with your own ears, didn't you? Now you know it ain't all in my head, what I suspected was going on!"

"Nilda," I intervened from her opposite flank, "she didn't say they actually did anything. She said Ernesto was trying to get her to."

Nilda redirected the gun at the trembling girl, who said defiantly, "It don't matter what I say. She's got her mind made up that she wants to kill me, so what's the use?"

"Go ahead, you little slut," Nilda hissed, sighting along the top of the revolver. "Might as well die with a lie on your lips, just the way you lived. Tell me you never led him on!"

Blanca shook her head with a beaten expression. "Oh, man! Well, I didn't beat him off, if that's what you mean. He *is* twice my size and I gotta live under the same roof with him—thanks to you."

"You don't have to live here or anywhere else, now," Nilda snarled, and extended her arm so that the gun barrel was less than six feet from her target's chest. Blanca let out a frightened little yelp and pushed her shoulders against the wall, as if trying to escape through it.

"Nilda, please let's talk this out!" I implored.

But Nilda didn't seem to hear me. She kept talking to Blanca in a voice that grew progressively louder and more agitated. "Before you die, I just want to make sure the last thing you think of is the way you turned against your own mother, the only person who loved you and cared for you, the person who gave you life and who's going to . . ."

In a desperate move, I threw myself between the two adversaries. "Nilda, listen to me!" I barked.

"Pat, get out of the way, for God's sake!" Vince screamed. "What the hell are you doing?"

Nilda blinked in consternation at the sudden change in the pistol range. "Look," I went on, trying to muster up a tone of stern authoritativeness I wasn't feeling, "you asked me to come all the way over here so that we could talk things out and you promised that you wouldn't do anything until we had our discussion. I expect you to live up to your end of the bargain, okay?"

Nilda gulped and stared at me as if I were speaking Chinese; finally, she lowered her head and her gun and murmured assent.

"Everyone back to her seat!" I announced, like a schoolteacher at the end of a fire drill. Obediently, Nilda and Blanca returned to the couch and chair respectively, and I resumed my seat beside Nilda.

"Nilda, you've got to understand what Blanca's been going through," I began. "She is only fifteen, after all. I'm sure she didn't ask for Ernesto's attentions, or even welcome them."

"That's for sure!" Blanca sighed. "What do I need with a drunken junkie like him, when I got *three* boyfriends of my own, real men!"

"Three men?" Nilda gasped. "And you're proud of that? Look at you, not even sixteen—a child yet! I should have let that orphanage take you back."

"Yeah, you should have," she agreed, "instead of pretending I had a mother. I'd do better on my own. I'm old enough to take care of myself. You're a fine one to talk about my being a child—you were married in P.R. when you were my age."

Nilda nodded sadly. "I was still a kid, though. I just didn't know it. What did I know about childhood? I left school to do housework when I was eight. I was taking care of baby brothers at nine. I had a job at eleven. Is that the kind of life you want? I wanted something more for you, to have a better life."

"I'll take any sort of life at this point," Blanca said sharply. "The way you're waving that gun around, you seem to want me to have a short one."

"I'd rather see you dead," Nilda warned, "than growing up to be . . ."

"Like you?" Blanca challenged. "Is that what you see ahead? A string of men who run out on you, a bunch of screaming dirty kids you can't manage, getting broken down, and old, and crazy? Well, Ma, you let me live out my life and you can be sure *I* won't end up that way. I wasn't born in a shack on a dirt road in P.R. Not that I've had much out of life that was good, between the slums and the institutions, but I've gotten just enough education to know what *is* out there in the world, and I'm gonna get some of the good . . ."

As Nilda was becoming more visibly tense under her daughter's verbal barrage, the telephone erupted with a piercing ring, sending a shock of alarm through us all. The effect of the telephone on our nervous systems was nothing compared to that of the pistol shot that followed as the startled Nilda jerked her right arm upward and sent a bullet flying into the ceiling at the opposite end of the

room. I threw myself sideways on the sofa and Vince sprang from
his chair to throw himself prostrate on the floor like a bearskin rug.
So much for the possibility of the gun's being harmless!

"Oh my God, what have I done!" wailed Nilda, staring in horror
at the smoking weapon in her hand as the phone rang persistently,
like an unheeded hungry infant crying to be picked up.

Vince slowly rose to one knee and then picked himself off the
floor, his mouth agape. I straightened up on the sofa, involuntarily
edging away from Nilda and her weapon.

"You've spoiled your fun, that's what you've done," Blanca
taunted. "Now the police will come and take you away to jail or a
crazy house, where you belong."

Nilda leaped to her feet and ran to the center of the room,
training the gun on us in a slowly sweeping arc, pointing it from
one to another. "They're not going to take me!" she shouted.

"Of course they won't," I said in a gentle voice. "We can tell
them it was just an accident. The gun is Ernesto's, you picked it
up, and it went off accidentally. That's all."

Nilda looked suspiciously at Vince. "He won't say that. He'll tell
them to lock me up."

"Honestly, I won't," Vince tried to reassure her. "If I'd wanted
to have you picked up, I would have already called the police
myself to come here."

Nilda shook her head. "I don't trust you. I don't trust any of you.
Besides, suppose the cops do come, take the gun, and leave me
alone. I'll be back where I started, played for a fool by my daughter
and that no-good rat. No, I'll kill the little bitch like I planned,
before they can stop me."

"Then you'll *never* get out of jail or the crazy house!" Blanca
chided with incredible nonchalance.

"Blanca, would you stop aggravating your mother!" Vince
ordered sharply.

"They can't take me anyway," Nilda proclaimed defiantly. "I've
got *hostages!*"

"Hostages?" Vince echoed. "What the hell are you talking
about?"

"You're my hostage," Nilda informed him. "So is Miss Patterson. With hostages, I can make them do whatever I want. I can get freedom, money, anything!"

"Hey, how about demanding a flight to Rio, Ma?" Blanca chirped excitedly. "I hear it's *beautiful* there. It's the only way we're ever going to see anything of this world besides New York and Puerto Rico."

"Shut up and sit still!" Nilda barked. "Don't move. Everybody sit right where you are. If the cops come to the door, the doctor will tell them, without opening the door, that I've got a gun and hostages and they'd better not try to break down the door 'cause I'll start shooting. Meanwhile, I gotta think of a list of demands to make."

The phone rang again, causing Nilda to jump so violently that I was amazed the gun didn't go off again. "Let it ring," she snarled at Blanca, who had half arisen from her chair as though to answer it. "Stay put!" The phone would not rest, however. It rang ten, twelve, fifteen times as we looked nervously from one to another.

"Ma, maybe it's one of the neighbors who heard the shot," Blanca urged. "If you don't answer and tell them everything is okay, they will call the police."

Nilda nodded grudgingly and picked up the receiver. "Hello," she grunted. An angry look came into her eyes as she said, "Yeah, he's here." Glowering, she extended the phone toward Vince, saying accusingly, "It's for you."

He walked over, warily eyeing the gun. "Hello. . . . Things are fine here, don't worry," he said calmly. "Well, no, not yet. But it's okay. . . . We can handle it ourselves, I'm sure. . . . Uh, I guess you can later, but don't panic if nobody answers. You can't tell how these things will go. . . . Of course, and I appreciate it. . . . Right. Thanks."

"You told somebody at the clinic you were coming here, huh?" Nilda said, looking betrayed, after Vince had hung up.

He shrugged as he resumed his seat. "You understand, Nilda. They had to know where to reach me. Suppose an emergency came up."

Sure, something that would take precedence over this routine home evaluation we were doing! "Who was that, Vince?" I asked. "One of the doctors?"

"No," he said, offering no further information.

"Not Rosie, I hope," I prodded. "You know how nervous she gets."

"Uh-uh." He saw I was still waiting for an answer. "Julie."

"Julie?" I said, incredulously. "Out of all the people in the clinic, you chose *her* to trust with this?"

"She had the emergency box in her office," he alibied. "I felt I owed her some explanation as to why I was skipping off with a sackful of medicinal goodies."

"You're the director," I harshly reminded him. "You can tell whatever you want or nothing at all to whomever you choose. And that was some choice!"

"What's wrong with my telling Julie?" he asked heatedly.

"Only that I can't understand why you'd pick one of the newest, youngest, and most inexperienced people on the staff to entrust such information to," I answered. "I mean, did you leave *her* in charge? Scrofetti?"

"Scovetti, damn it!" he corrected. "She's been on staff for a month and you still can't get her name straight."

"A rose by any other name is still a blooming incompetent," I declared.

"That's a bum rap, Pat," he snapped. "I don't see how you can call her incompetent after the way she handled that cardiac arrest."

"She may be an excellent medical nurse, but as far as her knowledge of community mental health, Slutteri's a green kid."

"Scovetti!" he shouted. "Just because she's younger than you, that doesn't make her a kid."

"See, they're all the same!" Nilda exclaimed, sitting beside me and patting my thigh with her free hand. "Soon as a younger woman comes along, she's all they think about. Even smart doctors like him, who ought to know better."

"Ma, would you butt out," Blanca reprimanded. "They're arguing about some business at the clinic, not about a girlfriend."

"Aaaah, what do you know?" Nilda scoffed. "I know a fight over another woman when I hear one. I been in enough of them myself." Then she looked at Vince. "Doctor, you take my advice. If you throw over Miss Patterson for this Scumbetti woman, you're a fool. Now, you promise me you won't never let her replace Miss Patterson."

"Nilda," he replied, "the best I can do is promise never to replace her as long as she's with us. When she leaves, it will be because she chose to do so."

"Vince, shut up," I said insubordinately. "There's no need to dredge that up now."

"You ain't leaving St. Dymphna's, are you, Miss Patterson?" Nilda asked anxiously. "Tell me the truth, now."

"Oh, Nilda," I sighed, "I was going to tell you at your next appointment. I'm afraid I will be leaving this month."

"Because of another woman?" Nilda scolded. "Don't you do it. You stay and fight. I'll help you keep your job, really. I got friends in this community . . ."

"You don't even have enemies, here," Blanca said with disgust. "You never talk to anyone except your crazy voices, and nobody even knows you're alive."

"She's wrong, Miss Patterson," Nilda said, looking at me with pleading eyes. "There are plenty of people who owe me favors. They'll remember when I go to them. I would do it for you, my therapist . . . my friend . . . if you stay."

"No, you don't understand," I explained. "Nobody's pushing me out. See, I want to go back to school."

"You're a dropout?" Blanca asked in amazement. "You been working all this time without a diploma?"

"That's okay," Nilda said, leaping to my defense. "She's plenty good enough, she'd don't need one. Doctor, nobody's gotta know about it, you can let her stay on without graduating, no?"

Ignoring Vince's snickering, I tried to break through to our patients. "I have a master's degree in psychiatric social work. But it's not enough for what I want to do. Now, I'm going to get a doctoral degree . . ."

"Oh, Ma, she's going to medical school!" Blanca said enthusiastically.

Nilda looked at me in awe. "Is that true? You're going to be a doctor? Just like him?"

"If she became dean of Harvard Medical School, she wouldn't be just like me!" Vince asserted.

"No, I'm not going to medical school," I corrected. "I'm going to be a doctor of *psychology*."

"You're not going to give injections and listen with a stethoscope?" Blanca asked, with obvious disappointment. When I shook my head, she asked, "Well, then, what exactly will you do?"

"Mostly psychotherapy," I said. "Helping people with emotional problems."

Nilda was even more perplexed. "But you do that now," she protested. "Why do you have to leave to study how to do what you're already doing?"

"Harken to her judgment!" proclaimed Vince. "Verily, a Daniel has come among us."

"There's still a lot more I can learn," I said modestly. "There are important books I should study, new techniques I can master."

"Go on!" Nilda disagreed. "You're plenty good now. Isn't she, Doctor?"

"I have no complaints," he agreed. "Of course," he added, staring directly at Nilda's gun, "some of her cases turn out better than others."

Nilda looked shamefacedly at her weapon. "Hey listen, Doc, don't blame her for this. I mean, this is something between me and my daughter. It's been going on a long time and don't have nothing to do with therapy."

"Yeah, Doc," Blanca chided, "you can't expect a social worker to straighten her out after they couldn't do anything with her at the state hospital, with shock treatments and enough tranquilizers to slow down a rhinoceros."

"You shut up!" Nilda screeched, jumping to her feet and lunging toward the girl. "It was you and your brothers and sisters that drove me into the hospital."

Blanca threw her hands up to shield her face, but said, nevertheless, "Yeah? Was it us little kids, or the dozen guys you kept bringing into the house to drink up your money and beat on you? This lady here could go to school for the next twenty years and not learn anything that's going to cure *you*."

Nilda's right hand, clutching the gun, swung out in a blur, sweeping Blanca's raised hands aside like two fluttering butterflies. Either the gun butt or Nilda's knuckles landed solidly on Blanca's cheek, as the girl and the chair tumbled to the floor. Blanca raised her quivering body on one elbow and brushed her long hair away from her battered face, revealing a scarlet trickle of blood from the corner of her mouth. Her dark eyes met the darker bore of the gun barrel.

"You see?" Nilda demanded shrilly. "You see why I want to kill the little bitch? Does that make me crazy?"

"You've got a right to be angry," Vince said. "But no right to use violence. Now, sit down!" Ignoring Nilda and her omnipresent gun, he knelt down beside Blanca. "Are you okay?" he asked.

Noting that Nilda had already turned to head sheepishly back to her seat, Blanca rubbed away some of the blood with the back of her hand and rose to her feet. "Yeah, sure," she said, resuming the old bravado. "I've been hit harder than that. And not just by her, either. I'm used to it."

"Yeah?" Nilda retorted. "See if you get used to bullets!"

"She wouldn't have the guts to do it," Blanca said to Vince as she picked up the chair from the floor and sat down again.

"Don't be too sure," Vince snapped at her. He looked impatiently at his watch, then glanced at the door expectantly. "Damn it, where are they?" he muttered, loudly enough to be heard.

"Where's who?" Blanca asked. "Expecting someone, Doc?"

Vince looked nervously at Nilda, wondering whether to guard his comments. Finally, in an exasperated voice, he said, "The police, of course! They should have been here by now. Aren't they coming?"

Blanca clasped her hands behind her head and grinned. "'Course not. You just figured that out? I realized it five minutes ago."

"But someone in the building must have heard the shot!" Vince protested.

"Sure," Blanca agreed casually. "Anybody who's home in this building today heard it. Not to mention people on the street and other buildings."

"Wouldn't *somebody* call the police?" he asked in consternation.

"What for?" Blanca shrugged.

"Well, somebody might have been *killed* by that shot," Vince argued.

"All the more reason for not getting involved," Blanca explained. "You put the finger on a killer and *your* life ain't worth a dime in this neighborhood. If the killer don't get you, his relatives or pals will. Ain't no percentage at all in getting mixed up in what ain't your business."

"I can't believe that in an entire building there wouldn't be one person with the courage and decency to try to help," Vince said.

"*I* can," I blurted. "I was attacked by a gang in the hallway this morning and screamed my lungs out, and nobody so much as stuck their head outside their doors."

"You what?" Vince gasped, bolting upright in his chair. "What happened? Were you hurt?"

Nilda grasped my arm with her left hand. "Oh my God, was that you, Miss Patterson? If I had known, I would have helped."

"You should have helped, whoever it was!" Vince scolded. "Pat, I warned you, didn't I? You and your pigheaded independence! But what happened? Did they hurt you . . . molest you?"

"Oh, forget it," I urged. "I was lucky enough to get away because somebody just happened to come out of his apartment."

"What did the guys look like, Miss Patterson?" Blanca asked. "Were they black?"

"I don't remember too much about their faces," I said. "There were four of them. Two didn't look any older than you. They were dressed all in black, but I don't remember any gang insignia. They were black Hispanics, I think."

Blanca nodded knowingly. "Serpents. I know the guys. Always hanging around here. They're a bunch of punks. Don't worry, Miss Patterson, my boyfriend, Rico, is with the Skulls. He'll get them for you."

"Oh, so *that's* the kind of 'real man' you go out with!" Nilda exclaimed. "I shoulda known he'd be a lousy hoodlum."

"Look, Blanca, I appreciate your wanting to help," I said, "but more violence isn't going to solve anything."

"Tell *her* that," Blanca said, nodding pointedly at her mother. Then, addressing Nilda directly, she said, "You're a great one to criticize my friends, waving that gun around like you've been doing."

"Yeah?" Nilda answered. "It's the only thing people like you will ever respect. And if you don't shut your dirty mouth, I'll shut it for good—with this!" She waved the pistol by way of demonstration.

"Nilda, stop talking that way," Vince snapped. "You know that's not the way you really feel. Have you ever been a violent person before? Have you ever threatened anyone with a gun or knife? Have you ever tried to kill someone?"

"Nilda's never been that way," I testified. "Angry, sure. But not violent."

"You know what's changed you, Nilda?" Vince added. "It's that damn gun. All of the things you've said today about your anger and frustration and depression made sense, except for the talk about killing. And if you didn't have that gun, you wouldn't be thinking of such things. Why don't you give it to me and then we'll talk things out sensibly." Vince rose from his chair and extended his hand.

Nilda leveled the gun at him. "Sit down, Doctor!" she commanded, and Vince instantly obeyed. "Yeah, you're right, the gun does make all the difference. The difference between being helpless and being able to do something. Ernesto thought he was a big man because he owned this, but when I grabbed it this morning and pointed it at him, he was a scared little rabbit. For the first time, he didn't yell at me and slap me around. You and Miss Patterson wouldn't be here if it wasn't for this gun. You'd have told me to take my medicine or you would have sent the police to take me off to the hospital. With this in my hand, you take me seriously, you listen to me."

"Nilda," I said, "I've always listened to you. I've always cared about you."

"Yeah, like you'd care for a child," she said. "Tell them to stop crying and go home to bed, to accept things like they are 'cause they won't get no better. Well, I'm not a child now, I'm dangerous. I got five bullets in here, enough to end five lives."

"Would you like me to go out and invite a friend?" Blanca smirked.

"The first bullet's still for you," Nilda said grimly. "It will teach your smart tongue to keep still, if nothing else has."

"Blanca, you're not going to get anywhere by baiting your mother that way," I said impatiently. "Nilda, I came here to talk things out with you. Can we talk quietly now?"

"Sure," she said. "Tell me why you want to leave St. Dymphna's."

"I didn't come here to discuss *my* situation," I protested. "I came to help you because you were upset."

"I'm upset about you leaving," she insisted. "Especially 'cause I don't understand why. This is what *I* say we talk about—if you want to talk."

"Better talk," Blanca advised. "It beats being used for target practice."

Nilda was obviously chairing this session, and while a gun wasn't a gavel, it was just as good. "Okay," I yielded, "but there's not much to say, really. I want to go as far in my field as I can. I want to learn more, I want to be more. I want to be able to take on more responsibility, to be good enough to teach others. In this world, you need credentials, you need the diplomas and papers to earn the respect of others."

"To earn money, too, I'll bet," Blanca interjected. "Women never get paid what they deserve."

"They don't pay you much, Miss Patterson?" Nilda asked, with a malevolent glare in the direction of my boss.

"Only twenty-two thousand dollars a year," Vince said casually. I felt my face flush with anger and embarrassment, as though my doctor had disclosed some intimate medical condition of mine at a cocktail party.

"Not quite half of what *he* makes!" I blurted in retaliation.

Nilda was staring at me in awe, as though I had been suddenly revealed as the missing heiress to the crown jewels of Imperial Russia. "I never realized you were so rich!" she exclaimed.

I didn't blame her, since it was too hot for me to wear my full-length sable and the chauffeur has such difficulty parking the limo in this neighborhood. "It's a decent living, but there are plenty of people who make a lot more," I informed her.

"Sure, Ma," affirmed Blanca, who knew from her magazines about the fabulous incomes of rock stars and Ph.D. psychologists. "If she goes back to school, she could earn two or three times as much. Right, Miss Patterson?"

"It's not the money," I said, feeling like an academic gold digger.

"Hah, people always say that!" Blanca laughed. "They act like wanting money is something to be ashamed of. When you've never had any at all, like us, you're a lot more honest about it. How will you feel when she's making as much as you, Doc?"

"Thoroughly amazed," Vince said. "Believe it or not, Blanca, she's telling the truth about the money. A starting-level Ph.D. psychologist at our clinic wouldn't even get what she's making now, at her level of experience, as a social worker."

"You mean after she goes back to school and studies for a year, maybe more, you're gonna pay her *less* to work for you?" Nilda asked incredulously. "That ain't fair."

"I don't set the salary standards," Vince declared. "See, despite what Ms. Patterson may lead you to believe, it's not just titles and diplomas that matter—experience counts for an awful lot."

"Maybe she could find a place to work that would pay her more," Blanca speculated.

"She *might*," Vince said, unconvincingly. "Of course, all I know is that whenever we have an opening, I get snowed under with resumes. Seems there's more degrees than jobs these days."

Nilda turned to me sympathetically. "Miss Patterson, I don't have no education myself, and maybe I got no right talking to you like this, but, if what he says is true, it sounds to me like you're making a big mistake to leave."

"All that Dr. Bellino said is true," I admitted. "Still, it doesn't change the fact that if I want to go farther in life, I've got to take some risks. I'll lose some years and I'll lose some money . . ."

"*Some* money?" Vince interrupted. "Multiply out the years of almost no income, add the years at starting levels, and figure out how long—*if* you land the right opportunities—it will take you to catch up. You'll be moonlighting in the nursing home where you spend your final days just to pay off your debts."

"Can't you think about anything but money?" I fumed. "I told you that's not what matters to me."

"Sure, you tell him," Blanca urged. "A pretty and smart lady like you can find plenty of guys willing to support her, right? Hey, you're probably married to a doctor or lawyer already. Are you, Miss Patterson?"

"Shut up, stupid!" Nilda said. "How can she be married if her name is 'Miss'?"

"No, she's not Miss Patterson," Vince goaded. "She's Ms. Spelled M–S."

"Oh," Nilda said uncomprehendingly. "That means she *is* married?"

"No, Ma, then she'd be a M–R–S," Blanca said pedantically. "A M–S doesn't have a husband, but that don't stop her from living with men, like it would a 'Miss.'"

"Well put, Blanca," Vince applauded.

"Stop misleading the child," I growled. "No, Blanca, it has nothing to do with marital status or men in a woman's life. That's the whole point: Ms. should be the title used by *all* woman, just as all men use Mr."

"*I* use Dr.," Vince chimed in irrascibly.

"You got a man, Miss . . . I mean, Ms. Patterson?" Blanca asked breathlessly.

"Shut up, Blanca, don't talk like that!" Nilda scolded. "She's a therapist."

"Yeah, a social worker . . . not a nun, for God's sake!" Blanca protested. "Even the nuns I ain't so sure about these days."

"Well, I personally wouldn't trust any sister who called herself Reverend Ms.," Vince confided.

Blanca gazed expectantly at me with the dogged persistence of a gossip columnist interviewing Farrah Fawcett-Majors about her activities after a hard day at the studio.

"Blanca, my personal life is totally irrelevant," I tried to explain. "As a professional, I would have to fulfill myself, whatever it took, regardless of who I was involved with or how much financial support he gave me. There's no point in discussing men."

"You're right," Nilda agreed. "They're all rotten—what's to discuss?" She looked at Vince and for a moment seemed about to make a qualifying remark to soothe his feelings. Then she looked at her gun and gave a small to-hell-with-him shrug. "Now, discuss why you got to leave if it ain't for money."

"There would be more possibilities open to me," I said. "I might be able to be director of a program somewhere. I could open up my own office and do private practice."

"What she's saying, Ma," Blanca interpreted, "is that she could get out of this lousy slum. She would work with a higher class of patients."

Nilda looked genuinely hurt. "Oh," she said softly. "Is that it, Miss Patterson? It's the community, huh?"

As I hesitated, Blanca hastily replied, "Of course it is! Shit, if I can't wait to get out of here, think how a lady like her, with all her education, must feel. Coming down to this sewer of a neighborhood every day, working with the scum that hangs around the streets, like Ernesto, trying to save hopeless wrecks like you . . ."

"At least I survived forty-two years!" Nilda said. "You and your fancy talk about getting out of here! Where are you going? With all your running around, you ain't even finished the eighth grade yet! What kind of a job are you ever gonna get? Or do you think those no-good boyfriends of yours are ever gonna do more for you than get you pregnant and then abandon you? Maybe Miss Patterson ain't made for the likes of this community, but, *muchacha*, you ain't never going anywhere that's any better, so get used to it!"

"Nilda, it's not that I don't want to work in this community," I intervened, doubting my sincerity at the moment. "I could have gotten a job in a richer neighborhood, if that were all that mattered. I suppose the thing I want most is to be my own boss, not to have to answer to anyone."

Nilda nodded and pointed to Vince. "Like him?"

"Hah!" Vince exclaimed. "If that's the lovely fantasy you're pursuing, abandon the chase and save your breath. I answer to the hospital administration and Sportin' Life and the rest of the community, don't I? I have to answer to the gripes and pleas of thirty staff members, most of them ridiculous, all of them conflicting. I have to answer to the needs of patients, not only my own fifty or so but the other thousand-plus on the clinic rolls. If you think a Ph.D. is going to make you Empress of Cathay, Pat, don't bet your imperial fan. You'll always have to answer . . ."

"The phone!" Blanca announced as the instrument went off. "Should I get it?" Nilda nodded wearily. Blanca designated me as the call's recipient.

"Pat, how are you? We're all so worried about you over here," cooed the irritating voice of Rosie McGonigle.

"We're hanging in, Rosie," I said.

"Oh, that's *such* a relief to hear," she warbled. "Well, now, the reason I'm calling . . . and I really hate to bother you at a time like this . . . you know, I wouldn't if I could avoid it . . ." Yeah, go on, Rosie, and spare me the prologue. You'd rap on my casket if you thought it would give you one last chance to bug me. "I need someone to cover the front desk between one and two. Dolores is out sick, as you know. Now, Evelyn would usually fill in, but *you* let her escort a patient to the welfare center, even though it isn't her day to go out and *is* her day to back up the desk. The only mental health assistants here right now are Pablo and Andy, and you know Pablo is useless out front, but I hesitate to ask . . ."

"Well, if Andy's the only one there, ask him, and stop harassing me!" I yelled, uncharacteristically. "For God's sake, Rosie, you know we've got a crisis here. Really!" I slammed down the receiver.

"*That's* what I mean about the clinic!" I grumbled at Vince. "This really petty nonsense. It's unprofessional and childish. It's . . . Mickey Mouse!"

"So it is," Vince said, with a bored yawn. "But the whole world is that way, from the schoolyard to the White House. Mickey Mouse rules not only Disneyland but the hearts of men everywhere. People *always* put their own little interests and feelings first. What do you think you're going to find, wherever your Ph.D. takes you?"

"A mouse!" I gasped, lunging at Vince and seizing his wrist.

He looked up at my gaping mouth, stunned at the intensity of my response. "Indeed," he said softly. "It's a Mickey Mouse world . . ."

Oblivious to his philosophical ramblings, I pointed in horror at a furry ball nestled against the leg of the sofa. "A m-m-mouse," I stammered. "A real mouse. Right there."

"Oh yeah," Blanca affirmed, her reaction a blend of disgust and resignation.

Nilda rose slowly from her seat on the sofa at the end opposite the offensive intruder, which was trying to make itself inconspicuous by remaining immobile. She circled around while I back-pedaled to the most remote corner of the room, then she crouched down a little and took a bead on the mouse with her gun.

"Ma!" shrieked Blanca, the sound convincing the mouse its camouflage had been blown and making it take cover under the sofa. "Are you crazy? You don't use a gun to kill a mouse!"

Nilda, not having had the luxury of a gun before and therefore not very sophisticated with regard to its appropriate uses, shrugged apologetically. She looked at my trembling body pressed rigidly against the wall and said solicitiously, "You okay, Miss Patterson? Come sit down."

"Nilda," I declined, "the mouse went under the sofa. I'm afraid of mice." I think she already suspected that.

"You'll *love* it here," Blanca smirked. "It's a house of horrors."

"Do you have many?" Vince asked, rising finally from the armchair and circling behind it to use it as a shield for his lower parts.

"Does this block have junkies?" she replied. "Man, you should see the *rats* we got—big as kittens, some of them." She extended both hands to encircle an imaginary rat the size of a cocker spaniel.

"What are you going to do about *that* one?" I asked, pointing with a quavering finger at the hiding place of the nonimaginary rodent.

"I'll kill it for you," Blanca casually volunteered. She sauntered into the kitchen in search of a weapon and emerged with a broom. "Now," she directed, swinging the broom, whisk-end up, like Reggie Jackson in the on-deck circle, "Doctor, you lift one end of the sofa and Miss Patterson . . ." I shook my head wordlessly.

There was no way I was going to get within a yard of that mouse. "Okay, Ma, get the other end, and I'll clobber the little bastard."

Vince reluctantly came out from behind his barrier and embraced the sofa, one hand behind its back and the other on its arm. Nilda halfheartedly slipped her right hand under its bottom at the opposite end, transferring the gun to her left hand. Blanca took her batting stance halfway between them. "Ready, get set . . . lift!" she commanded. I was experiencing very atypical pro-mouse feelings at the moment and was actually hoping the poor little animal had somehow sneaked to safety without our notice. No sooner had they gotten the sofa about two inches off the floor, which was about the best Nilda could manage with her one-handed grip, than a gray blur zipped out and darted under the skirt of the armchair. Blanca slapped the floor awkwardly with the broom as the mouse passed a foot to her right.

"Fine job you did!" Nilda scowled at her daughter. "Here, give me that broom before he gets away." Blanca uncomplainingly surrendered the broom to Nilda, who now found herself overly encumbered with weapons. She walked over to me after a moment's thought and handed the gun, its muzzle carefully directed to the side, out to me. "Will you hold this for me, Miss Patterson?" she asked politely. "You got to promise to give it back, though."

I obediently took the unfamiliar object, squeezing the handle with all my fingers as if to reassure myself that none of them was anywhere near the trigger. With my eyes riveted on Nilda, who was tiptoeing toward the armchair, I never noticed Vince until he was right at my elbow, startling me so badly I was grateful for my trigger phobia. "Great work, Pat," he said softly. "We've gotten the gun away from her."

"Don't be silly," I whispered, still watching Nilda, who was circling the chair planning her strategy. "I'm just holding it for her. I've got to give it back."

Nilda finally lifted her leg high and delivered a kick to the side of the chair, rocking it so badly it nearly toppled over. The mouse could have emerged from any of four sides and I was prepared to run myself if it headed in my direction. As luck would have it, the mouse took off perpendicular to Nilda, making for the far wall. The previously dispirited woman was after it like a cat, dealing one mighty blow before it reached the wall. It let out a dreadful squeak as its flight was halted. Nilda's hips mercifully shielded my eyes from its death throes as she brought the broom down again and again.

"Pat, please, be realistic," Vince begged. "You can't give that gun back to her. By keeping it, you could be saving her life, her daughter's life . . . our lives!" I shook my head stubbornly, as Nilda, her back still toward us, took a deep breath and stood triumphantly over her tiny victim. "Pat," he persisted in a whisper, "don't you see that her giving you the gun means that she wanted you to control things? It was the only way she could bring herself to give up the gun."

"Got it!" Nilda said, turning to us with a satisfied smile. She walked over to a stack of magazines and lifted the top one.

"Hey, Ma, not my new Betty and Veronica comic!" Blanca protested, charging at her. "Haven't you got a newspaper?"

"Vince," I said resolutely, "if she wants me to keep the gun, I'll be glad to. But if she asks for it back, I've got to give it to her, because I promised and I can't betray her. She'll have to work things out herself, regardless of the risk."

"Great!" Vince cried, flapping his arms in agitation. "I'm stuck here now with *two* crazy women!"

"Who can afford a newspaper?" Nilda replied to Blanca, with a scornful laugh. "You can waste good money on these junky comics when we're lucky enough to be able to buy a mouthful of food. I don't throw money away."

"My boyfriend bought it for me," Blanca argued sheepishly.

"I'd be ashamed to let a man know what a baby I was, reading little kids' stuff!" Nilda chided. She brandished the broom warningly in Blanca's direction, then flung the comic back in the direction of the stack where it had originated. "I got some old letters from the welfare center," she said, shuffling off toward the bedroom. "I'll use them for the mouse."

"Isn't she too much!" Blanca said, looking at us for approbation. "No respect for any of my property . . . or for me. I should have stayed at the home."

Nilda came back holding several sheets of paper. "Look at these!" she complained. "We paid you too much, we're going to give you less, we're taking away your food stamps, we're closing your case . . . lousy bastards! You gotta fight them for every scrap you eat." She knelt beside the fallen mouse.

"Aw, just pick it up by the tail with your hand," Blanca urged. "Don't be so damn fussy."

"Pick it up yourself, then," Nilda grumbled. "Tough-mouthed little bitch!" Nilda gripped the paper in one hand and, with it covering her palm, picked up the mouse.

"What are you going to do with it, Nilda?" I asked, with a weird fascination.

"If she's got something else for supper and doesn't have to cook it, she can keep it by the bed to remind her of Ernesto," teased Blanca.

"Aaaghh!" Nilda snarled, baring her teeth. She looked at her naive therapist. "Flush it down the toilet, what else? If the damn plumbing is working."

"Blanca, get out," Vince said, leaping with one bound to the girl's side as soon as the pallbearer had left. "Quick, before she comes back."

Blanca looked at him skeptically. "Go? Where am I gonna go?"

The toilet flushed. A pause, then again. The remains were resisting the trip to their final resting place.

"Anywhere, for God's sake!" Vince urged. "Go to the clinic and wait for us. You're in big danger here. Your mother has threatened to kill you."

"So what else is new?" grinned Blanca. "She's done that since I can remember."

Again, the sound of the flush, followed by some Spanish curses. Vince gripped the girl's arm. "Please, Blanca, she's not in her right mind—and she's got a gun."

Blanca shook her head and pointed to me. "No, she's got the gun."

Vince glared at me. "If my colleague has her addle-pated way, she'll give the gun back. She may feel your mother can be reasoned with, but in my opinion as an experienced psychiatrist your mother is very dangerous to both herself and you. She's a sick woman."

The cursing and flushing stopped, but Nilda still had not returned. Apparently she had decided, as long as she was in the bathroom, to take care of other related business.

"Yeah, Doc, I guess she is sick," Blanca acknowledged. She ambled over to the straight-backed chair and plopped herself down, stretching her long, tan legs in front of her. "That's why, I suppose, I really can't run out on her now. She's really all I got, bad as she is. And I know she must care about me in some crazy way, 'cause she took me back when she really didn't have to—and, God knows, she didn't need the expense and the trouble I bring." She looked up at me with a cheerful grin. "So hell, maybe Miss Patterson ain't got your diplomas and 'sperience, but if she thinks she can pull Ma through without any of us getting blown away, I say let her try. Us girls gotta stick together, right, Miss . . . I mean, Ms. Patterson?"

"Us women," I gently corrected.

"God help me, I've got three madwomen here," Vince groaned.

The phone rang just as Nilda had flushed the final time and returned from the burial at sea and associated activities. Since I had the gun, I didn't ask permission from anyone and answered the phone.

"Hello," a timid voice responded. "May I speak to Dr. Bellino?"

"Who is this?" I asked gruffly.

"This is Julia Scovetti," the caller reported, "psychiatric registered nurse at the Mental Health Clinic of St. Dymph . . ."

"He's busy now, he's with a patient," I interrupted.

"Is that you, Pat?"

No, it's Nilda. I've lost my accent through private elocution lessons with Rex Harrison. "Yes, Julia, it's me."

"Oh, is everything all right? I . . . we've all been so worried about Dr. Bellino. And you, too, of course."

Sure, you've probably got half your stuff moved into my office already. "We're all just fine, thanks."

"Is that Julie?" Vince panted. "Does she want to talk to me?"

I waved him off as the nightingale chirped, "Are you still in danger? Does the patient still have a . . . you know? . . ."

Did she think Nilda was rich enough to afford a Princess extension phone to listen in on? "I have that particular situation in my capable hands at the moment," I replied cleverly, perhaps too cleverly for the walking communication gap at the other end.

"*You* have the gun, Pat? Is that what you're saying?" she gushed.

"For the time being, yes."

"I don't quite understand. You're *not* going to give it back?"

"Look, just don't worry," I commanded my subordinate.

"But I *am* worried," she whimpered. "I don't understand what's going on there. Are you talking in some sort of code, Pat?"

"No," I sighed. "You've been watching too many TV shows."

"I *never* watch television!" she protested. "Only an occasional show that relates to my field of interest." That meant she hadn't gotten past *The Doctors* and *General Hospital*. "Can I do anything?" she persisted. "Does the doctor want me to call his family?" What the hell for? He's not dead yet, and with a little luck and fewer interruptions, he might be home in time for dinner.

"No, no, don't alarm anyone," I said. "We're all fine."

"Let me talk to her," Vince said, walking over to the phone.

I pressed down on the button and said, "She hung up."

"Well, what did she say?" he asked.

"Nothing important. She was just being nosy," I reported.

"She's concerned, Pat," he said. "I don't see why you have to be so hostile toward her."

"If she had something to contribute, I could see her involving herself," I explained, standing guard over the phone against further unwelcome intrusions. "As things stand, these calls by Miss Slobetti . . ."

"Scovetti!" he interjected.

". . . are a distracting nuisance."

"Excuse me, Miss Patterson," Nilda interrupted. "Can I have my gun back now?"

Vince hurled himself between us. "Nilda, you can't have the

gun. It can't possibly do any good, and it may lead you to do something you'll regret the rest of your life."

"It's mine," she whined. "Miss Patterson promised to give it back."

"I don't care what she said," he argued. "We, as therapists, have a responsibility to you and your daughter. When you think and act in an irresponsible way, you can't expect us to let you do whatever you please. You're free to talk things out with Ms. Patterson or myself—but not with a gun in your hand."

"Free?" she said in a loud, angry voice. "You know that unless I have that gun you people will do whatever you want with me. You'll let me talk, but you'll still tell me what to do, like you're doing now. If I have that gun, I'll know that whatever I decide, it *will* be a free choice." She took a step to the side to look me in the eye without his considerable bulk obstructing her vision. "Can I have my gun back like you promised, Miss Patterson?"

I gave Vince a long, deliberate look, then took a step toward Nilda, extending the gun.

"Hold it!" Vince shouted. "Pat, give *me* that gun. I'm still your superior and I have the clinical responsibility here. It's my decision to make, not yours." He held out his hand.

I swallowed hard and shook my head. "Sorry, I can't do it. I believe Nilda will ultimately make the right decision and I'm prepared to take this risk to let her make it."

"Pat," he persisted, his voice choking out the words in a rumbling growl, "if you don't give me that gun, I'll have you fired."

I shook my head resolutely. "I've already resigned."

"Well, you can forget about any letters of recommendation from me!" he threatened.

I shrugged. "It depends how this turns out, Vince. If you're right and I'm wrong in my judgment, I don't deserve one. Time will tell."

Vince was about four feet away from me, with Nilda practically looking over his shoulder. "For the last time, Pat, give me that gun. If you don't, I'm going to take it away from you by force. You know I can do it."

For the first time since I'd held the gun, I put my index finger on the trigger. "No, Vince," I said tremulously.

He stared at my trigger finger in disbelief. "You're out of your mind! You wouldn't shoot me!"

"Of course not, Vince," I said softly. "But you wouldn't try to take this away from me with my finger where it is, either. And if this is what it takes to stop you, I'm doing it. Nilda, come and get your gun."

"Shoot him in the arm, Miss Patterson!" Nilda urged. "That'll stop him for good. He deserves it."

"I don't intend to shoot anyone and neither do you," I said sharply. "Now stop talking nonsense and take this if you want it so badly."

Nilda slunk past Vince, who folded his arms and glared angrily at both of us. Without taking my eyes from Vince, I returned the weapon to Nilda, grateful to be rid of it even under such disquieting circumstances. "Fine doctor you are!" Nilda scolded Vince, who threw himself into the armchair with a moan. "Pushing patients around, breaking promises. You should be shot!"

"Welcome to the hit parade!" laughed Blanca. "I hate to lose my number one spot, but that's the breaks."

"Nobody will be hurt," Vince said in a mocking monotone. "Ms. Patterson, after all, has complete faith in your mother that she'll do the right thing."

Nilda strode to the center of the room, pointing the pistol ahead of her. "I'll do the right thing, for sure. But that don't mean no one will get hurt. Maybe the right thing is to kill all of us. Who's to say?"

"Well, if I may have a say, I'd like to object to that," Vince ventured.

"You got no say!" Nilda said, by way of informing him of his rights. "You didn't want to give me any rights, why should I give you any?"

"I wasn't depriving you of any right other than the one to bear arms," he protested.

"That one *is* covered by the Constitution," I reminded him.

"It pertains only to legally registered weapons," he retorted. "If she shows me a permit for that thing, I'll eat it."

"The permit or the gun?" Blanca asked.

"What difference does it make?" he roared. "There's no permit for that gun. And if there is, it doesn't make it legal to threaten innocent people with it. She's acting illegally—and Ms. Patterson is acting as an accomplice."

Blanca whistled. "You gonna have Ms. Patterson thrown in the slammer?"

"I would like to have her put somewhere where she's not a hazard to patients," he sneered. "Maybe a graduate school isn't such a bad idea. At least it will keep her from clinical malpractice for a couple of years."

"You'll be sorry when you don't have her at your clinic no more," Nilda warned. "You think you're gonna get her kind of work out of that Scungilli girl?"

"Scovetti!" he said. "And please don't mention *scungilli* or any other kind of food. I'm going mad with hunger! It's way past lunchtime, you know. What I wouldn't give now for a plate of *scungilli* with hot sauce. Or fried *calamari*. Listen, Nilda, don't you want some lunch? I'll treat."

"You ain't going nowhere," she told him, waving the gun.

"Then send Pat out," he suggested. "You know she always keeps her word."

"You hungry, Miss Patterson?" Nilda asked solicitously.

"Couldn't eat a bite," I answered truthfully, after a morning of mice and gunplay. "But I'll be glad to go out and buy some food for the rest of you."

"Hey, how about it, Ma?" Blanca urged. "The doc here is treating. We could have a real banquet for a change, instead of the old rice and beans."

"If Miss Patterson and I don't want to eat, you two can starve to death," Nilda said stubbornly.

"Then I'm going to help myself to something from the fridge," Blanca announced.

"That's *my* food in there," Nilda said ominously.

"Not *all* of it," Blanca countered. "There's some *cabrito* in there that I brought home from the restaurant when my boyfriend took me out to dinner." She stuck out her tongue at Nilda and sashayed into the kitchen, then returned with a platter of cold meat. "Want to try some, Doc?" she invited.

Vince asked, "What is it?"

"Goat meat," Blanca replied.

With anticipatory glee, I watched Vince's face for a reaction. I couldn't wait to see how the professed-liberal community leader would react to sharing the typical food of his alleged soul sisters. But to my consternation, instead of retching and making some feeble excuse, Vince seemed genuinely interested in Blanca's offer. "Hey, thanks," he exclaimed, reaching for a greasy gray slab adhering to a bone whose origin I was not about to identify. He bit into it with the gusto of Colonel Sanders attacking a finger-lickin'-good drumstick.

"Ever try goat meat before?" Blanca asked, fingering a smaller piece of meat with the delicacy of a debutante with a cocktail shrimp.

"Uh-huh," Vince affirmed indistinctly through his excessive mouthful. Then, having swallowed it, he said, "My family would often serve *caputzelle* around Easter."

"What's *that*?" Blanca asked, eager to learn the habits of the elite.

"The head of a kid, a young goat," he explained. "You split the skull in half and bake it. It's great."

"Yechhh," Blanca said with a little laugh. "I'll stick with *cabrito*."

"How come a rich doctor like you eats like poor folks?" Nilda asked suspiciously.

"Like poor folks?" Vince questioned. "Listen, do you know what a *caputzelle* costs? I don't think you can even get kids anymore— most of the time you have to settle for a lamb's head."

Blanca sauntered over to a radio on the dining table and flicked a knob, filling the room with a blare of human howls, drums, and electronic distortion of musical notes. Swinging her hips to her own internal rhythm, she grinned, "A little dinner music, huh?"

"Turn that garbage off!" Nilda bellowed.

"Aw," she pouted, "that's the Rolling Stones, my favorite group. You like 'em, Doc?"

"Since your mother and Miss Patterson aren't eating, maybe they'd like to talk in quiet," he said diplomatically. With a sigh of exasperation, Blanca put a quick end to the cacaphony.

"Who's *your* favorite group, Doc?" she asked.

"The Four Aces, I guess," he answered.

Blanca looked at him uncomprehendingly. "How about your favorite *rock* group?"

"Oh," he pondered, "like rock 'n' roll? Bill Haley and the Comets."

"I don't think they make records anymore," Blanca said, as though trying to break the news to him gently.

"That's why they're my favorite group," he said, undeterred.

Nilda watched Vince dexterously split joints apart with his greasy fingers, tearing indiscriminately with his teeth at meat, fat, and gristle. "You know," she whispered, "he don't seem like such a bad guy, once he loosens up a little. He acts high and mighty when he's in his office, but maybe it's just the suit and tie that does that to him. I bet you two could really work things out if you'd just talk things over."

"Work *what* things out?" I asked.

"You know, the reasons you want to leave and all."

"Nilda," I insisted, "I keep telling you my leaving to enter a doctoral program has nothing to do with the situation at St. Dymphna's."

"*Vaja!*" she exclaimed. "If you were happy there, you wouldn't even think of leaving, no matter how good the reason." Nilda looked at her daughter, who had now perched her bottom on the arm of Vince's chair, reaching at intervals into the plate he had balanced on his lap to deposit a bone or pick up another chunk of that loathsome carcass. I suddenly felt ashamed of my repugnance and wondered how I would be judged by my liberal sisters at Berkeley, though they never consumed anything more exotic than a *burrito* at a roadside stand off the Santa Monica Freeway.

"Look at the two of them," Nilda said, almost tenderly. "Know what crazy thought I just had?"

"If it had to do with your daughter marrying a psychiatrist someday, I'm calling nine-one-one," I warned.

Nilda laughed for the first time that day. "A woman could make a lot worse mistakes. I make you a deal. If you try to work things out with him, I'll talk to Blanca."

"I think you *should* talk to Blanca," I agreed, "but I have nothing to discuss . . ."

"Hey, Doc, come here," Nilda said, beckoning him with the gun. Vince obediently handed the girl what now appeared to be an elephant graveyard on a platter and rose to approach us. "I'm going to talk things over with my daughter," she said, giving him a wink I wasn't supposed to see. "And while we're discussing things, maybe there's a few things you and Miss Patterson can talk about."

"You two can use the bedroom if you want privacy," Blanca volunteered.

"Blanca!" Nilda reprimanded. "You expect Miss Patterson to go alone into a bedroom with this man?"

"I wouldn't trust *her* even with a chaperone present!" Vince said with theatrical horror.

"Come on, Blanca," Nilda urged. "We'll go in the bedroom and leave them alone out here for a while." Blanca gave Vince a flirtatious wave and followed her pistol-packing mama into the bedroom.

"*Now* what's going on?" Vince inquired. "A guy takes a lunch break and meanwhile all sorts of things are happening." He sat beside me on the sofa and looked at the closed bedroom door. "What's going on in there?"

"Hopefully, the calm discussion they should have had this morning," I said. "But actually, *we're* the main event. I think you're supposed to talk me into staying at St. Dymphna's."

"Can I?" he asked.

"No," I answered honestly.

"Too bad," he said. "It's not often I get a chance to talk to you alone like this, in quiet, comfortable surroundings, no one around except a sex-crazed girl in a minidress and a paranoid with a gun."

"Just like home, at the clinic," I noted. "I don't know why you would have waited this long if you had something to say to me."

"What do you say after, 'I accept your resignation'?" he asked.

"'Please don't go'? 'What can I say to change your mind'?"

"Not bad for openers," I commented.

"Pat, would you believe there were times when I started to say something along those lines? But then the telephone would ring, or the intercom would buzz, or an assistant would burst in with an emergency."

"It wouldn't have mattered, Vince. Honestly," I said.

"I'd like to have that talk now, anyway," he requested. "Seeing as there's not much to do here anyway."

"I can't stop you," I confessed, "now that Nilda's got the gun again."

"What do you *really* want, Pat?"

"A doctorate. You know that," I said.

"What will that give you that you don't have already?" he asked. "You're making a good salary now, with no guarantee that you could make more even if you put in the four or five years it will take you to get that Ph.D. you want so badly."

"You'll concede that program directors make more?" I ventured.

He nodded readily. "I'll even concede that they hire psychologists to head mental health programs—but you know that's often done so they can pay the psychologist less than they would have to give an M.D. There are programs where the psychologist-director is pulling less than the staff psychiatrists. And you know that in the big hospitals the medics have a lock on things."

"Am I better off now?" I challenged.

"*I* think so," he asserted. "I saw to it that you were promoted to supervisory social worker when you took on the headache of the mental health assistants, and your union saw to it that you got every possible raise that could be wheedled, at least semiannually. As clinic coordinator, you have a say in the way things are run throughout the whole operation and, most important, you have your pick of any therapy case that comes through intake. Think of it, Pat, over a hundred cases a month and you get your choice—if you're truly interested in doing therapy, and not in making money, where can you get a better deal than that?"

"If I get such great cases," I argued, "how come I wind up with trigger-happy grammar-school dropouts?"

"Maybe because that's where your heart is really at," he suggested. "Maybe you can't be happy unless you're taking on the cases everyone else has given up on and nobody else wants."

"Maybe," I added, "it's because by the end of the first year, all the more promising cases have gotten better or left therapy, and only the most helpless, dependent types keep coming back, making so many demands on you, you haven't time to pick up new cases."

"And you think it's going to be better in the wonderful world of private practice, huh?" he said. "Listen, I can assure you it's no different. You think there are hundreds of potential clients out there, with the mildest and most interesting of problems: the prize-winning novelist who has writer's block; the brilliant heiress coming to grips with her guilt over not making a personal contribution to society; the screen idol who feels compelled to review his sexual escapades over the last two decades. Pat, these people have no motivation for therapy, because they're not hurting enough. They'll come for one or two sessions and then cancel you for a boating invitation or a cocktail party. And the ones who really need you won't be able to afford you, because they can't work. Even the big names in our field get by mostly with a waiting list of hopefuls who expect miracles in two or three exorbitantly priced sessions and then drop out when their hopes and bankrolls run out."

"Don't tell me *nobody* makes it in private practice, Vince."

"I didn't say nobody makes a good living," he emphasized. "Just don't make the mistake of thinking that because our patients pay low fees or ride free on a Medicaid card it decreases their motivation for therapy. Human nature doesn't change with the addition of money. If you're hurting real bad, you come for therapy; if you're not, you'll spend your money elsewhere, no matter how much you've got. In private practice, your patients will pick you—and drop you. At least in the clinic you can pick *them*, and you'll never get that kind of deal again."

"Is that what keeps you tied to the ghetto?" I asked.

"That's part of it," he agreed. "Picking my own patients. Not having to worry about people failing to pay bills or not being able to pay at all. Being able to look at more than four diploma-filled walls and a couple of chairs every day. Sharing ideas and cases with other therapists, even if they are a bit far out at times."

"Being number one?" I pressed.

"It helps," he admitted.

"Can't you understand that I'd like to be more than a subordinate, no matter how much influence I might have and how well I'm treated? Don't you have pride in your title and your years of study to earn it?"

"Yeah, I sure can understand that," he said. "I'll tell you something funny. When I was a premed in college, and even when I was in medical school, I sometimes worried about dying before I finished. Mind you, I never worried about failure, just about death, the one thing that could stop me. And I used to think, All I ask is that I get that M.D. before I die. Whatever happens after that is okay, as long as my tombstone reads VINCENT BELLINO, M.D."

"And after *that*," I said with a tired smile, "you can't see how I would want a Ph.D.?"

"Oh, I see it perfectly," he assured me. "Only I'm trying to warn you, Pat. Because now, it's *not* okay if I die. I honestly don't think I give a damn anymore what it says on my tombstone. The magic inherent in those letters is gone now. All that's important is that I'm alive and doing what I want to do."

"And how far do you think you'd get without those letters after your name? Admit it, Vince, there's a hell of a lot more you can get and get away with if you're an M.D."

"Ah, now we come to the crux of the matter!" he exclaimed. "You're still angry at me because you feel I give the psychiatrists special treatment; because I let Dimitri come in late, and the Princess paint her face, and Chong put down talk-therapy, and Frau Krumpel take naps between patients . . ."

". . . while you let Rosie dock the pay of an assistant who comes in late because her kid woke up with vomiting, or make them pay a doctor twenty-five bucks for a note if they get sick on a Friday, or send one of them out into the snow to change a patient's appointment because the shrink took a day off to see his tax lawyer about a shelter," I continued.

"It's the system, Pat," he sighed, "but you've got to admit that I *have* bucked it for you and your precious underlings many times. I can't help it if master's-level professionals and paraprofessionals are flooding the job market, while I could probably sign up Reggie Jackson as a security guard with more ease than I can induce a psychiatrist to work in our run-down, non-university-affiliated, minimum-scale operation. Without the shrinks, we'd have no clinic. Without the clinic, Maria and Evelyn and Pablo would have no jobs. It's a fact of life, Pat, and your getting a Ph.D. won't change it. Sure, psychiatrists have their faults—maybe more than the average sinner, given our temptations—but we'll have our underlings in hell with us, as well as on earth. No doubt you grew up with the notion that social workers are all immaculate angels of mercy . . ."

"As a matter of fact," I confided, "the first social worker I was ever aware of struck me as the most heartless woman on earth."

"And where in the world did you meet such an atypical specimen of the breed?" he asked.

"I never actually met her," I related. "This goes back to my college days. As an overprivileged underclassman who'd spent every summer on the beach and Saturdays taking piano and ballet lessons, I was very susceptible to some of my freshman classmates who delighted in trying to make me feel guilty about not doing more for society than picking up my empty Tab cans when I left the beach. And so I volunteered my amateur services as a 'big sister' to a twelve-year-old girl named Barbara, who was in a group home for unwanted children. I'm not sure of the name, but I think it was St. Salvation for Lost Angels."

"No such saint!" Vince interrupted.

"What makes you so sure?" I challenged. "Just because *you've* never heard of him . . . or her? Maybe he wasn't Italian."

"There are a few non-Italians in heaven, I concede. But salvation is a state the soul reaches, it's not a person," Vince preached. "Don't you Protestants know anything about religion?"

"We agnostics know nothing about it," I professed. "Now, may I get on with my story? The home wasn't for bad kids, the juvenile delinquents who grow up to be murderers, burglars, and Medicaid defrauders, or for psychotic kids, who grow up to keep people like us in business. It was for kids whose parents simply didn't want them or couldn't cope with the demands of parenthood, because they were alcoholic or retarded or emotionally unstable or even just plain poor. Your wonderful modern medical science keeps parents alive long enough to rear their kids into adulthood, but it doesn't give them the emotional resources."

"We're working on it," Vince apologized. "What do you mean, just plain poor?"

"You mean they could always go on welfare," I nodded. "But you have to realize that some parents are better than others at managing to feed and clothe a school-age child on ninety-four dollars a month, which averages out to about three dollars a day. That figure, by the way, was for a one-member family; in larger families, each member was allotted much less, something more like one dollar a day."

Vince groaned. "I'd rather sit with Nilda and her gun than through an economics lecture. Can we get back to the institution?"

"Sorry. Well, you can imagine the effect an institution has on most kids. Even though they weren't in there through any fault of their own, the regimented atmosphere and the pecking order meant they had to become street-wise and tough to survive. I guess that's why St. Salvation seemed to recruit nice super-straight adolescents like me, ones who had a breadwinning father and the kind of thoroughly competent mother who treated everything from scraped knees to broken hearts. It gave these kids a glimpse of a different sort of family life than the one they had known. Barbara, my 'little sister,' came from what social workers like to call a multi-problem family. She had an alcoholic father who deserted and returned at intervals and the sort of inept mother who was too physically sick and emotionally unstable—now, in retrospect, I'd say depressed—to care for Barbara and her six siblings. One by one, they were all placed at St. Salvation."

"What did you do with her?" Vince asked, prodding the narrative along.

"Oh, sometimes we went for ice cream sodas in the commissary and other days we played Ping-Pong in the rec room, but usually we just walked around the grounds and talked. It doesn't sound like much, though I'm sure the staff psychologists wrote in records that I was functioning as a role model so Barbara could have a positive, achievement-oriented, middle-class woman to identify with, a person very different from her own defeated, ineffectual, and very limited mother."

"And all the while, you probably thought you were just playing Ping-Pong and drinking ice cream sodas," Vince said. "When does the wicked social worker come in?"

"It happened one day when I went there and found Barbara crying inconsolably. It took me a while to get it out, but bit by bit, between sobs, I pieced together the story. Her father had died suddenly—or as suddenly as a forty-year-old man with a twenty-year history of drinking a quart of whiskey a day and a liver twice normal size *could* die. The institution's social worker broke the news to Barbara and added that it was just as well, because he was no good anyway and had never done anything for her. It might have been true that Barbara's father was a 'hopeless' alcoholic, but he *was* her father and it was important for her to retain some positive feelings for him after his death."

"Did you believe it happened just as Barbara claimed?"

"I did then. Now, I realize how people often distort things, especially after painful experiences. I'm sure Barbara had unconscious hostile feelings about her father and may have listened selectively to what the social worker had to say about him. At that moment, though, I was shocked by how inhumane and cruelly judgmental social workers were."

"Did Barbara ever talk about the social worker after that?"

"Not that I recall," I said. "But I don't think after that incident Barbara ever trusted social workers or any other adult, including me. Things changed between us; Barbara no longer took me into her confidence. I wish I knew what finally became of her. All my fantasies about her are morbid ones. Maybe she became a hooker, or shot up and o.d.'d in a back apartment in some decaying tenement, or more likely, she married an alcoholic like her mother did and had a number of children she couldn't care for and abandoned them to St. Salvation for Lost Angels."

Vince shook his head. "And *that* influenced you to become a social worker? I don't see how."

I shrugged. "I didn't say it did. I only remember feeling what tremendous power for good and evil a social worker could have."

"Ah, the old power trip! *That* I can understand," Vince exclaimed. "So, that's where your interest in social work began."

"I suspect it went back a lot further," I confided. "Say, do you mind if I take off my shoes?"

"Feel free," he consented, as I slipped off my sandals and curled my feet under me on the sofa.

"Why don't you take off your jacket, Vince?" I invited. "I'm getting uncomfortable just looking at you."

With a self-conscious shrug, he followed my suggestion, carefully folding his jacket twice before laying it beside him on the shabby sofa.

"Now, why don't you loosen your tie and open your collar," I pressed.

"Okay," he consented. "But this is as far as I go on a first date." Having settled back beside me, he said, "Now, you were about to tell me what *really* started you in this profession you now want so desperately to escape."

"I'm not sure if it's really relevant," I said, rather embarrassed. "I remember, when I was about nine years old, pretending that I was head of an orphanage, and my sister's dolls—all sizes, shapes, and types—were my charges. The strange thing is that it wasn't a big, stony institution, it was an isolated farmhouse located somewhere in the Midwest, and there was usually a snowstorm raging outside. Hey, I feel like I'm talking to a shrink."

"You are," he reminded me. "Don't let the shirtsleeves fool you."

"Want me to lie down on the couch?" I teased.

"Not unless you're prepared to shake out your hair when I shake the roaches out of my jacket," he warned. "Whatever became of the fantasy?"

"I suspect the motley assortment of dolls grew up to be mental health assistants, in all sizes, shapes, and colors: plump old Maria and bouncy Jeanne, Evelyn with her long brown hair, and little Pablo. And I'm still trying to keep them from getting snowed under by the poverty outside, only now the storm has moved inside as well, a blizzard of memos and forms and regulations."

"And you're really ready to walk out on them?" he asked skeptically.

"Vince, I've turned thirty," I answered. "I've got to face the storm outside myself. I can't let myself get so comfortable protecting others that I stop taking risks myself."

"I certainly don't see you taking it easy at the clinic," he protested. "If anything, I've thrown too much responsibility on you. Now that we're just beginning to get the staff built up and organized, I can take some of the pressure off you. I can make things a lot easier."

"That's just what I can't let you do, Vince," I said softly. "I can't let you protect me as I protected those dolls. I can't let you be my good daddy, making me so secure I never want to go on."

"Whether you realize it or not," he said somewhat angrily, "you're forever projecting your fantasies on me. I am no more the overprotective father than I am the money-mad tycoon, the male chauvinist pig, or the Victorian prude. Whether I wanted to or not, circumstances compelled me to delegate just about every aspect of responsibility in that clinic to you . . . you've exercised perhaps more authority than you'll ever again possess in your career, degrees notwithstanding."

"Yes, that's true, I'll admit it. And, of all you've done, that's the thing I'm most grateful to you for, Vince. And it's probably the reason I'm leaving. Without the chance to take on that kind of responsibility, under the most chaotic and trying of conditions, I probably wouldn't have had the guts to push on. Thanks to you, I'll never be satisfied again with something less than my maximum potential."

"As Dr. Frankenstein realized, it's dangerous to give our creations too much power," he sighed. "I really corrupted you, didn't I? Do this much for me, though, if you're really determined to quit the clinic for graduate school—put in for a six-month l.o.a., an unpaid leave of absence. We'll claim you're only taking a six-month specialty course. Then if you're unhappy with your curriculum or can't make ends meet financially or just plain come to your senses, your old job will be waiting for you."

"No, thanks," I declined.

"No?" he exclaimed in disbelief. "But what have you possibly got to lose?"

"My sense of commitment to a new future," I explained. "As long as you make it easy to retreat, it will be that much harder to go forward."

"You are the most incredibly stubborn person I've ever met," he complained. "And that includes all my cases of obsessive-compulsive neurosis and passive-aggressive personality. Well, I won't be in any great hurry to fill your line. I can filibuster for several months at least."

"Take the light out of the window," I urged. "Don't wait up for me. We're still shorthanded at the clinic and you can use every therapist you can get."

"What about a part-time line?" he persisted. "Even with scholarship and loan money, you'll still need some additional income."

"I think I'd wait on tables before I'd come back to St. Dymphna's as just a part-time therapist," I said. "Don't be so guilt ridden."

"Who's guilt ridden?" he said defensively.

"Whence comes this urgent need to keep me on staff, after all our fights and disagreements during the past year?" I questioned.

"We've had our differences, sure," he said. "But I do respect you, you know that. You work hard, you care, and you believe in what you fight for . . . even if you get mixed up and fight against your own side at times, and feel you're being persecuted when you're not, and reject your femininity at times, and . . ."

"Please," I begged, holding up a hand for silence, "I really don't deserve all this respect."

"Sorry to have gone off the track," he apologized. "You really did change my thinking a little on several issues. When you've got a staff and a patient population as diversified as ours, maybe you need more than one viewpoint at the top."

"You can always hire a black, feminist, atheistic lesbian as your next clinic coordinator," I suggested.

Vince smiled ruefully. "I'm honestly thinking about going without one, at this point."

"How can you?" I protested. "Who's going to assign the intakes, supervise the assistants, handle phone inquiries, do liaison with other agencies . . ."

"Oh, I could parcel out what I can't handle myself to several other clinicians," he said. "I just can't see any single member of our present staff in that capacity."

"Not even Scovetti? It would seem to me she'd work ideally with you."

"If you mean she'd do what I told her, you're right," he replied. "If all my coordinator can do is exactly what I'd do in that situation, I may just as well do it myself."

"Now you're making me feel guilty."

"Good!" he said. "Maybe you'll change your mind, Patricia."

"Not *that* guilty," I hastened to remark. "And what's with 'Patricia?' You've never called me that before."

"Just thought I should be on a first-name basis with you," he explained.

"Haven't you been?"

"I honestly don't know," he confessed. "What is Pat short for, anyway? Patricia or Patterson? You're a tough girl to get to know."

"A tough *person*," I corrected. "And getting tougher, I hope." I looked toward the bedroom, where everything had been silent since we started talking. "What do you suppose those two are doing in there?" I asked, getting worried.

"Undoubtedly pressing their ears to the door," Vince said.

"Let's get them out here," I urged. "They're the patients, after all—not us."

"I think we were supposed to straighten something out between ourselves, though," he said. "What have we settled?"

"I'm leaving. That much is settled."

"Now, you're not going to leave poor Nilda without a ray of hope, are you?" he said dolefully. "Look, you've still got two weeks left at St. Dymphna's. Will you at least talk with me about your decision again, give me another chance to change your mind?"

I nodded. "I won't change it, but I'll listen. If we can get a few moments' peace at the clinic."

"I'll see to it," he said. "Let's go to lunch somewhere." I nodded. He continued, "I know this great Italian place that serves a wonderful *frutti di mare,* a cold seafood salad, with squid, conch, mussels, eels . . ."

I was simultaneously saying, "There's this terrific health food restaurant that has eggplant cutlets and chick-pea patties, with yogurt shakes . . ." We both stopped abruptly and started to laugh. "What's the use, Vince?"

"We'll go out for a drink," he compromised. "I'll bet you drink straight vodka, lemon twist."

"I prefer brandy alexanders. You're a martini man, six-to-one, right?"

He shook his head. "Irish whiskey on the rocks. Seems like we've still got a lot to learn about one another." He strode over to the bedroom, knocked, and said, "Hey, ladies, we're finished; how about you?"

The women emerged from the bedroom, smiling inquisitively, Nilda holding the gun at her side as casually as if she were toting a dustpan.

"You two look a lot more compatible than when I came here," Vince said cheerily. "What happened in there?"

Blanca grinned. "She's not going to shoot me. And we both decided to get rid of Ernesto. Like Ms. Patterson says, us women get pushed around by men too much."

"I guess I won't need this no more," Nilda said, handing me the gun, which I dropped onto the dining table as quickly as I could. "Thank you so much for coming, both of you. It really made all the difference."

"Part of our job, Nilda," Vince said gallantly. "Just another day's work."

But Nilda frowned and shook her head. "No, no, it was a lot different. Having the two of you here fighting with each other, getting excited, and acting like idiots really opened my eyes. See, at the clinic, you always seem so strong and calm and sensible, but now I've seen that you're not much different from me and everybody else. Maybe it didn't make my life no better, but I ain't going to go around feeling depressed anymore because I think everybody else in the world has their lives really together."

It was not the sort of compliment Vince expected, but he was relieved enough to see the day's activities drawing to a close that he accepted it with a gracious half-smile.

"How 'bout you two?" Nilda asked. "Did the doctor talk you into staying at the clinic?"

"I'm sorry, Nilda," I said resolutely. "I've given my decision to leave a lot of thought, and I'm sticking with it."

"However," Vince added hastily, "she is open to further discussion, and I'm sure once she sees things from a logical instead of an emotional point of view, she'll change her mind."

Nilda seemed even more optimistic than Vince. "She'll stay if you're nice to her, Doc," she assured him. "I don't have much brains, but I know how a woman's heart works."

Blanca let out an exasperated sigh. "Don't sell out, Ms. Patterson!" she urged. "Don't throw your life away just to please a man!"

Nilda whirled at her, pointing an index finger as though she still had the revolver. Realizing she had surrendered it, she made a token gesture of preparing to slap Blanca with the back of her hand. "Shut up, you dumb kid. Let her make up her own mind."

"That I will," I promised Nilda and Blanca. Blanca went back to the bedroom as Nilda extended her hand to me.

"You give me an appointment to see you soon at the clinic?" she asked.

"Sure, Nilda. I'll call you as soon as I get back and check my schedule."

"Don't forget to take this!" Blanca called, hurrying back with a paper sack.

"That's not more *cabrito*, is it?" I asked suspiciously.

"No," she giggled. "It's the needles and medicine and stuff the doctor brought. Don't forget anything."

While Vince meticulously unfolded and smoothed his jacket, I slipped on my sandals and scanned the room for stray belongings. "Shall we call the clinic and tell them we're on the way?" I asked.

"Naw," he said after a moment's deliberation. "Let's sneak in and see what goes on when we're not there."

We descended the rotting stairs side by side, barely able to fit in the narrow space together, but unwilling to separate and let one precede the other. I cradled the open paper sack in my left arm, gripping Vince's left arm for support with my free hand. Strange, I could not recall ever having touched him in the entire time I had known him.

It was still early afternoon when we left the building. The four hoods were no longer obstructing the staircase, but a similarly dressed clique of tough-looking males was camped on the corner with no apparent aim. A tall black man with a shaven head was angrily ranting on the opposite side of the street, and a sturdy, middle-aged drunk lurched along behind us as we walked.

"The community!" Vince proclaimed. "Behold the fruits of our lives' work. Pat, I don't know what drew you to this place, but I'm sure of one thing—having cared about it so much for so long, when the time comes, you won't want to leave."

"I'm sure I won't want to," I said, ambling slowly beside him and ignoring a rude remark in Spanish from the gang at the corner, "but I will leave all the same."

"And leave this all behind?"

"Vince, may I get personal for a moment?" I ventured. "Would you let your wife work in this community?"

"What a strange question!" he exclaimed. "I guess I'd feel the same way I feel about you. It's safe enough within the walls of the clinic, open asylum for the staff as well as the patients, but I wouldn't want her—or you—walking around in this neighborhood."

I smiled complacently. "I don't feel the least bit afraid now. Honestly."

He returned my smile, awkward as an adolescent boy, and said, with a catch in his voice, "Because I'm here with you?"

Oh, Vince, how ridiculously macho! I didn't want him to note my surprise, and I gave his shoulder a supportive pat. "That's one reason," I said charitably, "but it wasn't what I had in mind."

He shrugged philosophically. "Of course, I should have known by now. You're not afraid because you're a modern, liberated woman, ready for action and uncowed by displays of aggression. You have unshakable confidence in your ability to deal effectively with any crisis you encounter."

"Well put!" I said, without breaking stride. "But that's not quite it either."

"Tell me then, Patricia," he asked, looking nervously to both sides and behind him at the sinister figures lurking in every doorway and propped against every wall, "what's the source of your newfound confidence?"

I hefted the paper sack cradled in my left arm, a container considerably heavier than when Vince had brought it over, and reached my right hand across my chest to touch something nestled inside it among the syringes and ampules. Reassured, I informed Dr. Bellino, "I have the gun."